CONTROL AND DYNAMIC SYSTEMS

Advances in Theory and Applications

Volume 32

CONTRIBUTORS TO THIS VOLUME

HAIM BARUH
DENNIS S. BERNSTEIN
KANGYOUN CHOE
ROSALIE DE VILLIERS
WASSIM M. HADDAD
JOHN R. HOLDSWORTH
JOHN L. JUNKINS
C. T. LEONDES
SAM LIDÉN
LEONARD MEIROVITCH
DAVID F. MILLER
VIVEKANANDA MUKHOPADHYAY
MARK A. NORRIS
ROGER C. THOMPSON
YAAKOV YAVIN

CONTROL AND DYNAMIC SYSTEMS

ADVANCES IN THEORY AND APPLICATIONS

Edited by
C. T. LEONDES

School of Engineering and Applied Science
University of California, Los Angeles
Los Angeles, California

College of Engineering
University of Washington
Seattle, Washington

VOLUME 32: ADVANCES IN AEROSPACE SYSTEMS DYNAMICS AND CONTROL SYSTEMS
Part 2 of 3

ACADEMIC PRESS, INC.
Harcourt Brace Jovanovich, Publishers
San Diego New York Berkeley Boston
London Sydney Tokyo Toronto

This book is printed on acid-free paper. ♾

ACADEMIC PRESS, INC.
San Diego, California 92101

United Kingdom Edition published by
ACADEMIC PRESS LIMITED
24-28 Oval Road, London NW1 7DX

LIBRARY OF CONGRESS CATALOG CARD NUMBER: 64-8027

ISBN 0-12-012732-6 (alk. paper)

PRINTED IN THE UNITED STATES OF AMERICA
90 91 92 93 9 8 7 6 5 4 3 2 1

CONTROL AND DYNAMIC SYSTEMS

ADVANCES IN THEORY AND APPLICATIONS

Edited by
C. T. LEONDES

School of Engineering and Applied Science
University of California, Los Angeles
Los Angeles, California

College of Engineering
University of Washington
Seattle, Washington

VOLUME 32: ADVANCES IN AEROSPACE SYSTEMS DYNAMICS AND CONTROL SYSTEMS
Part 2 of 3

ACADEMIC PRESS, INC.
Harcourt Brace Jovanovich, Publishers
San Diego New York Berkeley Boston
London Sydney Tokyo Toronto

This book is printed on acid-free paper. ♾

ACADEMIC PRESS, INC.
San Diego, California 92101

United Kingdom Edition published by
ACADEMIC PRESS LIMITED
24-28 Oval Road, London NW1 7DX

LIBRARY OF CONGRESS CATALOG CARD NUMBER: 64-8027

ISBN 0-12-012732-6 (alk. paper)

PRINTED IN THE UNITED STATES OF AMERICA
90 91 92 93 9 8 7 6 5 4 3 2 1

CONTENTS

Proportional Navigation and the Game of Two Cars in Three Dimensions: A Time-Dependent Stochastic Differential Game

Yaakov Yavin and Rosalie de Villiers

Parameter Identification in Distributed Structures

Leonard Meirovitch and Mark A. Norris

Combined Structural and Control Optimization: A Steepest Descents Approach

David F. Miller

An Asymptotic Perturbation Method for Nonlinear Optimal Control Problems

Roger C. Thompson and John L. Junkins

Reliability Issues in Structural Control

Haim Baruh and Kangyoun Choe

Control Law Synthesis and Stability Robustness Improvement Using Constrained Optimization Techniques

Vivekananda Mukhopadhyay

Computational Methods for Decoy Discrimination and Optimal Targeting in Ballistic Missile Defense

John R. Holdsworth and C. T. Leondes

CONTRIBUTORS

Numbers in parentheses indicate the pages on which the authors' contributions begin.

Haim Baruh (135), *Department of Mechanical and Aerospace Engineering, Rutgers University, New Brunswick, New Jersey 08903*

Dennis S. Bernstein (23), *Harris Corporation, Melbourne, Florida 32902*

Kangyoun Choe (135), *Department of Mechanical and Aerospace Engineering, Rutgers University, New Brunswick, New Jersey 08903*

Rosalie de Villiers (39), *Centre for Advanced Computing and Decision Support, Council for Scientific and Industrial Research, Pretoria 0001, South Africa*

Wassim M. Haddad (23), *Department of Mechanical and Aerospace Engineering, Florida Institute of Technology, Melbourne, Florida 32901*

John R. Holdsworth (207), *Systems Analysis, Lockheed Aeronautical Systems, Burbank, California 91520*

John L. Junkins (115), *Department of Aerospace Engineering, Texas A&M University, College Station, Texas 77843*

C. T. Leondes (207), *Department of Mechanical, Aerospace, and Nuclear Engineering, School of Engineering and Applied Science, University of California, Los Angeles, Los Angeles, California 90024, and College of Engineering, University of Washington, Seattle, Washington 98195*

Sam Lidén (1), *Honeywell Inc., Sperry Commercial Flight Systems Group, Air Transport Systems Division, Phoenix, Arizona 85027*

Leonard Meirovitch (53), *Department of Engineering Science and Mechanics, Virginia Polytechnic Institute and State University, Blacksburg, Virginia 24061*

David F. Miller (89), *Department of Mathematics and Statistics, Wright State University, Dayton, Ohio, 45435*

Vivekananda Mukhopadhyay (163), *NASA Langley Research Center, Hampton, Virginia 23665*

Mark A. Norris (53), *Department of Engineering Science and Mechanics, Virginia Polytechnic Institute and State University, Blacksburg, Virginia 24061*

Roger C. Thompson (115), *Department of Aerospace Engineering, The Pennsylvania State University, University Park, Pennsylvania 16802*

Yaakov Yavin (39), *Centre for Advanced Computing and Decision Support, Council for Scientific and Industrial Research, Pretoria 0001, South Africa*

PREFACE

Expansion in the many technologies which support the development of aerospace systems has undergone an incredible revolution over the past 25–30 years. For example, integrated electronic circuits have increased in density by about eight orders of magnitude since 1960! This makes possible many advances in aerospace systems that were previously not possible. Advances in other areas such as sensor systems, materials structures, propulsion, software, and systems integration techniques all very clearly and strongly suggest that it is now most appropriate to treat these subjects in *Control and Dynamic Systems*. However, the proliferation of significant developments and advances has been so great that adequate coverage could not possibly be encompassed in one volume; thus this volume is the second of a trilogy devoted to the theme "Advances in Aerospace Systems Dynamics and Control Systems."

The first contribution, "Practical Considerations in Optimal and 4-Dimensional Flight Management Computations," by Sam Lidén, treats an area of major significance to commercial air transportation—flight management systems (FMS)—which provides new levels of flight automation, optimization, and information display for modern commercial aircraft. FMS facilitates and automates complete flight planning, from takeoff to touchdown, and controls the aircraft to follow the flight plan. It also does fast-time simulated flight (referred to as *prediction*), from the current aircraft position to the end of the flight plan, to obtain arrival time, fuel-on-board, and other data at all waypoints ahead. An optimum descent path is generated by computing backward prediction from the destination runway up to the cruise altitude. Since Lidén is deeply involved with the most advanced commercial FMS, his article provides this volume with a significant opening. The next contribution, "Optimal Reduced-Order Subspace-Observer Design with a Frequency-Domain Error Bound," by Wassim M. Haddad and Dennis S. Bernstein, presents techniques for treating complex aerospace system models that occur, for example, in large flexible space structures. These may involve numerous flexible modes, but only estimates of the rigid body attitude may be desired. There is a vast amount of literature on reduced-order observers and their design, and because of the frequently occurring problem of constraints on implementation complexity in aerospace systems, this contribution is most welcome.

Turning to the next contribution, "Proportional Navigation and The Game of Two Cars in Three Dimensions: A Time-Dependent Stochastic Differential Game," by Yaakov Yavin and Rosalie de Villiers, air-to-air systems are of substantial significance in many modern aerospace systems. In this contribution Yavin, a leading researcher in differential game theory, and his colleague, de Villiers, demonstrate that proportional navigation is a good approximation to an optimal feedback pursuit strategy for stochastic differential games. This is clearly a result of substantial significance for air-to-air systems. The next contribution to this volume, "Parameter Identification in Distibuted Structures," by Leonard Meirovitch and Mark A. Norris, is a rather comprehensive treatment of parameter identification techniques for distributed structures, a major issue in aircraft and space structures. Meirovitch is a leading contributor on the international scene in structural dynamics, and so this contribution by him and Norris will provide an excellent reference source for professionals working in this area.

The fifth contribution, "Combined Structural and Control Optimization: A Steepest Descents Approach," by David F. Miller, is an excellent example of the interdisciplinary nature of modern dynamic systems control. In this case, the power of the interdisciplinary nature of combined structural/control optimization is demonstrated by the development of techniques to reduce structural mass and simultaneously to reduce total system strain, kinetic, and control energies when a structure is excited. This is a fairly active area on the international scene because of its substantial applied significance, and so this article will be very useful for workers involved in this area. The next contribution, "An Asymptotic Perturbation Method for Nonlinear Optimal Control Problems," by Roger C. Thompson and John L. Junkins, develops a new and, in many instances, rather powerful means for solving the two-point boundary value problem (TPBVP) which is essential to the nonlinear optimal control problem. Currently used methods of algorithms for the solution of the TPBVP iterate on one of the three necessary conditions—the boundary conditions, the differential equations, or the minimization of the performance index—while simultaneously satisfying the other two necessary conditions. The results, respectively, are variation of extremals, quasilinearization, or the steepest descent algorithm. Thompson and Junkins's solution, instead, converts the system of nonlinear differential equations into a modal form plus what are frequently, if not generally, small nonlinear perturbation terms for the respective modal equations. As a result, the solution can be assumed to be an expansion in terms of linear plus perturbation terms. This technique promises to be useful in many applied instances.

The following contribution, "Reliability Issues in Structural Control," by Haim Baruh and Kangyoun Choe, develops significant results for the problem of reliability techniques associated with structural control laws, with additional reliability checks and redundancies around the control system. The effects of incorrect models and of sensor and actuator malfunctions on the performance of structures are presented. This contribution is also an excellent reference for research and professional workers in the field. The next contribution, "Control Law Synthesis and Stability Robustness Improvement Using Constrained Optimization Techniques," by Vivekananda Mukhopadhyay, presents results for dealing with the conflicting design requirements on dynamic loads, responses, actuator deflections, and rate limitations for the optimal control of modern flexible aircraft or large space structures with active control. Such systems are typically modeled by a large order state-space system of equations in order to represent accurately the rigid and flexible body modes, unsteady aerodynamic forces, actuator dynamics, antialiasing filters, and gust spectrum. The control laws for such multiinput–multioutput (MIMO) systems must satisfy the conflicting requirements mentioned above. This contribution develops the equations of motion and system description for such systems, and then presents algorithms for the solution of the complex optimization problems posed by such systems and their performance requirements. The power and utility of the techniques developed in this contribution are then verified by computer simulation studies for several complex systems applications.

The final contribution, "Computation Methods for Decoy Discrimination and Optimal Targeting in Ballistic Missile Defense," by John R. Holdsworth and C. T. Leondes, presents results of substantial significance to the complex problem of the assignment of intercept systems, a limited resource, to threat clouds which include both reentry vehicles (RVs) and decoys. The problem is complicated by the fact that the decoys will typically outnumber the RVs by an order of magnitude, and, again, it should be bourne in mind that the intercept systems represent limited resources. Of course, this is a highly dynamic and very time-limited environment. Research in this major problem area virtually came to a stop in the early 1970s, and so this contribution will be a valuable source for problems of this general category extending to other areas.

This second volume in the trilogy is a particularly appropriate volume with which to continue this series. The authors are all to be commended for their superb contributions, which will most certainly be a significant reference source for workers on the international scene for many years to come.

PRACTICAL CONSIDERATIONS IN OPTIMAL AND 4-DIMENSIONAL FLIGHT MANAGEMENT COMPUTATIONS

SAM LIDÉN

Honeywell Inc.
Sperry Commercial Flight Systems Group
Air Transport Systems Division
Phoenix, Arizona 85027

I. FLIGHT MANAGEMENT SYSTEMS BACKGROUND

Modern commercial transport aircraft, such as the Boeing 757 and 767, Airbus A310 and A320, McDonnell-Douglas MD-80 and MD-11, and Fokker-100, are equipped with a flight management system (FMS) that provides new levels of flight automation, optimization, and information display for this category of aircraft. The FMS facilitates and automates complete flight planning from takeoff to touchdown and controls the aircraft to follow the flight plan. It also does fast-time simulated flight, referred to as prediction, from the current aircraft position to the end of the flight plan to obtain arrival time, fuel-on-board, and other data at all waypoints ahead of the aircraft. An optimum descent path is generated by doing backward prediction from the destination runway to the cruise altitude.

The FMS contains a large data base, referred to as the navigation data base (NDB), of navaids, airways, airports, runways, departure and arrival procedures, and other map data covering the geographical area where the aircraft is intended to operate. A flight plan is constructed by appropriately linking such data base elements. The NDB also contains preassembled standard company routes that may be selected between a given city pair. The pilot can construct and/or modify a flight plan at any time and, before a flight plan is activated, can observe the prediction results (such as fuel consumption and arrival time) for the new plan.

The FMS automatically selects and tunes in the optimum VOR (very high-frequency omnirange) and DME (distance-measuring equipment) navaid stations based on their locations and directions relative to the aircraft. The DME range and VOR omnibearing signals are optimally mixed with position and velocity inputs from the inertial reference system (IRS) to compute the position and velocity of the aircraft. The FMS also generates display data including data for a moving map display on a color CRT.

A principal objective of an FMS is to minimize the cost of flight. The current FMS attempts to achieve this objective by selecting vertical and lateral profiles that minimize direct operating cost (DOC), which is the cost of fuel and other costs that are proportional to flight time. A significant share of the savings achieved by the current FMS is due to effective lateral planning and navigation, which results in reduced air distance, taking winds into account. The remaining share of the savings is due to optimal selection of cruise altitudes, step climb points, thrust settings, and speed commands. When the "economy" performance mode is selected, the FMS computes the speed and thrust commands that minimize DOC.

Flight-time cost, such as the crew cost and maintenance and repair cost that may reasonably be prorated with flight time, is represented in the FMS calculations in terms of a cost index (CI), which is defined as the ratio of time cost to fuel cost. CI usually has units of 100 lb/hr or kg/min. The scaling is chosen to provide a 3-digit entry on a keyboard. The cost index is a predetermined parameter that theoretically should be fixed for a given aircraft and flight, but it can be set by the pilot to any value from 0 to 999. A normal range of values is from 25 to 100 in the English CI unit.

The FMS then attempts to compute the climb, cruise, and descent profiles that minimize the DOC, expressed as

$$J_{\mathrm{DOC}} = C_{\mathrm{f}} \int_0^{t_{\mathrm{f}}} (f + K)\, dt \tag{1}$$

where

C_{f} = unit cost of fuel (\$/lb or \$/kg)

f = fuel flow (lb/hr or kg/hr)

K = cost index scaled to the units of fuel flow

t_{f} = flight time

The flight profile is constrained to a fixed lateral path and ATC-approved cruise flight levels (ATC, air traffic control), and is subject to airframe and ATC-imposed speed limits. Pilot-entered speed limits and altitude constraints are also observed.

The current FMS designs have been found to adequately solve the problem of computing the optimum speed, thrust, altitude, and so forth to minimize DOC. The methods are based on the energy state approach formulated by Erzberger and Lee [1], but with some practical constraints such as constant CAS/Mach (CAS, calibrated air speed) profiles for climb and descent.

A significant drawback to the DOC approach is that it does not properly reflect costs associated with arrival-time error, such as crew overtime cost, losses due to missed connections in a hubbing operation, and potential losses due to customer dissatisfaction with the airline. The airlines have used the CI as a means for adjusting the average flight time for a given flight, based on normal wind conditions and schedule considerations.

When the CI is used in this way it no longer represents the flight-time cost initially intended but becomes a means for adjusting arrival time. It has been shown [2,3] that this use of CI provides the minimum-fuel solution for the resulting arrival time. Methods for finding the cost index that result in a desired arrival time are therefore a basic issue in optimal 4-D guidance.

A major objective in 4-D guidance is to increase the efficiency of air traffic control in a congested terminal-area environment by controlling the spacing of aircraft so that overall flow rate is maximized. Ground-based ATC computations generate landing orders and arrival times at a metering fix, and the arrival time at the fix needs to be controlled very accurately (± 5 sec is desired). A fundamental problem is the control of a mixture of aircraft types, only some of which may be equipped with arrival-time guidance capability. Efficient terminal area control is a significant factor in minimizing flight cost, but this work does not deal with multiple aircraft speed strategies or constraints that may be required to maximize terminal area flow rate. It is primarily concerned with adjusting the speed of an aircraft, within prescribed constraints, to effect arrival-time accuracy at minimum cost. In the 4-D guidance case, the arrival time is prescribed; in the minimum cost case, it is computed.

This article also does not deal with modifying the path, such as path stretching or early descent, for efficient time absorption. Chakravarty [4] has shown that cruise altitude should be reduced for large negative cost index and has developed optimal 4-D trajectory algorithms. Some savings are available by such algorithms, but they require extensive computation and are deemed impractical on the current or near-term FMS.

II. A SIMULATION STUDY

To gain understanding of the relationships between cost index, speed, flight time, fuel burn, and winds, a simulation study was undertaken of a representative flight of a wide-body aircraft over a 1000-nmi flight plan. The initial and final altitudes were 1000 ft, and a cruise altitude of 35,000 ft was selected. No step climbs or step descents were considered. The International Standard Atmosphere (ISA) was assumed, and the initial gross weight was 350,000 lb. Takeoff and final approach phases were not included in the profiles, and a clean configuration was assumed throughout the flight. The 250-kn ATC speed limit was observed below 10,000 ft, and the aircraft speed was initialized at the commanded speed at the initial altitude.

Three wind conditions were applied: NW (no wind), HW (head wind), and TW (tail wind). The HW and TW conditions had 50-kn magnitude at 35,000 ft and decreased linearly to zero at sea level. Simulation runs were made at each wind condition with the following values of cost index (in 100 lb/hr): -100, -75, -50, -25, -10, 0, 10, 25, 50, 75, 100, 150, 200, 300, 400, 600, 800, and 1000. The value of cost index that represents real flight-time cost usually lies in the range of 25 to 75. A negative value for the cost index (not selectable on the current FMS) results in lower speed than the minimum-fuel speed and more fuel consumption than the minimum for unconstrained arrival time. When time absorption is required, the minimum-fuel solution for the required arrival time is obtained with a negative cost index. However, the cost index should not be less than minus the minimum cruise fuel-flow value (i.e., the speed should not go below the maximum endurance speed). Further time delay should be implemented by increased path length (usually a holding pattern) at maximum endurance speed. (These results are described in [2].) The maximum endurance speed is not investigated in this study.

Figure 1a shows the effect of cost index on average true airspeed (air distance divided by flight time) at the three wind conditions and points out the significant nonlinearities. The speed for a given cost index is very dependent on the wind, and this dependency is nonlinear. Also, the speed sensitivity to cost index is high at small and negative values and low at large values. Cost index is evidently not easily related to airspeed and is not a practical parameter for controlling airspeed.

Figure 1b shows the effects on flight time, with the analogous sensitivities at large and small values of cost index. The high sensitivity to wind is evident, as is the large increase in cost index required to make up for an unexpected head wind.

Figure 1c shows fuel burn versus cost index. Theoretically, $\mathrm{CI} = 0$ should yield minimum fuel burn, but the figure shows the minimum point to be at a slightly negative value of cost index. A few simplifying assumptions and

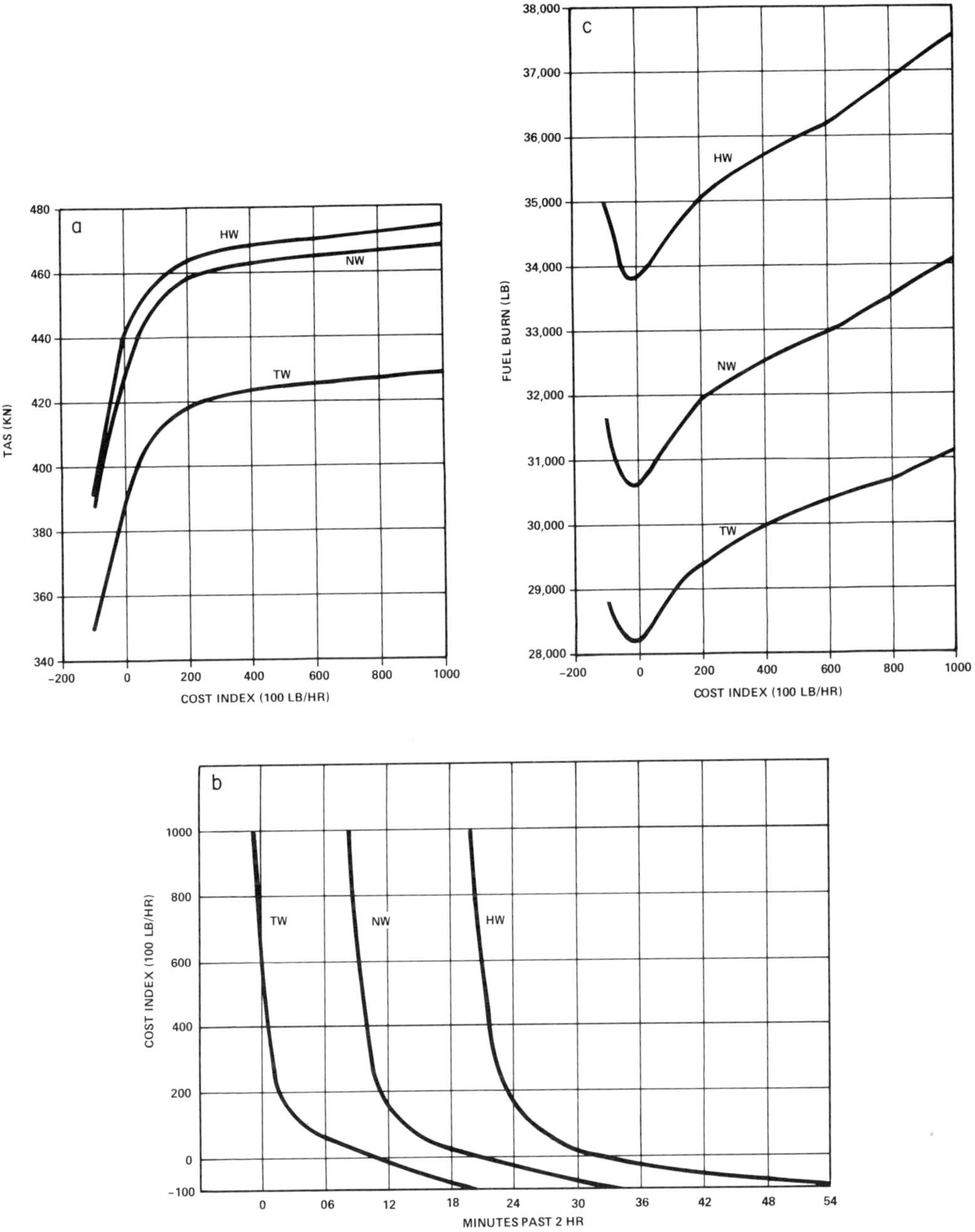

Fig. 1. (a) Average true airspeed versus cost index. (b) Flight time versus cost index. (c) Fuel burn versus cost index.

approximations were made in the FMS speed command algorithms, however, such as constant CAS/Mach profiles in climb and descent. (Such profiles do not quite yield minimum fuel.)

Figure 2 shows minimum fuel burn versus flight time for the three wind conditions, with the CI points marked. The figure also shows that a flight time

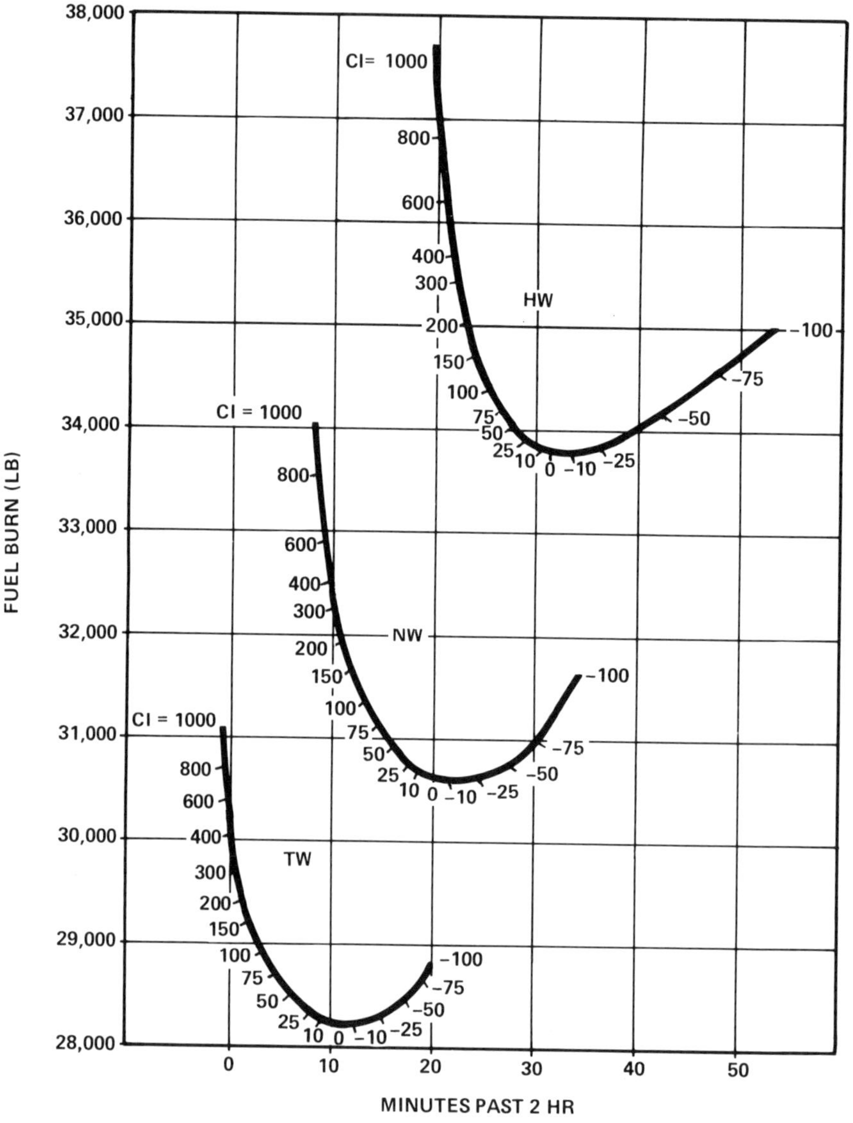

Fig. 2. Minimum fuel versus flight time.

of 2:20 results for CI = 0 and no wind. To have the same flight time under a 50-kn head wind requires CI = 900 and approximately 6600 more pounds of fuel.

The results are based on controlling the speed over the entire 1000-nmi trip. Also, the cruise altitude and the initial fuel-on-board are the same in all cases. Because fuel planning takes wind forecasts into account, the head-wind case would normally have more initial fuel than the tail-wind case, which would tend to separate the curves in Fig. 2 even further. A fully optimized trajectory would mitigate the fuel penalty to some degree.

The curves are obtainable only by doing a prediction to the destination in question for each set of given cost index values, taking into account winds, flight plan constraints, guidance laws, and so forth, at every point along the flight plan. Such predictions consume considerable processing time in an FMS because they must accurately simulate aircraft drag, thrust, fuel flow, and so on. Furthermore, they must include temporary auxiliary predictions, such as the generation of a descent path by backward prediction from the destination waypoint. Each prediction iteration is costly in terms of processing time, so the number of iterations undertaken to search for an optimum cost index must be minimized.

III. OPTIMUM COST INDEX SEARCH

We define total flight cost (TFC) to be the sum of direct operating cost (DOC) and arrival error cost (AEC), expressed as

$$J(K) = C_{\mathrm{f}} \int_{0}^{t_{\mathrm{f}}(K)} [f_K(t) + K_0]\, dt + g(t_{\mathrm{e}}) \tag{2}$$

where

C_{f} = unit cost of fuel

K = cost index in units of fuel flow (a variable)

K_0 = the value of K that represents the actual flight-hour cost (a constant)

$f_K(t)$ = the fuel flow consumed at each point in the profile when optimized for cost index K

$t_{\mathrm{f}}(K)$ = the flight time that results for cost index K

t_{e} = arrival-time error (actual arrival time minus scheduled arrival time)

$g(t_{\mathrm{e}})$ = arrival error cost function

As the result of a prediction pass for a given K, we have t_f, t_e, and fuel burn F, so we can evaluate

$$J(K) = C_f(F + K_0 t_f) + g(t_e) \tag{3}$$

Constants C_f and K_0 and function $g(t_e)$ must be provided. The optimum cost index is the one that minimizes J.

The arrival error cost function $g(t_e)$ is a composite of several cost elements associated with arrival-time error, such as overtime cost, customer dissatisfaction cost, and losses due to missed connections. Overtime cost usually begins at the expiration of the scheduled flight time, which may be later than the scheduled arrival time if the flight starts late. The choice of $g(t_e)$ is somewhat arbitrary and is airline dependent. Appropriate functions must be provided but require studies beyond the scope of this work. Figure 3 shows an example of such a function, made up of a linear component at \$600/hr for $t_e > 0$ and of two steps representing missed-connection costs. No cost is assigned to early arrival. The arrival error costs are expected to be different for each termination, so a convenient way must be found for storing such

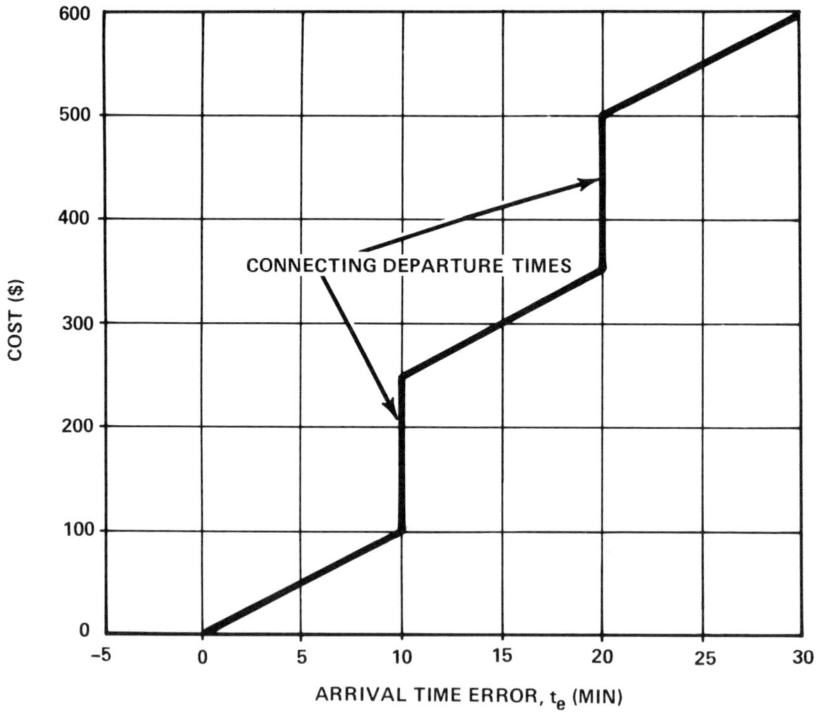

Fig. 3. Arrival error cost function.

functions in the FMS data base, and possibly for modifying them by keyboard entry. The following format is suggested:

$$g(t_e) = \sum_i \sigma(t_i, s_i, m_i) \tag{4}$$

where $\sigma(t_i, s_i, m_i)$ is a sloping step function of time that steps up for increasing positive t_e and also for decreasing negative t_e (to allow cost associated with early arrival). It is defined in terms of step point t_i, step size s_i, and slope m_i by

$$\sigma(t_i, s_i, m_i) = \begin{cases} s_i + m_i(t_i - t_e) & \text{if } t_e < t_i \leq 0 \\ 0 & \text{if } (t_i < t_e < 0) \text{ or } (0 < t_e < t_i) \\ s_i + m_i(t_e - t_i) & \text{if } 0 \leq t_i < t_e \end{cases} \tag{5}$$

The variable t_e is omitted in the σ parameter list for the sake of brevity. The time points $\{t_i\}$ are important in the search for the optimum cost index as described later; they are referred to as the AEC critical points.

The arrival error cost function in Fig. 3 can then be expressed as

$$g(t_e) = \sigma(0, 0, 10) + \sigma(10, 150, 0) + \sigma(20, 150, 0) \tag{6}$$

A window-type function of width $2t_w$, centered at $t_e = 0$, and with cost C_w outside the window, is defined by

$$g(t_e) = \sigma(-t_w, C_w, 0) + \sigma(t_w, C_w, 0) \tag{7}$$

Figure 4 shows how total flight cost is constructed. The DOC curve corresponds to the head-wind case described earlier, with $C_f = 13$¢/lb and $C_f K_0 = \$650$/hr (CI = 50). The scheduled arrival time is based on the no-wind case with CI = 0, which corresponds to a flight time of 2:20. The arrival-time cost function of Fig. 3 is then referenced to this time, and the total cost is as shown. By inspection we see that the optimum arrival time is around 2:26, or 6 min late, and the optimum cost index is in the range of 75 to 100. On-time arrival would require a cost index of 900 and would cost around \$250 more. At CI = 0, a connecting flight is missed, and so the total cost would be around \$200 more than the optimum. An important point is that sizeable variations in cost index near the optimum value have a negligible effect on total cost unless the minimum point lies near a critical point. In this example, the cost index can vary from about 30 to 130 with only a \$10 variation in total cost. This variation in CI corresponds to a variation in arrival time of over 4 min.

For the general case, the procedure for finding the optimum cost index is as follows:

1. Find the time t_{opt} that minimizes total flight cost from a TFC versus flight time curve (such as Fig. 4).
2. Find the corresponding cost index from a cost index versus flight time curve (such as Fig. 1b).

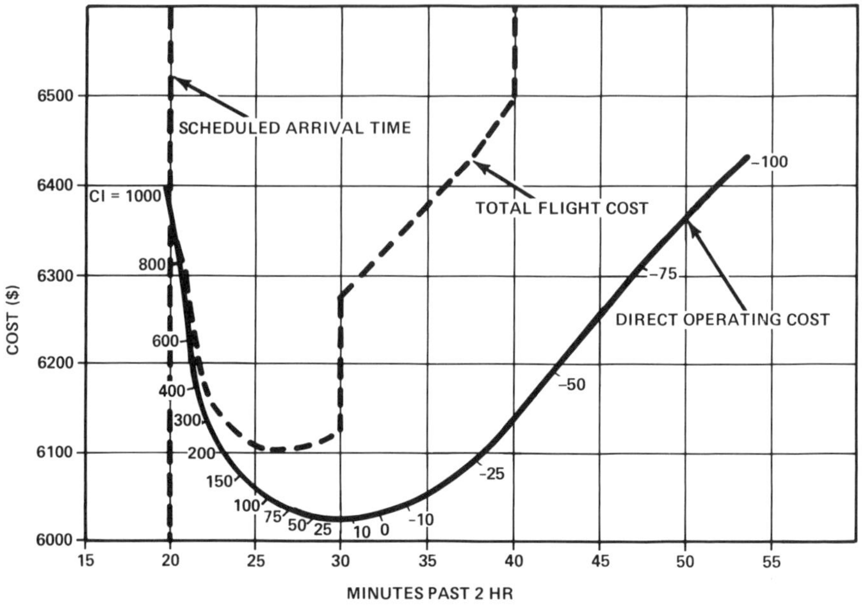

Fig. 4. Flight cost versus flight time.

However, every point on such curves requires a prediction pass for a trial cost index. For practical reasons, the number of such predictions must be minimized, so the trial cost index values must be carefully chosen. The procedure to be described uses CI values from a reference set, in which parabolic interpolation is employed to estimate intermediate values. Suggested CI reference values are

$$(-100, -50, -25, -10, 25, 150, 400, 1000)$$

The following procedure is then used to estimate the optimum cost index:

1. Select three cost index values from the reference set that are expected to lie in the vicinity of the optimum value. With no advance knowledge, select -10, 25, and 150.
2. Perform predictions with the three CI values to obtain corresponding values for DOC and flight time.
3. Fit a parabola to the three points to approximate DOC versus flight time, then add the AEC function to approximate TFC.
4. Do a simple linear search on TFC versus time to find the minimum point. The search intervals can be fairly large (60 sec) but must include the AEC critical points.

5. If the resulting minimum point lies outside the span of the three prediction times, select a new adjacent trial cost index from the reference set, in the appropriate direction, and do another prediction that replaces the previous one furthest removed. Repeat from item 3.
6. Find the optimum cost index by doing parabolic interpolation on the three prediction values of cost index versus flight time. This procedure represents a practical compromise between accuracy and processing load, based on the observations that TFC is relatively insensitive to cost index per se and that sensitivity to arrival time is significant only in the vicinity of AEC critical points. Because such time points are predefined, the accuracy of an optimum point at a critical time is ensured. This procedure usually requires just three prediction passes.

V. FINE SPEED ADJUSTMENT

With an optimal arrival time and a near-optimal cost index, the corresponding speed should result in arrival near the optimal time. However, the approximations are likely to result in inadequate arrival time accuracy. The second part of the procedure is to fine-tune the speed obtained with the computed cost index to achieve high arrival-time accuracy. The speed adjustment is assumed to be fairly small so that cost is not significantly affected.

The following discussion attempts to explain a speed-adjustment algorithm that was developed somewhat heuristically but has been found to be effective in adjusting the speed to reduce the arrival-time error. A method was sought for finding a speed command in the following form:

$$V_{\mathrm{R}} = V_0 + V_{\mathrm{SA}} \tag{8}$$

where V_{R} is the required true airspeed for causing the aircraft to arrive at a destination point at a required arrival time T_{R}, and V_0 is the speed command generated by the FMS, normally the optimum speed for a given cost index but often subject to speed and acceleration limits. V_0 is computed at every point in the prediction profile by the usual FMS algorithms. The speed adjustment term V_{SA} should be much simpler to compute. The method is explained as follows.

Let X be the horizontal distance to the destination waypoint along the flight path. Then

$$X = \int_0^T V_{\mathrm{G}}\, dt = \bar{V}_{\mathrm{G}} T \tag{9}$$

where V_G is ground speed, T is flight time to the destination, and $\bar{V}_G$ is the time-averaged V_G. Let $\bar{V}_{G0}$ be the $\bar{V}_G$ for a prediction that uses the FMS-generated speed command without speed adjustment, let T_0 be the resulting arrival time, let T_R be the required arrival time, and let $\bar{V}_{GR}$ be the $\bar{V}_G$ required to arrive on time. Then

$$X = \bar{V}_{G0} T_0 = \bar{V}_{GR} T_R \tag{10}$$

so

$$\bar{V}_{GR} = \frac{T_0}{T_R} \bar{V}_{G0} \tag{11}$$

We now make the assumption that the time average of V_G very nearly equals the distance average; that is

$$\frac{1}{T}\int_0^T V_G(t)\,dt = \frac{1}{X}\int_0^X V_G(x)\,dx \tag{12}$$

Then

$$\frac{1}{X}\int_0^X V_{GR}\,dx = \frac{1}{X}\int_0^X \frac{T_0}{T_R} V_{G0}\,dx \tag{13}$$

which is satisfied by letting

$$V_{GR} = \frac{T_0}{T_R} V_{G0} \tag{14}$$

at every distance point along the trajectory. In terms of true airspeed V_T and tail wind V_W, this becomes

$$V_R + V_W = \frac{T_0}{T_R}(V_0 + V_W) \tag{15}$$

or

$$V_R = V_0 + \left(\frac{T_0}{T_R} - 1\right)(V_0 + V_W) \tag{16}$$

By reapplying Eq. (14), we get

$$V_R = V_0 + \frac{\Delta T_0}{T_0} V_{GR} \tag{17}$$

Let V_1 denote the first estimate of V_R based on one prediction pass; that is, let

$$V_1 = V_0 + \frac{\Delta T_0}{T_0} V_{G1} \tag{18}$$

where T_0 is the arrival time with V_0 as the speed function and $\Delta T_0 = T_0 - T_R$. After another iteration, we similarly have

$$V_2 = V_1 + \frac{\Delta T_1}{T_1} V_{G2} \tag{19}$$

$$= V_0 + \frac{\Delta T_0}{T_0} V_{G1} + \frac{\Delta T_1}{T_1} V_{G2}$$

After N predictions, we obtain for the estimate of V_R

$$V_N = V_0 + \sum_{i=0}^{N-1} \frac{\Delta T_i}{T_i} V_G(i+1) \tag{20}$$

We now observe that V_G does not change much for small speed corrections, so we replace Eq. (20) by

$$V_N = V_0 + \left(\sum_{i=0}^{N-1} \frac{\Delta T_i}{T_i} \right) V_N \tag{21}$$

Defining the speed-adjustment factor as

$$K_{SA} = \sum_{i=0}^{N-1} \frac{\Delta T_i}{T_i} \tag{22}$$

we then have the adjusted speed in the form that was sought:

$$V_R = V_0 + K_{SA} V_{GR} \tag{23}$$

V_0 is obtainable at every point from the normal FMS speed command, and K_{SA} is updated at the end of each prediction pass. V_{GR} is the adjusted ground speed at the current prediction position and is given by

$$V_{GR} = V_R + V_W \tag{24}$$

where V_W is obtained from a wind forecast model. Equation (23) can then be rearranged to give the final result:

$$V_R = \frac{V_0 + K_{SA} V_W}{1 - K_{SA}} \tag{25}$$

This form is slightly different from the one initially sought, but it meets the same basic objective of being simple to evaluate at every point.

The formulation so far assumes that the aircraft is able to fly at the adjusted speed. However, speed and acceleration limits prevent speed adjustments over certain segments of the flight, which must be made up for by greater speed

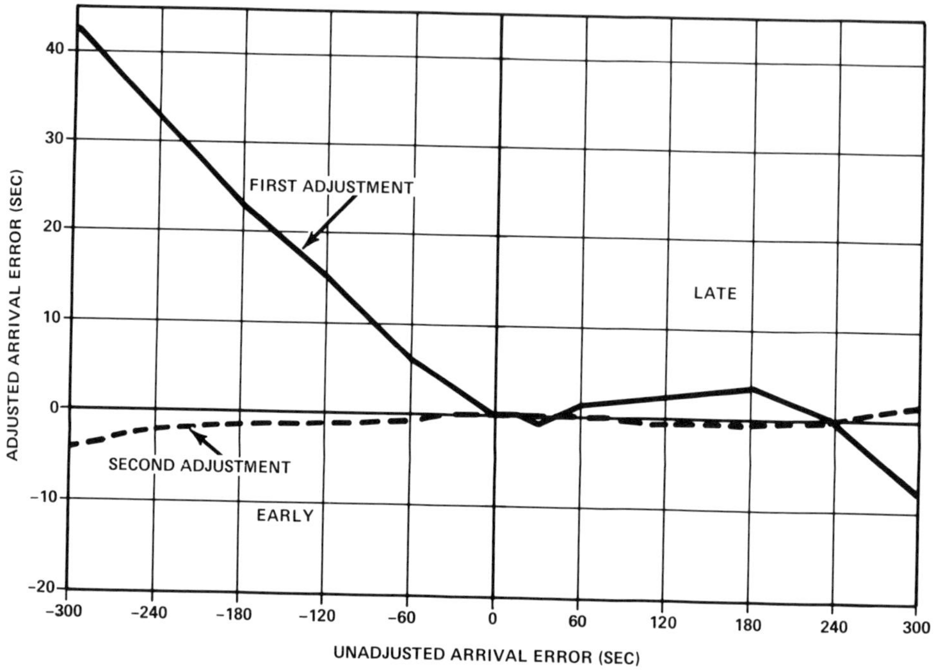

Fig. 5. Speed adjustment results.

adjustments over the remaining segments. We account for this by including two additional time variables in the prediction algorithm: T_U, the accumulated time during which speed can be increased, and T_D, the accumulated time during which speed can be decreased. The time segments excluded are those at which a speed limit, imposed either by the flight plan or by aircraft limits, prevents the speed from being increased or decreased, respectively. Also excluded are the periods during which the aircraft is accelerating or decelerating at a limited value. If, at the end of the prediction pass, the arrival time is found to be late, T_{Ui} is used instead of T_i in the updating of K_{SA} in Eq. (22). Similarly, if the arrival time is found to be early, T_{Di} is used instead of T_i.

Figure 5 illustrates some results obtained with this method. The previously described simulation was run with no wind and CI = 0, which resulted in a flight time of 2:19:58. Fourteen cases of time constraints were run, corresponding to required arrival times that deviated from the above time by ± 15 sec, ± 30 sec, ± 1 min, ± 2 min, ± 3 min, ± 4 min, and ± 5 min. Figure 5 shows the result of the speed adjustment after one and two adjustments. For example, if the nonadjusted speed resulted in a 3-min late arrival, then the first adjustment reduced the arrival error to 3.6 sec and the second adjustment to −0.5 sec. The early-arrival cases tended to overadjust somewhat on the first adjustment. For example, when the nonadjusted speed corresponded to a 5-min early arrival, the result of the first adjustment was a 43-sec late arrival. The second adjustment resulted in a 4.3-sec early arrival.

These results illustrate how rapidly the speed-adjustment algorithm converges. Another important advantage is that it uses the predictions that are already required by the FMS in normal operation. Hence, this method may not require any additional prediction passes. By comparison, the trial predictions to search for the optimum cost index are not usable for normal FMS predictions.

V. WIND FORECAST ERROR COMPENSATION

The ability to control an aircraft so that it will arrive precisely at a prescribed time is very dependent on having accurate arrival-time predictions, which in turn depends on accurate wind forecast information. Future systems with direct ground-to-air transfer of weather information will be capable of providing significant improvements in estimates of the current wind conditions over the future flight profile. However, because the wind assuredly will change from the time of the prediction to the time the aircraft arrives at each point in the profile, forecast error will always be present.

If it were practical to control an aircraft to fly a prescribed ground speed profile, forecast error would be less of a problem. Menga and Erzberger [5] have demonstrated excellent arrival-time performance for such cases. However, aircraft are normally controlled to fly airspeed because of the aerodynamic characteristics that affect performance and because of the speed limits that must always be observed by a flight control system. Imposed speed limits such as the 250-kn CAS limit required below 10,000 ft are always in terms of airspeed, and the optimum descent profile almost always bumps against this speed limit. An unexpected head wind in such a segment reduces ground speed, delaying arrival time, and cannot be made up for by increasing speed downstream.

Current FMS prediction methods correct forecast error in the vicinity of the aircraft by using the known wind at the aircraft position. This wind is blended with the forecast wind as a function of the distance of the prediction away from the aircraft. As an example of this general approach, let W_P be a component (north or east) of the wind vector at the prediction position, computed by

$$W_P = W_{FP} + (W_{AA} - W_{FA})f_{FO}(\Delta X, \Delta H) \tag{26}$$

where

$$W_{FP} = \text{forecast wind component at the prediction position}$$

$$W_{AA} = \text{actual wind component at the aircraft position}$$

$$W_{FA} = \text{forecast wind component at the aircraft position}$$

$$f_{FO}(\Delta X, \Delta H) = \text{fadeout function}$$

$$= \frac{1}{1 + (\Delta X/K_X)^2 + (\Delta H/K_H)^2} \tag{27}$$

ΔX = horizontal separation between the aircraft and prediction positions (nmi)

ΔH = vertical separation between the aircraft and prediction positions (ft)

K_X = distance blend coefficient (nmi)

K_H = altitude blend coefficient (ft)

The fadeout function is an heuristically defined weighting function that represents a confidence measure of the persistence of the known forecast error at the current aircraft position through points ahead of the aircraft and at future times. Values for blend coefficients used in current systems are $K_X = 200$ nmi and $K_H = 5000$ ft.

To evaluate this and other methods of forecast error compensation, a simulation study was conducted [6] of a cruise-only flight at 37,000 ft with a speed limit of 250 kn CAS [true airspeed (TAS) = 443.4 kn, Mach = 0.773] for the last 150 nmi. Such a speed limit is not usually applied at cruise altitude, but the 150-nmi segment is representative of the descent phase where speed adjustment is severely limited. This simple plan eliminates extraneous variables, constraints, and procedures associated with descent (such as the generation of, and guidance to, a descent path) and simplifies analysis of forecast error compensation methods.

For similar reasons, one of the forecast error cases of the cited study consisted of a constant 10-kn head wind over the entire flight, with forecast of no wind. This level of wind forecast error is usually considered to be small, yet it has significant impact on arrival-time performance. A constant forecast error may not represent reality but can be thought of as the mean component of a variable error. The deviations from the mean tend to compensate for each other in terms of arrival-time error.

In Fig. 6, curve A shows the true airspeed profile adjusted for a required flight time of 2:13:00 when the wind forecast (10-kn head wind) is correct. This curve represents the ideal speed profile. The speed adjustment has taken the speed-limited segment into account by increasing the speed ahead of this

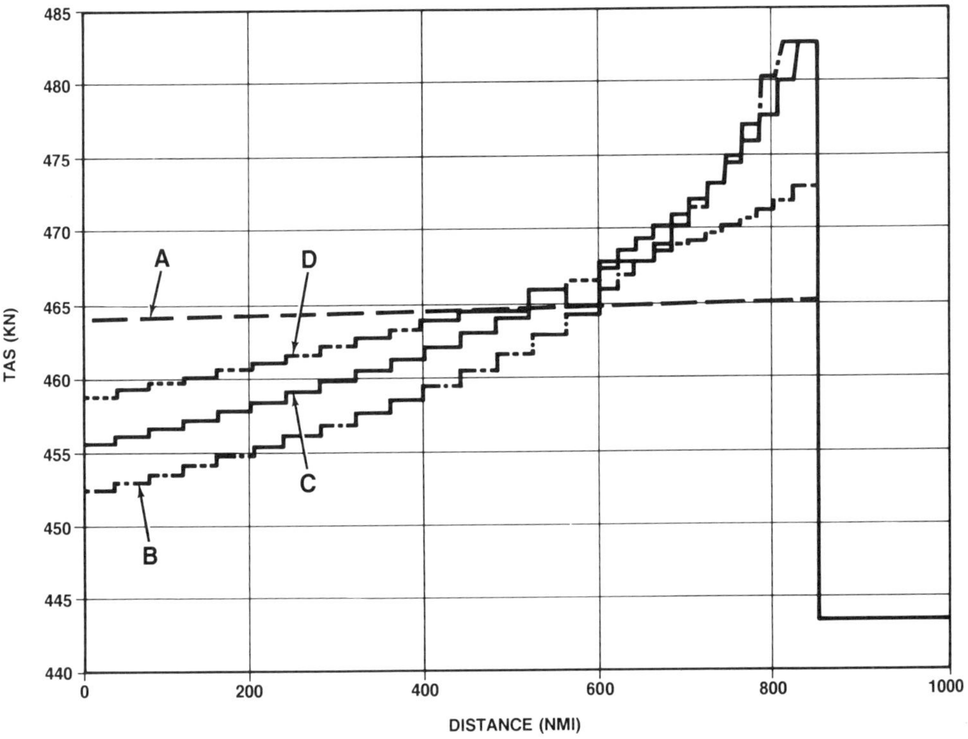

Fig. 6. Prediction blend compensation for forecast error.

segment by the amount required to achieve on-time arrival. At 850 nmi the aircraft decelerates to 250 kn CAS at 0.05 G (0.95 kn/sec); this slope is not apparent in the figure due to the scaling.

For the remaining three curves, the forecast wind is zero and therefore in error by 10 kn. Every 5 min for the first 800 nmi and every 2 min thereafter, a prediction cycle is initiated and the speed is consequently readjusted at each point for on-time arrival. For curve B, the blend function is not applied, and the speed adjustment assumes that the forecast is correct throughout. The initial adjusted speed is therefore lower than the ideal (by 11.5 kn), but the early underspeed eventually leads to overspeed, as shown. An aerodynamic speed limit of 482 kn is briefly encountered after 800 nmi. The flight arrives 36 sec late.

The effect of blending aircraft wind with the forecast wind is shown in curves C and D. For curve C, the nominal value for the distance blend coefficient ($K_X = 200$ nmi) is used and results in speed slightly closer to the ideal. This flight arrives 6 sec late. For curve D, a larger value of $K_X = 500$ nmi is used. Its speed is still closer to the ideal and results in 1.0 sec late arrival. However, this large value for K_X may not be representative of actual forecast error persistence. A general observation with this prediction blend method of forecast error compensation is that it does not compensate sufficiently in the early phases of flight and is therefore required to make large corrections later on.

Instead of trying to compensate for forecast error during prediction, where this error is not known, a method is proposed that compensates during flight where this error is precisely known. The first part of this method is to adjust the flight speed by the forecast wind error at the aircraft position as follows:

$$V_C = V_A + V_{FE} \tag{28}$$

where

V_A = speed command adjusted for predicted arrival time without forecast blend

$$V_{FE} = \text{forecast error speed adjustment}$$
$$= (W_{TF} - W_{TA})/\mathrm{Cos}(FPA) \tag{29}$$

W_{TF} = forecast tail wind at aircraft position

W_{TA} = actual tail wind at aircraft position

FPA = flight path angle

Because the forecast error signal V_{FE} may be noisy during wind turbulence, some form of filtering may be needed to smooth out this signal to prevent undesirable throttle activity.

For the above example in which the forecast wind is zero, the adjusted airspeed V_c amounts to controlling to the prediction ground speed profile. However, the forecast error is expected to be significantly smaller than the wind magnitude, which, in cruise, often exceeds 100 kn, making V_c significantly closer to the optimum airspeed profile than would result by controlling to the prediction ground speed profile.

As with ground speed control, a problem with merely making this adjustment is that speed limits may prevent the aircraft from flying at this adjusted speed. The second part of the method is, therefore, to adjust the speed limits during prediction (only) so that the arrival-time speed adjustment, which is based on the prediction, makes corresponding speed adjustments in the previous segments that are not speed limited. The adjustment of the speed limit during prediction should also be by the amount of the forecast error there, which again is not known. The blended forecast error is used to estimate the amount of speed limit adjustment required for prediction. The prediction speed limit for both maximum and minimum speed is computed as

$$V_{PL} = V_L + V_{LA} \tag{30}$$

where

V_L = the complete aircraft speed limit, including aero/engine and imposed limits, either maximum or minimum as appropriate

$$V_{LA} = (W_{TP} - W_{TF})/\text{Cos}(FPA) \tag{31}$$

W_{TF} = forecast tail wind

W_{TP} = predicted tail wind

= projection of W_P, the blended wind model described earlier, on the aircraft velocity vector.

W_{TP} is an estimate of the tail wind at the prediction point in the speed limited segment, which improves as the aircraft approaches that segment.

Figure 7 shows runs that use this method. Run A, the ideal profile with no forecast error, is shown again for comparison. Run E makes the forecast error

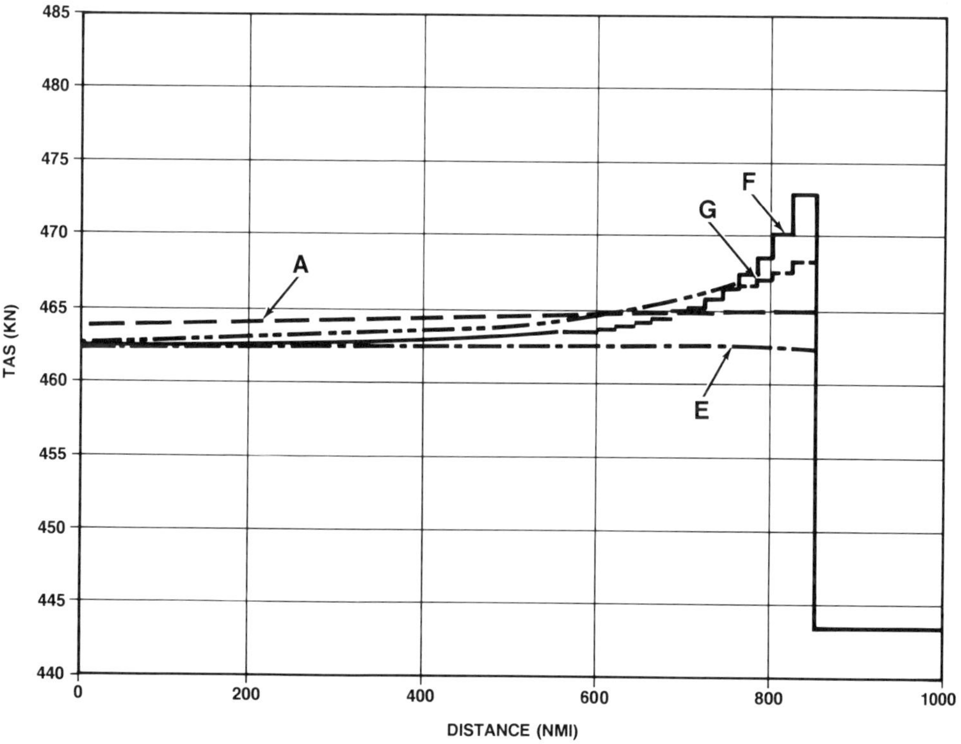

Fig. 7. Flight speed compensation for forecast error.

speed adjustment in the first segment; but it does not plan ahead for the upcoming speed limit at which adjustment is not possible, and therefore the aircraft arrives 27.4 sec late. Runs F and G anticipate the speed-limited section with blend coefficients of 200 and 500 nmi, respectively. Their arrival times are 6.0 and 1.3 sec late, respectively. This arrival-time performance is essentially the same as with the previous method (runs C and D), but the speed profile is significantly closer to the ideal. Fuel burn is reduced by 162 and 53 pounds, respectively.

Other forecast error profiles were studied [6] with similar results, showing improved performance with the proposed forecast error compensation method.

VI. CONCLUSIONS

The simulation studies and the optimization methods that have been described lead to the following conclusions:

1. Total flight cost, composed of direct operating cost plus arrival error cost, is relatively insensitive to cost index in the vicinity of the optimum arrival time, unless this time is near a critical point in the arrival error cost function (such as the scheduled arrival time or connecting flight times).
2. The optimum arrival time and cost index can be found with adequate accuracy for minimizing cost by a procedure that usually requires three trial prediction passes.
3. Precise speed adjustment for required arrival-time prediction can be found by a simple algorithm that requires very few, if any, extra prediction passes to converge. However, wind forecast error compromises prediction accuracy.
4. A simple method of adjusting the flight speed by the forecast error, and adjusting the prediction speed limits by estimated forecast error, provides improved arrival-time performance.
5. Speed control that minimizes total flight cost, or results in accurate arrival time, is achievable with relatively modest modification to the current FMS design. However, valid arrival error cost functions, which are generally different for each arrival situation, must be defined and stored in the FMS data base.

ACKNOWLEDGMENTS

Portions of technical papers "Practical Considerations in Optimal Flight Management Computations," copyright © 1986, AIAA [7], and "Arrival-Time Guidance in Variable Winds," copyright © 1988, AIAA [6], were reproduced with the permission of the American Institute of Aeronautics and Astronautics.

REFERENCES

1. H. ERZBERGER and H. LEE, "Constrained Optimum Trajectories with Specified Range," *J. Guidance Control* **3**, 78–85 (1980).
2. J. A. SORENSEN and M. H. WATERS, "Airborne Method to Minimize Fuel with Fixed Time-of-Arrival Constraints," *J. Guidance Control* **4**, 348–349 (1981).
3. J. W. BURROWS, "Fuel-Optimal Aircraft Trajectories with Fixed Arrival Times," *J. Guidance Control* **6**, 14–19 (1983).
4. A. CHAKRAVARTY, "4-D Fuel-Optimal Guidance in the Presence of Winds," *AIAA Guidance Control Conf., Gatlinburg Ten.* (1983).
5. G. MENGA and H. ERZBERGER, "Time-Controlled Descent Guidance in Uncertain Winds," *J. Guidance Control* **1**, 123–129 (1978).
6. S. LIDÉN, "Arrival-Time Guidance in Variable Winds," *AIAA/IEEE 8th Digital Avion. Syst. Conf. San Jose, Calif.* (1988).
7. S. LIDÉN, "Practical Considerations in Optimal Flight Management Computations," *J. Guidance, Control Dyn.* **9**, No. 4, 427–432 (1986).

OPTIMAL REDUCED-ORDER SUBSPACE-OBSERVER DESIGN WITH A FREQUENCY-DOMAIN ERROR BOUND

WASSIM M. HADDAD

Department of Mechanical and Aerospace Engineering
Florida Institute of Technology
Melbourne, Florida 32901

DENNIS S. BERNSTEIN

Harris Corporation
Melbourne, Florida 32902

I. INTRODUCTION

Constraints on implementation complexity often make it desirable in practice to design estimators of reduced order. Such low-order estimators are also of interest when estimates of only a few state variables are required. For example, although a large flexible space structure may involve numerous flexible modes, only estimates of the rigid body attitude may be desired. The literature on reduced-order estimator design is vast, and we note a representative collection of papers [1–11] as an indication of long-standing interest in this problem.

The starting point for this article is the Riccati equation approach developed in [1]. There it was shown that optimal reduced-order, steady-state estimators can be characterized by means of an algebraic system of equations consisting of one modified Riccati equation and two modified Lyapunov equations coupled by a projection matrix τ. As shown in [1] this projection arises directly from the fixed-order constraint on the estimator order. We note that the order projection τ derived in [1] is given by

$$\tau \triangleq \hat{Q}\hat{P}(\hat{Q}\hat{P})^{\#}, \tag{1}$$

where $(\ )^{\#}$ denotes group generalized inverse, and $\hat{Q}$ and $\hat{P}$ are rank-deficient nonnegative-definite matrices analogous to the controllability and observability Gramians of the estimator. As discussed in [1], the order projection τ arises as a direct consequence of optimality and is not the result of an *a priori* assumption on the structure of the reduced-order estimator. Indeed, no assumption was made in [1] concerning the internal structure of the estimator.

The solution given in [1], however, was confined to problems in which the plant is asymptotically stable though in practice it is often necessary to obtain estimators for plants with unstable modes. Intuitively, it is clear that finite, steady-state state-estimation error for unstable plants is only achievable when the estimator retains, or duplicates in some sense, the unstable modes. The solution given in [1] is inapplicable to the unstable plant problem for the simple reason that the range of the order projection τ may not fully encompass all of the unstable modes. Hence, in this article we derive a new and completely distinct reduced-order solution in which the observation subspace of the estimator is constrained *a priori* to include all of the unstable modes and selected stable modes. Specifically, for a plant with $\hat{n}_{\mathrm{u}}$ unstable modes, we characterize the optimal estimator of order $n_{\mathrm{u}} \geq \hat{n}_{\mathrm{u}}$ which generates estimates of all of the $\hat{n}_{\mathrm{u}}$ unstable states and $n_{\mathrm{u}} - \hat{n}_{\mathrm{u}}$ prespecified stable states. Hence this estimator effectively serves as an *observer* for a designated plant subspace.

The subspace observation constraint is embedded within the optimization process by fixing the internal structure of the reduced-order estimator. This structure gives rise to a projection μ defined by

$$\mu \triangleq \begin{bmatrix} I_{n_{\mathrm{u}}} & P_{\mathrm{u}}^{-1}P_{\mathrm{us}} \\ 0_{n_{\mathrm{s}} \times n_{\mathrm{u}}} & 0_{n_{\mathrm{s}}} \end{bmatrix}, \tag{2}$$

where $P_{\mathrm{u}} \in \mathbb{R}^{n_{\mathrm{u}} \times n_{\mathrm{u}}}$ and $P_{\mathrm{us}} \in \mathbb{R}^{n_{\mathrm{u}} \times n_{\mathrm{s}}}$ are subblocks of an $n \times n$ matrix P satisfying a modified algebraic Lyapunov equation, $n_{\mathrm{u}} \geq \hat{n}_{\mathrm{u}}$ is the dimension of the observation subspace of the estimator containing all of the $\hat{n}_{\mathrm{u}}$ unstable modes and $n_{\mathrm{u}} - \hat{n}_{\mathrm{u}}$ selected stable modes, and $n_{\mathrm{s}} \triangleq n - n_{\mathrm{u}}$ is the dimension of the remaining subspace containing only stable modes. It turns out that the subspace projection μ, which is completely distinct from the order projection τ appearing in [1], plays a crucial role in characterizing the optimal estimator gains. Furthermore, in contrast to the lone observer Riccati equation of the standard full-order theory, in the constrained-subspace case the reduced-order solution consists of one modified Riccati equation and one modified Lyapunov equation coupled by the subspace projection μ.

In addition to the subspace-observation problem just discussed, this article includes the treatment of a worst-case frequency-domain design criterion for the state-estimation error. Specifically, we consider the least-squares state-estimation problem with a constraint on the frequency-domain (i.e., H_∞)

estimation error [12]. This generalization provides additional design flexibility by yielding a reduction of the frequency content of the estimation error in addition to its mean-square magnitude. The principal result in this case is a sufficient condition that yields subspace-constrained estimators satisfying an optimized L_2 bound as well as a prespecified H_∞ bound. The sufficient condition is a direct generalization of the subspace-observation problem developed previously for the least-squares estimation problem. Once again, the optimal reduced-order estimator is characterized by an algebraic system consisting of one modified Riccati equation and one modified Lyapunov equation coupled by the constrained-subspace projection μ with additional coupling arising due to the H_∞ constraint. This result is analogous to recent developments in H_∞ control theory [13–16].

An additional feature of this article is the inclusion of a static estimator gain in conjunction with the dynamic estimator. Thus, our results also represent a generalization of the standard steady-state Kalman filter result to the case of nonstrictly proper estimation. Specifically, noise-free measurements

$$\hat{y} = \hat{C}x(t) \tag{3}$$

multiplied by a static estimator gain lead to the static-gain projection

$$\nu \triangleq Q\hat{C}^{\mathrm{T}}(\hat{C}Q\hat{C}^{\mathrm{T}})^{-1}\hat{C}, \tag{4}$$

where Q is the steady-state estimation-error covariance. This projection has been discussed earlier, for example [17–19]. In the H_∞-constrained case, the static-gain projection ν becomes

$$\nu_\infty \triangleq (\mathcal{Q}\hat{C}^{\mathrm{T}} + \gamma^{-2}\mathcal{Q}\mathcal{P}\mathcal{Q}\hat{C}^{\mathrm{T}})(\hat{C}\mathcal{Q}\hat{C}^{\mathrm{T}} + \gamma^{-2}\hat{C}\mathcal{Q}\mathcal{P}\mathcal{Q}\hat{C}^{\mathrm{T}})^{-1}\hat{C}, \tag{5}$$

where $\mathcal{Q}$ is a bound on the steady-state estimation-error covariance, $\mathcal{P}$ satisfies a modified Lyapunov equation, and γ is the prespecified frequency-domain error bound. If this bound is sufficiently relaxed (i.e., $\gamma \to \infty$), then $\nu_\infty \to \nu$ and the "pure" least-squares nonstrictly proper estimator is recovered. Of course, if nonnoisy measurements of the form (3) are not available for a particular application, then this design aspect can be ignored in both the least-squares and frequency-domain problems. Such specializations are pointed out in later sections.

It should be stressed that all three projections τ, μ, and ν are completely distinct and arise from different design objectives. Specifically, as discussed in [1,2], the order projection τ arises due to a constraint on the order of the estimator, the subspace projection μ arises from a constraint on the structure of the estimator, and the static-gain projection ν arises due to the presence of noise-free measurements. Designing a nonstrictly proper reduced-order estimator that includes all of the unstable modes and an optimal choice of some of the stable modes would involve all three projections and four matrix equations. This unified solution is considerably more complex and thus is deferred to a future paper.

After presenting notation in Section II, we give in Section III the statement of the optimal reduced-order subspace-observer problem. Theorem 1 shows that the reduced-order subspace-constrained estimator is characterized by one modified Riccati equation and one modified Lyapunov equation. The H_∞-constrained reduced-order subspace-observer problem is considered in Section IV. The principal result of this section (Lemma 1) shows that if the algebraic Lyapunov equation for the error covariance is replaced by a modified Riccati equation possessing a nonnegative-definite solution, then the H_∞ estimation constraint is satisfied, and the least-squares state-estimation error criterion is bounded above by an auxiliary cost function. The problem of determining reduced-order estimators that minimize this upper bound subject to the Riccati equation constraint is considered as the auxiliary minimization problem. Necessary conditions for the auxiliary minimization problem (Theorem 2) are again given in the form of a coupled system of algebraic Riccati and Lyapunov equations. To develop connections with the standard Kalman filter theory, the results of Theorem 2 are specialized to the full-order case (see Remark 11). In Section V the necessary conditions of Theorem 2 are combined with Lemma 1 to yield sufficient conditions for stability of the estimation-error dynamics, constrained H_∞ estimation error, and bounded least-squares state-estimation error.

II. NOTATION AND DEFINITIONS

$\mathbb{R}, \mathbb{R}^{r\times s}, \mathbb{R}^r, \mathbb{E}$	Real numbers, $r \times s$ real matrices, $\mathbb{R}^{r\times 1}$, expected value
$I_r, (\ )^{\mathrm{T}}, 0_{r\times s}, 0_r$	$r \times r$ identity matrix, transpose, $r \times s$ zero matrix, $0_{r\times r}$
tr	Trace
$\sigma_{\max}(Z)$	Largest singular value of matrix Z
$\|H(s)\|_\infty$	$\sup_{\omega\in\mathbb{R}} \sigma_{\max}[H(j\omega)]$
$\mathcal{N}(Z), \mathcal{R}(Z)$	Null space, range of matrix Z
$\mathbb{S}^r, \mathbb{N}^r, \mathbb{P}^r$	$r \times r$ symmetric, nonnegative-definite, positive-definite matrices
$Z_1 \leq Z_2, Z_1 < Z_2$	$Z_2 - Z_1 \in \mathbb{N}^r, Z_2 - Z_1 \in \mathbb{P}^r, Z_2, Z_1 \in \mathbb{S}^r$
$n, l, \hat{l}, n_e, n_u, n_s, q, p$	Positive integers
$x, y, \hat{y}, x_e, x_u, x_s, y_e$	$n, l, \hat{l}, n_e, n_u, n_s, q$-dimensional vectors
$A, C, \hat{C}$	$n \times n, l \times n, \hat{l} \times n$ matrices
A_u, A_{us}, A_s	$n_u \times n_u, n_u \times n_s, n_s \times n_s$ matrices
$C_u, C_s, \hat{C}_u, \hat{C}_s$	$l \times n_u, l \times n_s, \hat{l} \times n_u, \hat{l} \times n_s$ matrices

D_1, D_2, E, L	$n \times p, l \times p, r \times q, q \times n$ matrices
D_{1u}, D_{1s}, L_u, L_s	$n_u \times p, n_s \times p, q \times n_u, q \times n_s$ matrices
R	$E^T E$, estimation-error weighting in $\mathbb{P}^q$
A_e, B_e, C_e, D_e	$n_e \times n_e, n_e \times l, q \times n_e, q \times \hat{l}$ matrices
$w(\cdot)$	p-dimensional standard white noise process
V_1, V_2	Intensity of $D_1 w(\cdot)$, $D_2 w(\cdot)$; $V_1 = D_1 D_1^T \in \mathbb{N}^n$, $V_2 = D_2 D_2^T \in \mathbb{P}^l$
V_{12}	Cross intensity of $D_1 w(\cdot)$, $D_2 w(\cdot)$; $V_{12} = D_1 D_2^T \in \mathbb{R}^{n \times l}$
$\tilde{A}$	$A - \begin{bmatrix} I_{n_u} \\ 0_{n_s \times n_u} \end{bmatrix} B_e C$, $n_u < n$; $A - B_e C$, $n_u = n$
$\tilde{D}$	$D_1 - \begin{bmatrix} I_{n_u} \\ 0_{n_s \times n_u} \end{bmatrix} B_e D_2$, $n_u < n$; $D_1 - B_e D_2$, $n_u = n$
$\tilde{E}$	$E(L - D_e C)$
$\tilde{R}$	$\tilde{E}^T \tilde{E} = (L - D_e C)^T R (L - D_e C)$
$\tilde{V}$	$\tilde{D}\tilde{D}^T$

III. THE OPTIMAL REDUCED-ORDER SUBSPACE-OBSERVER PROBLEM

The problem is addressed as follows: Given the nth-order system

$$\dot{x}(t) = Ax(t) + D_1 w(t), \quad t \in [0, \infty), \tag{6}$$

with noisy and nonnoisy measurements

$$y(t) = Cx(t) + D_2 w(t), \tag{7}$$

$$\hat{y}(t) = \hat{C}x(t), \tag{8}$$

and with the partitioning

$$\begin{bmatrix} \dot{x}_u(t) \\ \dot{x}_s(t) \end{bmatrix} = \begin{bmatrix} A_u & A_{us} \\ 0_{n_s \times n_u} & A_s \end{bmatrix} \begin{bmatrix} x_u(t) \\ x_s(t) \end{bmatrix} + \begin{bmatrix} D_{1u} \\ D_{1s} \end{bmatrix} w(t), \tag{9}$$

$$y(t) = [C_u \quad C_s] \begin{bmatrix} x_u(t) \\ x_s(t) \end{bmatrix} + D_2 w(t), \tag{10}$$

$$\hat{y}(t) = [\hat{C}_u \quad \hat{C}_s] \begin{bmatrix} x_u(t) \\ x_s(t) \end{bmatrix}, \tag{11}$$

design an n_uth-order nonstrictly proper state estimator

$$\dot{x}_e(t) = A_e x_e(t) + B_e y(t), \tag{12}$$

$$y_e(t) = C_e x_e(t) + D_e \hat{y}(t), \tag{13}$$

such that the state-estimation error criterion

$$J(A_e, B_e, C_e, D_e) \triangleq \lim_{t \to \infty} \mathbb{E}[Lx(t) - y_e(t)]^{\mathrm{T}} R [Lx(t) - y_e(t)] \tag{14}$$

is minimized and

$$\lim_{t \to \infty} [x_u(t) - x_e(t)] = 0, \tag{15}$$

for all $x(0)$ and $x_e(0)$ when $D_1 = 0$ and $D_2 = 0$.

Remark 1. Note that (13) allows the additional feature of a static feedthrough gain D_e when nonnoisy measurements (8) are available. This corresponds to a static least-squares estimator in conjunction with the dynamic (Wiener–Kalman) estimator. For the special case in which only noisy measurements are available, one needs only to set $D_e = 0$, which leads to a strictly proper state estimator.

Remark 2. Note that (14) is the usual least-squares state-estimation error criterion whereas (15) implies that perfect observation is achieved at steady state for the plant and observer dynamics under zero external disturbances and arbitrary initial conditions.

In this formulation the plant state $x(t)$ is partitioned into subsystems for $x_u(t)$ and $x_s(t)$ of dimension n_u and n_s, respectively. Furthermore, we assume that if λ is an eigenvalue of A such that $\mathrm{Re}(\lambda) \geq 0$, then λ is also an eigenvalue of A_u with the same multiplicity. That is, the n_u-dimensional subspace for $x_u(t)$ contains all the unstable modes of the system (if there are any) and possibly selected stable modes. Thus, if the unstable subspace of A has dimension $\hat{n}_u$, then we have $n_u \geq \hat{n}_u$, and the n_s-dimensional subspace for $x_s(t)$ contains the remaining stable modes. Furthermore, the matrix L, which is partitioned as

$$L \triangleq [L_u \quad L_s], \tag{16}$$

where L_u and L_s are $q \times n_u$ and $q \times n_s$ matrices, identifies the states or linear combinations of states whose estimates are desired. The order n_e of the estimator state x_e is fixed to be equal to the order of the n_u-dimensional subspace for $x_u(t)$. Thus, the goal of the optimal reduced-order subspace-observer problem is to design an estimator of order n_u which yields quadratically optimal linear least-squares estimates of specified linear combinations of the states of the system. To satisfy the observation constraint (15), define the error state $z(t) \triangleq x_u(t) - x_e(t)$ satisfying

$$\begin{aligned}\dot{z}(t) &= \dot{x}_u(t) - \dot{x}_e(t) \\ &= (A_u - B_e C_u)x_u(t) - A_e x_e(t) + (A_{us} - B_e C_s)x_s(t) + D_{1u}w(t) - B_e D_2 w(t).\end{aligned} \tag{17}$$

Note that the explicit dependence of the error states $z(t)$ on the states $x_u(t)$ can be eliminated by constraining

$$A_e = A_u - B_e C_u. \tag{18}$$

Thus, (17) becomes

$$\dot{z}(t) = A_e z(t) + (A_{us} - B_e C_s)x_s(t) + D_{1u}w(t) - B_e D_2 w(t). \tag{19}$$

Furthermore, the explicit dependence of the estimation error (14) on the $x_u(t)$ subsystem can be eliminated by constraining

$$C_e = L_u - D_e \hat{C}_u. \tag{20}$$

Henceforth, we assume that A_e and C_e are given by (18) and (20). Now, from (9)–(13) it follows that

$$\dot{\tilde{x}}(t) = \tilde{A}\tilde{x}(t) + \tilde{D}w(t), \tag{21}$$

where

$$\tilde{x}(t) \triangleq \begin{bmatrix} z(t) \\ x_s(t) \end{bmatrix}, \qquad \tilde{A} \triangleq \begin{bmatrix} A_u - B_e C_u & A_{us} - B_e C_s \\ 0_{n_s \times n_u} & A_s \end{bmatrix}.$$

To guarantee that J is finite, consider the set of asymptotically stable reduced-order estimators,

$$\mathscr{S} \triangleq \{(A_e, B_e, C_e, D_e)\colon A_e = A_u - B_e C_u \quad \text{is asymptotically stable}\},$$

which is nonempty if (A_u, C_u) is detectable.

Before continuing, we note that if A_e is asymptotically stable, then since A_s is asymptotically stable, $\tilde{A}$ is also asymptotically stable. Hence the least-squares state-estimation error criterion (14) is given by

$$J(A_e, B_e, C_e, D_e) = \operatorname{tr} Q\tilde{R}, \tag{22}$$

where the $n \times n$ steady-state error covariance,

$$Q \triangleq \lim_{t \to \infty} \mathbb{E}[\tilde{x}(t)\tilde{x}^{\mathrm{T}}(t)] \geq 0, \tag{23}$$

exists and satisfies the algebraic Lyapunov equation

$$0 = \tilde{A}Q + Q\tilde{A}^{\mathrm{T}} + \tilde{V}. \tag{24}$$

Furthermore, for nondegeneracy we restrict our attention to the set of admissible estimators,

$$\mathscr{S}^+ \triangleq \{(A_e, B_e, C_e, D_e) \in \mathscr{S}\colon (A_e, C_e) \quad \text{is observable and} \quad \hat{C}Q\hat{C}^{\mathrm{T}} > 0\}.$$

The definiteness condition $\hat{C}Q\hat{C}^{\mathrm{T}} > 0$ holds if $\hat{C}$ has full row rank and Q is positive definite. Conversely, if $\hat{C}Q\hat{C}^{\mathrm{T}} > 0$, then $\hat{C}$ must have full row rank but Q need not necessarily be positive definite. As shown in the appendix, this condition implies the existence of the static-gain projection ν, which is defined in (35).

The following result gives necessary conditions that characterize solutions to the optimal reduced-order subspace-observer problem. For convenience in stating this result, define

$$Q_{\mathrm{a}} \triangleq QC^{\mathrm{T}} + V_{12}.$$

Theorem 1. If $(A_{\mathrm{e}}, B_{\mathrm{e}}, C_{\mathrm{e}}, D_{\mathrm{e}}) \in \mathscr{S}^+$ solves the optimal reduced-order subspace-observer problem with constraints (18) and (19) and Q given by (24), then there exists $P \in \mathbb{N}^n$ such that

$$A_{\mathrm{e}} = \Phi(A - Q_{\mathrm{a}}V_2^{-1}C)F^{\mathrm{T}}, \tag{25}$$

$$B_{\mathrm{e}} = \Phi Q_{\mathrm{a}}V_2^{-1}, \tag{26}$$

$$C_{\mathrm{e}} = L\nu_{\perp}F^{\mathrm{T}}, \tag{27}$$

$$D_{\mathrm{e}} = LQ\hat{C}^{\mathrm{T}}(\hat{C}Q\hat{C}^{\mathrm{T}})^{-1}, \tag{28}$$

and such that Q and P satisfy

$$0 = AQ + QA^{\mathrm{T}} + V_1 - Q_{\mathrm{a}}V_2^{-1}Q_{\mathrm{a}}^{\mathrm{T}} + \mu_{\perp}Q_{\mathrm{a}}V_2^{-1}Q_{\mathrm{a}}^{\mathrm{T}}\mu_{\perp}^{\mathrm{T}}, \tag{29}$$

$$0 = (A - \mu Q_{\mathrm{a}}V_2^{-1}C)^{\mathrm{T}}P + P(A - \mu Q_{\mathrm{a}}V_2^{-1}C) + \nu_{\perp}^{\mathrm{T}}L^{\mathrm{T}}RL\nu_{\perp}, \tag{30}$$

where

$$P = \begin{bmatrix} P_{\mathrm{u}} & P_{\mathrm{us}} \\ P_{\mathrm{us}}^{\mathrm{T}} & P_{\mathrm{s}} \end{bmatrix} \in \mathbb{R}^{(n_{\mathrm{u}}+n_{\mathrm{s}})\times(n_{\mathrm{u}}+n_{\mathrm{s}})}, \tag{31}$$

$$P_{\mathrm{u}} > 0, \tag{32}$$

$$F \triangleq [I_{n_{\mathrm{u}}} \quad 0_{n_{\mathrm{u}}\times n_{\mathrm{s}}}], \qquad \Phi \triangleq [I_{n_{\mathrm{u}}} \quad P_{\mathrm{u}}^{-1}P_{\mathrm{us}}], \tag{33}$$

$$\mu \triangleq F^{\mathrm{T}}\Phi = \begin{bmatrix} I_{n_{\mathrm{u}}} & P_{\mathrm{u}}^{-1}P_{\mathrm{us}} \\ 0_{n_{\mathrm{s}}\times n_{\mathrm{u}}} & 0_{n_{\mathrm{s}}} \end{bmatrix}, \qquad \mu_{\perp} \triangleq I_n - \mu, \tag{34}$$

$$\nu \triangleq Q\hat{C}^{\mathrm{T}}(\hat{C}Q\hat{C}^{\mathrm{T}})^{-1}\hat{C}, \qquad \nu_{\perp} \triangleq I_n - \nu. \tag{35}$$

Furthermore, the minimal cost is given by

$$J(A_{\mathrm{e}}, B_{\mathrm{e}}, C_{\mathrm{e}}, D_{\mathrm{e}}) = \operatorname{tr} Q\nu_{\perp}^{\mathrm{T}}L^{\mathrm{T}}RL\nu_{\perp}. \tag{36}$$

Conversely, if there exist $Q, P \in \mathbb{N}^n$ satisfying (29) and (30), and such that $\hat{C}Q\hat{C}^{\mathrm{T}} > 0$, then Q satisfies (24) with $(A_{\mathrm{e}}, B_{\mathrm{e}}, C_{\mathrm{e}}, D_{\mathrm{e}})$ given by (25)–(28). Furthermore, $(\tilde{A}, \tilde{D})$ is stabilizable if and only if A_{e} is asymptotically stable. In this case $(A_{\mathrm{e}}, C_{\mathrm{e}})$ is observable.

Proof. The result follows as a special case of Theorem 2. See Remark 9 for details. □

Remark 3. Equations (29) and (30) involve two distinct projections, namely, v and μ. Note that v and μ are idempotent since $v^2 = v$ and $\mu^2 = \mu$. As discussed earlier, the presence of noise-free measurements $\hat{y}(t) = \hat{C}x(t)$ gives rise to the static-gain projection v whereas the observation constraint (15) gives rise to the subspace projection μ. It is easy to see that rank $\mu = n_u$; and with Sylvester's inequality, it follows that rank $v = \hat{l}$. Finally, it should be stressed that the subspace projection μ is completely distinct from the order projection τ appearing in [1].

Remark 4. Note that with B_e and D_e given by (26) and (28), the expressions (25) and (27) for A_e and C_e are equivalent to the constraints (28) and (29).

Remark 5. As a first step in analyzing these equations, consider the extreme case $\hat{l} = n$ and $\hat{C} = I_n$ so that perfect measurements of the entire state are available. It then follows from Theorem 1 with Q positive definite that $v = I_n$, $v_\perp = 0$, $C_e = 0$ (i.e., the dynamic filter is disabled), $D_e = L$, and by (36), $J = 0$. More generally, suppose that $\mathscr{R}(L) \subset \mathscr{R}(\hat{C})$, which implies that perfect measurements of Lx are available. In this case,

$$\text{rank}\begin{bmatrix} \hat{C} \\ L \end{bmatrix} = \text{rank } \hat{C},$$

and thus $L = \hat{L}\hat{C}$ for some $\hat{L} \in \mathbb{R}^{q \times \hat{l}}$ without loss of generality. Thus, it follows from Theorem 1 that $C_e = 0$, $D_e = L$, and $J = 0$ since $L^T R L = \hat{C}^T \hat{L}^T R \hat{L} \hat{C}$ and $\hat{C} v_\perp = 0$. These are, of course, expected results because perfect estimation is achievable in both cases.

Remark 6. Note that for A_e, B_e, C_e, D_e given by (25)–(28), the estimator assumes the innovations form

$$\dot{x}_e(t) = \Phi A F^T x_e(t) + \Phi Q_a V_2^{-1}[y(t) - CF^T x_e(t)]. \tag{37}$$

By introducing the quasi full-state estimate $\hat{x}(t) \triangleq F^T x_e(t) \in \mathbb{R}^n$, so that $\mu\hat{x}(t) = \hat{x}(t)$ and $x_e(t) = \Phi\hat{x}(t) \in \mathbb{R}^{n_u}$, we can write (37) as

$$\dot{\hat{x}}(t) = \mu A \mu \hat{x}(t) + \mu Q_a V_2^{-1}(y(t) - C\hat{x}(t)). \tag{38}$$

Note that although the implemented estimator (37) has the state $x_e(t) \in \mathbb{R}^{n_u}$ (38) can be viewed as a quasi full-order estimator whose geometric structure is entirely dictated by the projection μ. Specifically, error inputs $Q_a V_2^{-1}(y(t) - \hat{C}\hat{x}(t))$ are annihilated unless they are contained in $[\mathscr{N}(\mu)]^\perp = \mathscr{R}(\mu^T)$. Hence the observation subspace of the estimator is precisely $\mathscr{R}(\mu^T)$.

Remark 7. In the full-order case $n_u = n$, Theorem 1 yields a steady-state nonstrictly proper Kalman filter. To see this, formally set $\Phi = F = \mu = I_n$ and $\mu_\perp = 0$ so that (22) is superfluous and (21) becomes

$$0 = AQ + QA^T + V_1 - Q_a V_2^{-1} Q_a^T, \tag{39}$$

with gains

$$A_e = A - Q_a V_2^{-1} C, \tag{40}$$

$$B_e = Q_a V_2^{-1}, \tag{41}$$

$$C_e = L v_\perp, \tag{42}$$

$$D_e = LQ\hat{C}^T(\hat{C}Q\hat{C}^T)^{-1}. \tag{43}$$

Finally, to recover the standard steady-state Kalman filter, which involves only noisy measurements, set $\hat{C} = 0$, delete (43), and define $v = 0$ and $v_\perp = I_n$.

IV. THE OPTIMAL REDUCED-ORDER SUBSPACE-OBSERVER PROBLEM WITH AN H_∞ ERROR CONSTRAINT

We now introduce the reduced-order subspace-observer problem with an H_∞ constraint on the H_∞-norm of the state-estimation error. Specifically, we constrain the transfer function between disturbances and error states to have H_∞ norm less than γ. Given the nth-order observed system (6)–(11), determine an n_uth-order subspace observer, (12) and (13), that satisfies the following design criteria:

1. $A_e = A_u - B_e C_u$ is asymptotically stable.
2. The $r \times p$ transfer function

$$H(s) \triangleq \tilde{E}(sI_{\tilde{n}} - \tilde{A})^{-1}\tilde{D} \tag{44}$$

   from disturbances $w(t)$ to error states $E[Lx(t) - y_e(t)]$ satisfies the constraint

$$\|H(s)\|_\infty \leq \gamma, \tag{45}$$

   where $\gamma > 0$ is a given constant.
3. The least-squares state-estimation error criterion (14) is minimized, and the observation constraint (15) holds.

The key step in enforcing (45) is to replace the algebraic Lyapunov equation (24) by an algebraic Riccati equation. Justification for this technique is provided by the following result.

Lemma 1. Let (A_e, B_e, C_e, D_e) be given and assume there exists an $n \times n$ matrix $\mathcal{Q}$ satisfying

$$\mathcal{Q} \in \mathbb{N}^n \tag{46}$$

and

$$0 = \tilde{A}\mathcal{Q} + \mathcal{Q}\tilde{A}^T + \gamma^{-2}\mathcal{Q}\tilde{R}\mathcal{Q} + \tilde{V}. \tag{47}$$

Then,

$$(\tilde{A}, \tilde{D}) \text{ is stabilizable} \tag{48}$$

if and only if

$$A_e \text{ is asymptotically stable.} \tag{49}$$

Furthermore, in this case,

$$\|H(s)\|_\infty \leq \gamma, \tag{50}$$

$$Q \leq \mathcal{Q}, \tag{51}$$

and

$$J(A_e, B_e, C_e, D_e) \leq \mathcal{J}(A_e, B_e, C_e, D_e, \mathcal{Q}), \tag{52}$$

where

$$\mathcal{J}(A_e, B_e, C_e, D_e, \mathcal{Q}) \triangleq \operatorname{tr} \mathcal{Q}\tilde{R}. \tag{53}$$

Proof. See [16]. □

Lemma 1 shows that the H_∞ constraint is automatically enforced when a nonnegative-definite solution to (47) is known to exist. Furthermore, the solution $\mathcal{Q}$ provides an upper bound for the actual closed-loop state covariance Q, which in turn yields an upper bound for the least-squares state-estimation error criterion. That is, given a fixed-order estimator (A_e, B_e, C_e, D_e) satisfying the H_∞ estimation constraint, the actual least-squares state-estimation error is guaranteed to be no worse than the bound given by $\mathcal{J}(A_e, B_e, C_e, D_e, \mathcal{Q})$ if (47) is solvable. Hence $\mathcal{J}(A_e, B_e, C_e, D_e, \mathcal{Q})$ can be interpreted as an auxiliary cost, which leads to the following optimization problem.

To solve the auxiliary minimization problem, determine the $(A_e, B_e, C_e, D_e, \mathcal{Q})$ that minimizes $\mathcal{J}(A_e, B_e, C_e, D_e, \mathcal{Q})$ subject to (46) and (47).

Rigorous derivation of the necessary conditions for the auxiliary minimization problem requires additional technical assumptions. Specifically, we restrict $(A_e, B_e, C_e, D_e, \mathcal{Q})$ to the open set

$$\begin{aligned} \mathcal{S}_\infty \triangleq \{(A_e, B_e, C_e, D_e, \mathcal{Q})\colon & \tilde{A} + \gamma^{-2}\mathcal{Q}\tilde{R} \text{ is asymptotically stable,} \\ & (A_e, B_e, C_e) \text{ is minimal, and } \hat{C}\mathcal{Q}\hat{C}^{\mathrm{T}} + \gamma^{-2}\hat{C}\mathcal{Q}\mathcal{P}\mathcal{Q}\hat{C}^{\mathrm{T}} > 0\}, \end{aligned} \tag{54}$$

where $\mathcal{P} \in \mathbb{N}^n$ satisfies

$$0 = (\tilde{A} + \gamma^{-2}\mathcal{Q}\tilde{R})^{\mathrm{T}}\mathcal{P} + \mathcal{P}(\tilde{A} + \gamma^{-2}\mathcal{Q}\tilde{R}) + \tilde{R}.$$

Remark 8. The set $\mathcal{S}_\infty$ constitutes sufficient conditions under which the Lagrange multiplier technique is applicable to the auxiliary minimization problem. Specifically, the requirement that $\mathcal{Q}$ be positive definite replaces (46) by an open-set constraint, the stability of $\tilde{A} + \gamma^{-2}\mathcal{Q}\tilde{R}$ serves as a normality condition, (A_e, B_e, C_e) minimal is a nondegeneracy condition, and the definiteness condition implies the existence of the static-gain projection v_∞, defined in (62) for the H_∞-constrained problem. Finally, for arbitrary $\mathcal{Q} \in \mathbb{R}^{n \times n}$, define the notation

$$\mathcal{Q}_a \triangleq \mathcal{Q}C^T + V_{12}. \tag{55}$$

Theorem 2. If $(A_e, B_e, C_e, D_e, \mathcal{Q}) \in \mathcal{S}_\infty$ solves the auxiliary minimization problem with constraints (18) and (20) and $\mathcal{Q}$ given by (47), then there exists $\mathcal{P} \in \mathbb{N}^n$ such that

$$A_e = \Phi(A - \mathcal{Q}_a V_2^{-1} C)F^T, \tag{56}$$

$$B_e = \Phi \mathcal{Q}_a V_2^{-1}, \tag{57}$$

$$C_e = L v_{\infty\perp} F^T, \tag{58}$$

$$D_e = L(\mathcal{Q}\hat{C}^T + \gamma^{-2}\mathcal{Q}\mathcal{P}\mathcal{Q}\hat{C}^T)(\hat{C}\mathcal{Q}\hat{C}^T + \gamma^{-2}\hat{C}\mathcal{Q}\mathcal{P}\mathcal{Q}\hat{C}^T)^{-1}, \tag{59}$$

and such that $\mathcal{Q}$ and $\mathcal{P}$ satisfy

$$\begin{aligned} 0 = {} & A\mathcal{Q} + \mathcal{Q}A^T + V_1 + \gamma^{-2}\mathcal{Q}v_{\infty\perp}^T L^T R L v_{\infty\perp}\mathcal{Q} - \mathcal{Q}_a V_2^{-1}\mathcal{Q}_a^T \\ & + \mu_\perp \mathcal{Q}_a V_2^{-1}\mathcal{Q}_a^T \mu_\perp^T, \end{aligned} \tag{60}$$

$$\begin{aligned} 0 = {} & (A - \mu\mathcal{Q}_a V_2^{-1}C + \gamma^{-2}\mathcal{Q}v_{\infty\perp}^T L^T R L v_{\infty\perp})^T\mathcal{P} + \mathcal{P}(A - \mu\mathcal{Q}_a V_2^{-1}C \\ & + \gamma^{-2}\mathcal{Q}v_{\infty\perp}^T L^T R L v_{\infty\perp}) + v_{\infty\perp}^T L^T R L v_{\infty\perp}, \end{aligned} \tag{61}$$

where F, Φ, μ, and $\mu_\perp$ are defined by (33) and (34), $\mathcal{P}$ is partitioned as in (31), and v_∞ and $v_{\infty\perp}$ are defined by

$$\begin{aligned} v_\infty &\triangleq (\mathcal{Q}\hat{C}^T + \gamma^{-2}\mathcal{Q}\mathcal{P}\mathcal{Q}\hat{C}^T)(\hat{C}\mathcal{Q}\hat{C}^T + \gamma^{-2}\hat{C}\mathcal{Q}\mathcal{P}\mathcal{Q}\hat{C}^T)^{-1}\hat{C}, \\ v_{\infty\perp} &\triangleq I_n - v_\infty. \end{aligned} \tag{62}$$

Furthermore, the auxiliary cost (53) is given by

$$\mathcal{J}(A_e, B_e, C_e, D_e, \mathcal{Q}) = \operatorname{tr} \mathcal{Q}v_{\infty\perp}^T L^T R L v_{\infty\perp}. \tag{63}$$

Conversely, if there exist $\mathcal{Q}, \mathcal{P} \in \mathbb{N}^n$ satisfying (60) and (61), and such that $\hat{C}\mathcal{Q}\hat{C}^T + \gamma^{-2}\hat{C}\mathcal{Q}\mathcal{P}\mathcal{Q}\hat{C}^T > 0$, then $(A_e, B_e, C_e, D_e, \mathcal{Q})$ given by (56)–(60) satisfy (46) and (47) with the auxiliary cost (53) given by (63).

Proof. See Appendix. □

Remark 9. Theorem 2 presents necessary conditions for the auxiliary minimization problem that explicitly synthesize full- and reduced-order estimators (A_e, B_e, C_e, D_e). If the H_∞ estimation constraint is sufficiently relaxed (i.e., $\gamma \to \infty$), then $v_\infty = v$ and (60) and (61) reduce to (29) and (30), thus recovering the result of Theorem 1.

Remark 10. Since $\hat{C}\mathcal{Q}\hat{C}^T \le \hat{C}\mathcal{Q}\hat{C}^T + \gamma^{-2}\hat{C}\mathcal{Q}\mathcal{P}\mathcal{Q}\hat{C}^T$, it follows that if $\hat{C}\mathcal{Q}\hat{C}^T$

is positive definite, then so is $\hat{C}\mathcal{Q}\hat{C}^{\mathrm{T}} + \gamma^{-2}\hat{C}\mathcal{Q}\mathcal{P}\mathcal{Q}\hat{C}^{\mathrm{T}}$. Also, note that since $Q \leq \mathcal{Q}$, it follows that if $\hat{C}Q\hat{C}^{\mathrm{T}}$ is positive definite, then so is $\hat{C}\mathcal{Q}\hat{C}^{\mathrm{T}}$. Hence, if v exists for an unconstrained problem, it follows that v_{∞} will not fail to exist due to the singularity of $\hat{C}\mathcal{Q}\hat{C}^{\mathrm{T}} + \gamma^{-2}\hat{C}\mathcal{Q}\mathcal{P}\mathcal{Q}\hat{C}^{\mathrm{T}}$ for the H_{∞}-constrained problem.

As discussed in Remark 7, in the full-order (Kalman-filter) case, set $n_{\mathrm{u}} = n$, $F = \Phi = \mu = I_n$, and $\mu_{\perp} = 0$. To develop further connections with standard steady-state Kalman filter theory assume that

$$V_{12} = 0. \tag{64}$$

In this case, the gain expressions (56)–(59) become

$$A_{\mathrm{e}} = A - \mathcal{Q}C^{\mathrm{T}}V_2^{-1}C, \tag{65}$$

$$B_{\mathrm{e}} = \mathcal{Q}C^{\mathrm{T}}V_2^{-1}, \tag{66}$$

$$C_{\mathrm{e}} = Lv_{\infty\perp}, \tag{67}$$

$$D_{\mathrm{e}} = L(\mathcal{Q}\hat{C}^{\mathrm{T}} + \gamma^{-2}\mathcal{Q}\mathcal{P}\mathcal{Q}\hat{C}^{\mathrm{T}})(\hat{C}\mathcal{Q}\hat{C}^{\mathrm{T}} + \gamma^{-2}\hat{C}\mathcal{Q}\mathcal{P}\mathcal{Q}\hat{C}^{\mathrm{T}})^{-1}, \tag{68}$$

whereas (60) and (61) specialize to

$$0 = A\mathcal{Q} + \mathcal{Q}A^{\mathrm{T}} + V_1 + \gamma^{-2}\mathcal{Q}v_{\infty\perp}^{\mathrm{T}}L^{\mathrm{T}}RLv_{\infty\perp}\mathcal{Q} - \mathcal{Q}C^{\mathrm{T}}V_2^{-1}C\mathcal{Q}, \tag{69a}$$

$$\begin{aligned} 0 = {} & (A - \mathcal{Q}C^{\mathrm{T}}V_2^{-1}C + \gamma^{-2}\mathcal{Q}v_{\infty\perp}^{\mathrm{T}}L^{\mathrm{T}}RLv_{\infty\perp})^{\mathrm{T}}\mathcal{P} \\ & + \mathcal{P}(A - \mathcal{Q}C^{\mathrm{T}}V_2^{-1}C + \gamma^{-2}\mathcal{Q}v_{\infty\perp}^{\mathrm{T}}L^{\mathrm{T}}RLv_{\infty\perp}) + v_{\infty\perp}^{\mathrm{T}}L^{\mathrm{T}}RLv_{\infty\perp}. \end{aligned} \tag{69b}$$

Remark 11. Note that the necessary conditions for the full-order non-strictly proper filter problem consist of one modified Riccati equation and one modified Lyapunov equation. To recover the case involving only noisy measurements, set $\hat{C} = 0$, delete (68), and define $v_{\infty} = 0$. In this case, (69) becomes

$$0 = A\mathcal{Q} + \mathcal{Q}A^{\mathrm{T}} + V_1 + \gamma^{-2}\mathcal{Q}L^{\mathrm{T}}RL\mathcal{Q} - \mathcal{Q}C^{\mathrm{T}}V_2^{-1}C\mathcal{Q}. \tag{70}$$

Finally, by relaxing the H_{∞}-constraint (i.e., $\gamma \to \infty$), (70) reduces to the standard observer Riccati equation.

V. SUFFICIENT CONDITIONS FOR COMBINED LEAST-SQUARES AND FREQUENCY-DOMAIN ERROR ESTIMATION

In this section we combine Lemma 1 with the converse of Theorem 2 to obtain our main result, guaranteeing H_{∞}-constrained estimation with an optimized least-squares bound on the state-estimation error criterion.

Theorem 3. Suppose there exist $\mathcal{Q}, \mathcal{P} \in \mathbb{N}^n$ satisfying (60) and (61), and let (A_e, B_e, C_e, D_e) be given by (56)–(59). Then (48) is satisfied if and only if A_e is asymptotically stable. In this case, the transfer function (44) satisfies the H_∞ estimation-error constraint

$$\|H(s)\|_\infty \leq \gamma, \tag{71}$$

and the least-squares state-estimation error criterion (14) satisfies the bound

$$J(A_e, B_e, C_e, D_e) \leq \operatorname{tr} \mathcal{Q} v_{\infty\perp}^{\mathrm{T}} L^{\mathrm{T}} R L v_{\infty\perp}. \tag{72}$$

Proof. The converse portion of Theorem 2 implies that $\mathcal{Q}$ given by (60) satisfies (46) and (47). It now follows from Lemma 1 that the stabilizability condition (48) is equivalent to the asymptotic stability of A_e, the H_∞ estimation-error constraint (50) holds, and the least-squares state-estimation error criterion satisfies the bound (53) which is equivalent to (72). □

APPENDIX. PROOF OF THEOREM 2

To optimize (53) over the open set $\mathcal{S}_\infty$ subject to the constraint (47), form the Lagrangian

$$\mathcal{L}(B_e, D_e, \mathcal{Q}, \mathcal{P}, \lambda) \triangleq \operatorname{tr}\{\lambda \mathcal{Q} \tilde{R} + [\tilde{A}\mathcal{Q} + \mathcal{Q}\tilde{A}^{\mathrm{T}} + \gamma^{-2}\mathcal{Q}\tilde{R}\mathcal{Q} + \tilde{V}]\mathcal{P}\}, \tag{73}$$

where the Lagrange multipliers $\lambda \geq 0$ and $\mathcal{P} \in \mathbb{R}^{n \times n}$ are not both zero. We thus obtain

$$\frac{\partial \mathcal{L}}{\partial \mathcal{Q}} = (\tilde{A} + \gamma^{-2}\mathcal{Q}\tilde{R})^{\mathrm{T}}\mathcal{P} + \mathcal{P}(\tilde{A} + \gamma^{-2}\mathcal{Q}\tilde{R}) + \lambda \tilde{R}. \tag{74}$$

Setting $\partial \mathcal{L}/\partial Q = 0$ yields

$$0 = (\tilde{A} + \gamma^{-2}\mathcal{Q}\tilde{R})^{\mathrm{T}}\mathcal{P} + \mathcal{P}(\tilde{A} + \gamma^{-2}\mathcal{Q}\tilde{R}) + \lambda \tilde{R}. \tag{75}$$

Since $\tilde{A} + \gamma^{-2}\mathcal{Q}\tilde{R}$ is assumed to be stable, $\lambda = 0$ implies $\mathcal{P} = 0$. Hence it can be assumed without loss of generality that $\lambda = 1$. Furthermore, $\mathcal{P}$ is nonnegative definite.

Now partition $n \times n$ $\mathcal{Q}, \mathcal{P}$ into $n_u \times n_u$, $n_u \times n_s$, and $n_s \times n_s$ subblocks as

$$\mathcal{Q} = \begin{bmatrix} Q_u & Q_{us} \\ Q_{us}^{\mathrm{T}} & Q_s \end{bmatrix}, \qquad \mathcal{P} = \begin{bmatrix} P_u & P_{us} \\ P_{us}^{\mathrm{T}} & P_s \end{bmatrix}.$$

Thus, the stationarity conditions are given by

$$\frac{\partial \mathcal{L}}{\partial B_e} = P_u B_e V_2 - [P_u \quad P_{us}](\mathcal{Q}C^{\mathrm{T}} + V_{12}) = 0, \tag{76}$$

$$\frac{\partial \mathcal{L}}{\partial D_e} = D_e[\hat{C}\mathcal{Q}\hat{C}^{\mathrm{T}} + \gamma^{-2}\hat{C}\mathcal{Q}\mathcal{P}\mathcal{Q}\hat{C}^{\mathrm{T}}] - L[\mathcal{Q}\hat{C}^{\mathrm{T}} + \gamma^{-2}\mathcal{Q}\mathcal{P}\mathcal{Q}\hat{C}^{\mathrm{T}}] = 0. \tag{77}$$

Expanding the $n_u \times n_u$ subblock of (75) yields

$$0 = (A_e + \gamma^{-2}Q_u C_e^T R C_e)^T P_u + P_u(A_e + \gamma^{-2}Q_u C_e^T R C_e) + \gamma^{-2}Q_{us}P_{us}^T C_e^T R C_e P_{us} Q_{us}^T + C_e^T R C_e. \tag{78}$$

Since $(A_e, B_e, C_e, D_e) \in \mathscr{S}_\infty$, it follows from [20, Lemmas 2.1 and 12.2] that P_u is positive definite. Since P_u is thus invertible, define the $n_u \times n$ matrices

$$F \triangleq [I_{n_u} \quad 0_{n_u \times n_s}], \qquad \Phi \triangleq [I_{n_u} \quad P_u^{-1}P_{us}], \tag{79}$$

and the $n \times n$ matrix $\mu \triangleq F^T\Phi$. Note that since $\Phi F^T = I_n$, μ is idempotent, that is, $\mu^2 = \mu$.

Next note that (76), (77), and (79) imply (57) and (59). Similarly, (56) and (58) are equivalent to (18) and (20) with B_e and D_e given by (57) and (59), respectively. Now, using the expression for B_e, $\tilde{A}$ and $\tilde{V}$ become

$$\tilde{A} = A - \mu Q_a V_2^{-1} C, \tag{80}$$

$$\tilde{V} = V_1 - V_{12}V_2^{-1}Q_a^T\mu^T - \mu Q_a V_2^{-1}V_{12}^T + \mu Q_a V_2^{-1} Q_a^T \mu^T. \tag{81}$$

Now (60) and (61) follow from (47) and (75) by using (80) and (81).

Finally, to prove the converse, we use (56)–(61) to obtain (47) and (75)–(77). Let A_e, B_e, C_e, D_e, F, Φ, μ, $\mathscr{P}$ be as in the statement of Theorem 2. With $\Phi F^T = I_n$, it is easy to verify (76) and (77). Finally, substitute the definitions of F, Φ, and μ into (60) and (61), along with $\Phi F^T = I_n$, (33), and (34), to obtain (47) and (75). □

ACKNOWLEDGMENT

The research for this article was supported in part by the Air Force Office of Scientific Research under contract F49620-86-C-0002.

REFERENCES

1. D. S. BERNSTEIN and D. C. HYLAND, "The Optimal Projection Equations for Reduced-Order State Estimation," *IEEE Trans. Autom. Control* **AC-30**, 583–585 (1985).
2. D. S. BERNSTEIN, L. D. DAVIS, and D. C. HYLAND. "The Optimal Projection Equations for Reduced-Order, Discrete-Time Modelling, Estimation and Control," *AIAA J. Guidance, Control Dyn.* **9**, 288–293 (1986).
3. D. A. WILSON and R. N. MISHRA, "Design of Low Order Estimators Using Reduced Models," *Int. J. Control* **23**, 447–456 (1979).
4. C. S. SIMS, "Reduced-order Modelling and Filtering," *Control Dyn. Syst.* **18**, 55–103 (1982).
5. R. B. ASHER, K. D. HERRING, and J. C. RYLES, "Bias Variance and Estimation Error in Reduced-Order Filters," *Automatica* **12**, 289–600 (1976).
6. F. W. FAIRMAN, "On Stochastic Observer Estimators for Continuous-Time Systems," *IEEE Trans. Autom. Control* **AC-22**, 874–876 (1977).
7. C. S. SIMS and R. B. ASHER, "Optimal and Suboptimal Results in Full and Reduced-Order Linear Filtering," *IEEE Trans. Autom. Control* **AC-23**, 469–472 (1978).

8. F. W. FAIRMAN and R. D. GUPTA, "Design of Multi-functional Reduced-Order Observers," *Int. J. Syst. Sci.* **11**, 1083–1094 (1980).
9. C. S. SIMS and L. G. STOTTS, "Linear Discrete Reduced-Order Filtering," *Proc. IEEE Conf. Decision Control*, 1172–1177 (1979).
10. T. E. FORTMAN and D. WILLIAMS, "Design of Low-Order Observers for Linear Feedback Control Laws," *IEEE Trans. Autom. Control* **AC-17**, 301–308 (1972).
11. C. S. SIMS, "An Algorithm for Estimating a Portion of a State Vector," *IEEE Trans. Autom. Control* **AC-19**, 391–393 (1974).
12. B. A. FRANCIS, "A Course in H_∞ Control Theory," Springer-Verlag, New York, 1987.
13. I. R. PETERSEN, "Disturbance Attenuation and H^∞ Optimization: A Design Method Based on the Algebraic Riccati Equation," *IEEE Trans. Autom. Control* **AC-32**, 427–429 (1987).
14. P. P. KHARGONEKAR, I. R. PETERSEN, and M. A. ROTEA, "H^∞ Optimal Control with State Feedback," *IEEE Trans. Autom. Control* **AC-33**, 786–788 (1988).
15. I. R. PETERSEN, "Complete Results for a Class of State Feedback Disturbance Attenuation Problems," *Proc. IEEE Conf. Decision Control,* 1349–1353 (1988).
16. D. S. BERNSTEIN and W. M. HADDAD, "LQG Control with an H_∞ Performance Bound: A Riccati Equation Approach," *Proc. Am. Control Conf., Atlanta, Ga.*, 796–802 (1988); *IEEE Trans. Autom. Control* **AC-34**, 293–305 (1989).
17. W. M. HADDAD and D. S. BERNSTEIN, "The Optimal Projection Equations for Reduced-Order State Estimation: The Singular Measurement Noise Case," *IEEE Trans. Autom. Control* **AC-32**, 1135–1139 (1987).
18. W. M. HADDAD and D. S. BERNSTEIN, "Robust, Reduced-Order Nonstrictly Proper State Estimation via the Optimal Projection Equations with Guaranteed Cost Bounds," *IEEE Trans. Autom. Control* **AC-33**, 591–595 (1988).
19. Y. HALEVI, "The Optimal Reduced-Order Estimator for Systems with Singular Measurement Noise," *IEEE Trans. Autom. Control* **34** (1989).
20. W. M. WONHAM, "Linear Multivariable Control: A Geometric Approach," Springer-Verlag, New York, 1979.

PROPORTIONAL NAVIGATION AND THE GAME OF TWO CARS IN THREE DIMENSIONS: A TIME-DEPENDENT STOCHASTIC DIFFERENTIAL GAME

YAAKOV YAVIN
ROSALIE DE VILLIERS

Centre for Advanced Computing and Decision Support
Council for Scientific and Industrial Research
Pretoria 0001, South Africa

I. INTRODUCTION

A stochastic pursuit–evasion differential game involving two players, E (the evader) and P (the pursuer), moving in the (x, y, z) space is considered. The differential game dealt with here is based on a noise-perturbed kinematic model, in which both players have fixed speeds and bounded turning rates. Denote by $\bar{r}(t)$ the range vector from P to E at the time t, and let $r(t)$ denote its magnitude. We assume that player P has (1) an *effective operation zone* D_P, defined by $0 < r < R_0$, $\langle \bar{r}, \bar{v}_P \rangle > 0$, and $dr/dt < -v_0$, where R_0 and v_0 are given positive numbers, $\bar{v}_P$ is P's velocity vector, and $\langle \bar{a}, \bar{b} \rangle$ denotes the inner product between $\bar{a}$ and $\bar{b}$; and (2) a *killing zone* K_P, defined by $0 \leq r \leq \rho$, $\langle \bar{r}, \bar{v}_P \rangle > 0$, and $dr/dt < -v_0$, where ρ, $0 < \rho < R_0$, is a given number.

Player E, on the other hand, has a *safe zone* given by $r \geq R_0$, or $\langle \bar{r}, \bar{v}_P \rangle \leq 0$ and $r > \rho$, or $dr/dt \geq -v_0$ and $r > \rho$. The rigorous definitions of all these zones are given in Section II. Let Ξ be the event {before player E enters the safe zone, E enters K_P at some t, $0 \leq t \leq T$, or player E stays at the domain $D_P - K_P$ for all $t \in [0, t_0]$, for some $t_0 > T$}. Player E steers by choosing, at each instant, control functions in such a manner as to minimize Prob.(Ξ), whereas player P steers by choosing, at each instant, control functions in such a manner as to maximize Prob.(Ξ).

In the past few years pursuit–evasion problems in three dimensions have been dealt with in, for example, [1–7]. Although these references and others not mentioned here consider a variety of aspects of pursuit-evasion problems, the aim of this work is to establish the conditions under which a proportional navigation guidance law is an optimal feedback pursuit strategy in an encounter in the (x, y, z) space where both players have fixed speeds and bounded turning rates.

Recently, a study conducted on two stochastic versions of the game of two cars showed, by numerically solving a nonlinear elliptic boundary-value problem on a generalized torus in $\mathbb{R}^4$ [8] or by numerically solving a nonlinear parabolic partial differential equation on a cylinder whose base is a generalized torus in $\mathbb{R}^3$ [9], that for a large range of values of some parameters, a proportional navigation guidance law is an optimal feedback pursuit strategy. (See [10] for the deterministic planar game of two cars.) In a subsequent study, [11,12] conducted two stochastic versions of the game of two cars with the pursuer having a variable speed and showed, by numerically solving a nonlinear elliptic boundary-value problem on a generalized torus in $\mathbb{R}^5$ [11] or by numerically solving a nonlinear parabolic partial differential equation on a cylinder whose base is a generalized torus in $\mathbb{R}^4$ [12], that for a great variety of values of some parameters, a proportional navigation guidance law (as used in the games in [8,9] is a suboptimal feedback pursuit strategy.

Continuing this line of investigation, [13] considered a stochastic version of the game of two cars in the (x, y, z) space. In that study a containment probability was used as a cost function. By numerically solving a nonlinear elliptic boundary value problem on a generalized torus in $\mathbb{R}^7$, the investigators showed that for a large range of values of some parameters, a proportional navigation guidance law (a 3-D extension of the one mentioned before) is an optimal feedback pursuit strategy. Thus, the study undertaken here directly continues that carried out in [8,9] and is complementary to that carried out in [13].

In the past, proportional navigation has been proved to be an optimal pursuit strategy in some differential games involving linear systems [14,15] or has been found to be an optimal control solution for a linear quadratic problem (see, e.g., [16]). In this work, we show by numerically solving a nonlinear parabolic partial differential equation on a cylinder whose base is a generalized torus in $\mathbb{R}^6$ that, for some ranges of values of some parameters, a proportional navigation guidance law is a good approximation to an optimal feedback pursuit strategy. To the first author's knowledge, the differential games dealt with here and in [13] are the first cases in which a proportional navigation guidance law is shown to be an optimal feedback pursuit strategy, or a good approximation to it, in a game in (x, y, z) space in which a nonlinear system is involved. The study carried out here is of importance because most modern air-to-air and surface-to-air missile systems use a form of proportional navigation in the homing phase of flight.

II. THE FUNDAMENTAL EQUATIONS

Let (X, Y, Z) denote an inertial coordinate system with origin 0 and three unit vectors $(\hat{I}, \hat{J}, \hat{K})$ along the axes, which we consider to be fixed in space. It is assumed here that the equations of motion for E and P are given by

$$dX_{\mathrm{E}}/dt = V_{\mathrm{E}} \cos \gamma_{\mathrm{E}} \cos \psi_{\mathrm{E}}, \tag{1}$$

$$dY_{\mathrm{E}}/dt = V_{\mathrm{E}} \cos \gamma_{\mathrm{E}} \sin \psi_{\mathrm{E}}, \tag{2}$$

$$dZ_{\mathrm{E}}/dt = V_{\mathrm{E}} \sin \gamma_{\mathrm{E}}, \tag{3}$$

$$d\gamma_{\mathrm{E}}/dt = v_{\mathrm{E}1}, \qquad d\psi_{\mathrm{E}}/dt = v_{\mathrm{E}2}, \tag{4}$$

$$-\pi/2 \le \gamma_{\mathrm{E}} \le \pi/2, \qquad 0 \le \psi_{\mathrm{E}} \le 2\pi, \tag{5}$$

and

$$dX_{\mathrm{P}}/dt = V_{\mathrm{P}} \cos \gamma_{\mathrm{P}} \cos \psi_{\mathrm{P}}, \tag{6}$$

$$dY_{\mathrm{P}}/dt = V_{\mathrm{P}} \cos \gamma_{\mathrm{P}} \sin \psi_{\mathrm{P}}, \tag{7}$$

$$dZ_{\mathrm{P}}/dt = V_{\mathrm{P}} \sin \gamma_{\mathrm{P}}, \tag{8}$$

$$d\gamma_{\mathrm{P}}/dt = v_{\mathrm{P}1}, \qquad d\psi_{\mathrm{P}}/dt = v_{\mathrm{P}2}, \tag{9}$$

$$-\pi/2 \le \gamma_{\mathrm{P}} \le \pi/2, \qquad 0 \le \psi_{\mathrm{P}} \le 2\pi, \tag{10}$$

where $(X_{\mathrm{E}}, Y_{\mathrm{E}}, Z_{\mathrm{E}})$ and $(X_{\mathrm{P}}, Y_{\mathrm{P}}, Z_{\mathrm{P}})$ denote the coordinates in the (X, Y, Z) coordinate system of players E and P, respectively; V_{E} and V_{P} denote their respective speeds, γ_{E} and γ_{P} their respective path inclinations, and ψ_{E} and ψ_{P} their respective azimuths; $v_{\mathrm{E}i}$, $i = 1, 2$, denote the control functions of E; and $v_{\mathrm{P}i}$, $i = 1, 2$, denote the control functions of P.

Let $(x_{\mathrm{P}}, y_{\mathrm{P}}, z_{\mathrm{P}})$ denote a coordinate system fixed at and moving with P and such that, at each instant, $\bar{v}_{\mathrm{P}}$, the velocity of P, is along the x_{P} axis, and let $(\hat{i}_{\mathrm{P}}, \hat{j}_{\mathrm{P}}, \hat{k}_{\mathrm{P}})$ be three unit vectors along the x_{P}, y_{P}, and z_{P} axes, respectively. Hence from Eqs. (6)–(8) it follows that

$$\hat{i}_{\mathrm{P}} = \cos \gamma_{\mathrm{P}} \cos \psi_{\mathrm{P}} \hat{I} + \cos \gamma_{\mathrm{P}} \sin \psi_{\mathrm{P}} \hat{J} + \sin \gamma_{\mathrm{P}} \hat{K}, \tag{11}$$

and consequently, $\hat{j}_{\mathrm{P}}$ and $\hat{k}_{\mathrm{P}}$ are chosen to be given by

$$\hat{j}_{\mathrm{P}} := -\sin \psi_{\mathrm{P}} \hat{I} + \cos \psi_{\mathrm{P}} \hat{J}, \tag{12}$$

$$\hat{k}_{\mathrm{P}} := -\sin \gamma_{\mathrm{P}} \cos \psi_{\mathrm{P}} \hat{I} - \sin \gamma_{\mathrm{P}} \sin \psi_{\mathrm{P}} \hat{J} + \cos \gamma_{\mathrm{P}} \hat{K}. \tag{13}$$

Define

$$\bar{r} := (X_{\mathrm{E}} - X_{\mathrm{P}})\hat{I} + (Y_{\mathrm{E}} - Y_{\mathrm{P}})\hat{J} + (Z_{\mathrm{E}} - Z_{\mathrm{P}})\hat{K}, \tag{14}$$

and let the representation of $\bar{r}$ in the $(x_{\mathrm{P}}, y_{\mathrm{P}}, z_{\mathrm{P}})$ coordinate system be given by

$$\bar{r} = x_1 \hat{i}_{\mathrm{P}} + x_2 \hat{j}_{\mathrm{P}} + x_3 \hat{k}_{\mathrm{P}}. \tag{15}$$

Then, by applying the same techniques as in [6], we obtain the following equations for x_i, $i = 1, 2, 3$:

$$dx_1/dt = v_{P1}x_3 + v_{P2}x_2 \cos\gamma_P + V_E[\cos\gamma_P \cos\gamma_E \cos(\psi_E - \psi_P) + \sin\gamma_P \sin\gamma_E] - V_P, \quad (16)$$

$$dx_2/dt = v_{P2}(-x_1 \cos\gamma_P + x_3 \sin\gamma_P) + V_E \cos\gamma_E \sin(\psi_E - \psi_P), \quad (17)$$

$$dx_3/dt = -v_{P1}x_1 - v_{P2}x_2 \sin\gamma_P + V_E[-\sin\gamma_P \cos\gamma_E \cos(\psi_E - \psi_P) + \cos\gamma_P \sin\gamma_E], \quad (18)$$

$$d\gamma_P/dt = v_{P1}, \quad (19)$$

$$d\gamma_E/dt = v_{E1}, \quad (20)$$

$$d(\psi_E - \psi_P)/dt = v_{E2} - v_{P2}. \quad (21)$$

Equations (16)–(21) constitute a mathematical model for a game of two cars in three dimensions. The aim of this work is twofold: to find optimal feedback pursuit strategies for P and to find simple representations of optimal or suboptimal feedback pursuit strategies. Denote

$$x_4 := \gamma_P, \qquad x_5 := \gamma_E, \qquad \text{and} \qquad x_6 := \psi_E - \psi_P.$$

It is assumed here that the motion of E and P relative to the coordinate system (x_P, y_P, z_P) is perturbed by Gaussian white noise processes that model the uncertainties in the kinematics, the effect of external random perturbations arising from the environment, and noises in the measurements received by E and P. Thus, with this reasoning, Eqs. (16)–(21) yield

$$dx_1/dt = v_{P1}x_3 + v_{P2}x_2 \cos x_4 + V_E(\cos x_4 \cos x_5 \cos x_6 + \sin x_4 \sin x_5) - V_P + \sigma_1\, dW_1/dt, \quad (22)$$

$$dx_2/dt = v_{P2}(-x_1 \cos x_4 + x_3 \sin x_4) + V_E \cos x_5 \sin x_6 + \sigma_2\, dW_2/dt, \quad (23)$$

$$dx_3/dt = -v_{P1}x_1 - v_{P2}x_2 \sin x_4 + V_E(-\sin x_4 \cos x_5 \cos x_6 + \cos x_4 \sin x_5) + \sigma_3\, dW_3/dt, \quad (24)$$

$$dx_4/dt = v_{P1} + \sigma_4\, dW_4/dt, \quad (25)$$

$$dx_5/dt = v_{E1} + \sigma_5\, dW_5/dt, \quad (26)$$

$$dx_6/dt = v_{E2} - v_{P2} + \sigma_6\, dW_6/dt \quad (27)$$

where $W = \{W(t) = (W_1(t), W_2(t), W_3(t), W_4(t), W_5(t), W_6(t)),\ t \geq 0\}$ is an $\mathbb{R}^6$-valued standard Wiener process and σ_i, $i = 1, \ldots, 6$, are given positive numbers such that $0 < \sigma_i \ll \min(V_E, V_P)$, $i = 1, 2, 3$, and $0 < \sigma_j \ll \pi$, $j = 4, 5, 6$.

Equations (22)–(27) constitute the fundamental equations of motion of players E and P. We redefine player P's effective operation zone and killing zone in the x-coordinate system, where $x = (x_1, x_2, x_3, x_4, x_5, x_6)$, to be given by the sets D_0 and K, respectively:

$$D_0 := \{x: 0 < r < R_0, r(V_E + v_0)V_P^{-1} < x_1 < R_0, (x_4, x_5, x_6) \in \mathbb{R}^3\} \quad (28)$$

$$K := \{x: 0 \leq r \leq \rho, r(V_E + v_0 + \delta)V_P^{-1} \leq x_1 \leq \rho, (x_4, x_5, x_6) \in \mathbb{R}^3\},$$
$$0 < \delta \ll 1, r = [x_1^2 + x_2^2 + x_3^2]^{1/2}. \quad (29)$$

Also, denote

$$D := D_0 - K. \quad (30)$$

Player E's safe zone, on the other hand, is given by

$$B := K^c \cap D_0^c, \quad (31)$$

where D_0^c and K^c denote the complements of D_0 and K, respectively.

Let $\hat{i}_r$ be a unit vector in the direction of $\bar{r}$. Then, in the deterministic case, in which $\sigma_i = 0$, $i = 1, \ldots, 6$, it can be shown that

$$dr/dt = \langle \hat{i}_r, d\bar{r}/dt \rangle \leq r^{-1}(V_E r - V_P x_1). \quad (32)$$

Hence, if we require the right-hand side of inequality (32) to be smaller than $-v_0$, the following domain is defined:

$$V_P^{-1}(V_E + v_0)r < x_1. \quad (33)$$

Also, note that

$$\langle \bar{r}, \bar{v}_P \rangle = V_P x_1. \quad (34)$$

Hence, inequality (33) and Eq. (34) lead to the preceding definition of the sets D_0 and K.

Denote by

$$x^u = \{x^u(t) = (x_1^u(t), x_2^u(t), x_3^u(t), x_4^u(t), x_5^u(t), x_6^u(t)), t \geq 0\},$$

$u = (v_{E1}, v_{E2}, v_{P1}, v_{P2})$, the state of the game (see the next section for a rigorous definition of a solution to a set of stochastic differential equations). It is assumed that the game begins at $t = 0$ and that $x^u(0) \in D_0 \cup K$. Hence, if for some $t \in [0, T]$, $x^u(t) \in K$ and $x^u(s) \in D$ for all $s \in [0, t)$, then we say that player E has been intercepted by P, whereas, if for some $t \in [0, T]$, $x^u(t) \in B$ and $x^u(s) \in D$ for all $s \in [0, t)$, then we say that player E has escaped from player P. Furthermore, if $x^u(t) \in D$ for all $t \in [0, T]$, player P still wins. Thus, player E's goal is to choose his control functions (v_{E1}, v_{E2}) in such a manner as to minimize the probability of the event $\{x^u(t) \in K$ for some $t \in [0, T]$ and

$x^u(s) \in D$ for all $s \in [0, t)$, or $x^u(t) \in D$ for all $t \in [0, T]\}$, whereas player P's goal is to choose his control functions (v_{P1}, v_{P2}) in such a manner as to maximize the probability of the event.

III. FORMULATION OF THE PROBLEM

In the sequel the following set of stochastic differential equations will serve as the model for the motion of players E and P:

$$\begin{aligned} dx_1 &= [I(x)(x_3 v_{P1}(t,x) + v_{P2}(t,x)x_2 \cos x_4) \\ &\quad + V_E(\cos x_4 \cos x_5 \cos x_6 + \sin x_4 \sin x_5) - V_P]\,dt + \sigma_1\,dW_1 \quad (35) \\ dx_2 &= [I(x)v_{P2}(t,x)(-x_1 \cos x_4 + x_3 \sin x_4) + V_E \cos x_5 \sin x_6]\,dt \\ &\quad + \sigma_2\,dW_2, \quad (36) \\ dx_3 &= [I(x)(-x_1 v_{P1}(t,x) - v_{P2}(t,x)x_2 \sin x_4) \\ &\quad + V_E(-\sin x_4 \cos x_5 \cos x_6 + \cos x_4 \sin x_5)]\,dt + \sigma_3\,dW_3, \quad (37) \\ dx_4 &= v_{P1}(t,x)\,dt + \sigma_4\,dW_4, \quad (38) \\ dx_5 &= v_{E1}(t,x)\,dt + \sigma_5\,dW_5, \quad (39) \\ dx_6 &= (v_{E2}(t,x) - v_{P2}(t,x))\,dt + \sigma_6\,dW_6. \quad (40) \end{aligned}$$

The function I is introduced here to guarantee the existence of solutions to Eqs. (35)–(40) over $\mathbb{R}^6 \times [0, \infty)$. In fact, we are interested in these solutions only over $\bar{D}_0 \times [0, \infty)$, where $\bar{D}_0$ denotes the closure of D_0. Thus, I is given by $I(x) = 1$ if $0 \le r \le R_0$, and $I(x) = 0$ otherwise.

Denote by U_0 the class of all feedback strategies

$$\begin{aligned} u &= (v_{E1}, v_{E2}, v_{P1}, v_{P2}) \\ &= \{(v_{E1}(t,x), v_{E2}(t,x), v_{P1}(t,x), v_{P2}(t,x)), (t,x) \in [0,\infty) \times \mathbb{R}^6\} \end{aligned}$$

such that u: $[0,\infty) \times \mathbb{R}^6 \to \mathbb{R}^4$ is a measurable function and $v_{E1}^2(t,x) + v_{E2}^2(t,x) \le v_{E0}^2$ and $v_{P1}^2(t,x) + v_{P2}^2(t,x) \le v_{P0}^2$ for all $(t,x) \in [0,\infty) \times \mathbb{R}^6$.

Let $u \in U_0$. Then, according to [17], Eqs. (35)–(40) determine a family of stochastic processes

$$\zeta_{s,x}^u = \{\zeta_{s,x}^u(t) = (\zeta_{s,x1}^u(t), \zeta_{s,x2}^u(t), \zeta_{s,x3}^u(t), \zeta_{s,x4}^u(t), \zeta_{s,x5}^u(t), \zeta_{s,x6}^u(t)), t \in [0,\infty)\},$$
$$(s,x) \in [0,\infty) \times \mathbb{R}^6,$$

and an associated family of probability measures $\{P_{s,x}^u, (s,x) \in [0,\infty) \times \mathbb{R}^6\}$ on $\Omega = C([0,\infty), [0,\infty) \times \mathbb{R}^6)$, such that $P_{s,x}^u$ is the solution to the martingale problem for $L_t(u)$,

$$\begin{aligned} L_t(u) = {} & [I(x)(x_3 v_{P1}(t,x) + v_{P2}(t,x)x_2 \cos x_4) \\ & + V_E(\cos x_4 \cos x_5 \cos x_6 + \sin x_4 \sin x_5) - V_P]\,\partial/\partial x_1 \\ & + [I(x)v_{P2}(t,x)(-x_1 \cos x_4 + x_3 \sin x_4) + V_E \cos x_5 \sin x_6]\,\partial/\partial x_2 \\ & + [I(x)(-x_1 v_{P1}(t,x) - v_{P2}(t,x)x_2 \sin x_4) \\ & + V_E(-\sin x_4 \cos x_5 \cos x_6 + \cos x_4 \sin x_5)]\,\partial/\partial x_3 \\ & + v_{P1}(t,x)\,\partial/\partial x_4 + v_{E1}(t,x)\,\partial/\partial x_5 \\ & + [v_{E2}(t,x) - v_{P2}(t,x)]\,\partial/\partial x_6 \\ & + (1/2)\sum_{i=1}^{6} \sigma_i^2\,\partial^2/\partial x_i^2, \end{aligned} \tag{41}$$

and has the following properties:

(a) $$P^u_{s,x}(\{\zeta^u_{s,x}(t) = x, 0 \le t \le s\}) = 1. \tag{42}$$

(b) $$F(\zeta^u_{s,x}(t)) - \int_s^t L_v(u)F(\zeta^u_{s,x}(v))\,dv, \tag{43}$$

which is a $P^u_{s,x}$-martingale after time s for all $F \in C_0^\infty(\mathbb{R}^6)$.

Denote by $\tau(s,x;u)$ the following exit time:

$$\tau(s,x;u) := \begin{cases} \inf\{t \ge s\colon \zeta^u_{s,x}(t) \notin D \quad \text{where} \quad \zeta^u_{s,x}(s) = x \in D\} \\ 0 \quad \text{if} \quad \zeta^u_{s,x}(s) = x \notin D \\ \infty \quad \text{if} \quad \zeta^u_{s,x}(t) \in D \quad \text{for all} \quad t \ge s,\ (s,x) \in [0,\infty) \times \mathbb{R}^6. \end{cases} \tag{44}$$

The quantity $\tau(s,x;u)$ is the first exit time after s of $\zeta^u_{s,x}$ from D. Also, define the following class of admissible feedback strategies:

$$U := \{u = (v_{E1}, v_{E2}, v_{P1}, v_{P2}) \in U_0\colon \sup_{(s,x)\in[0,\infty)\times D} E^u_{s,x}\tau(s,x;u) < \infty\}, \tag{45}$$

where $E^u_{s,x}$ denotes the expectation operator with respect to $P^u_{s,x}$.

Let $u \in U$. Then, player E is intercepted by P or escapes from P if

$$\zeta^u_{s,x}(\tau(s,x;u)) \in K \quad \text{or} \quad \zeta^u_{s,x}(\tau(s,x;u)) \in B.$$

Furthermore, if $\tau(s,x;u) > T$, player P still wins.

Define the following family of functionals:

$$\begin{aligned} V(t,x;u) := {} & P^u_{t,x}(\{\tau(t,x;u) \le T \quad \text{and} \quad \zeta^u_{t,x}(\tau(t,x;u)) \in K\} \\ & \cup \{\tau(t,x;u) > T\}), \quad u \in U, \quad (t,x) \in [0,T] \times \mathbb{R}^6. \end{aligned} \tag{46}$$

The problem dealt with in this paper is to find a feedback strategy $u^* = (v^*_{E1}, v^*_{E2}, v^*_{P1}, v^*_{P2}) \in U$ such that

$$V(t,x;(v^*_{E1}, v^*_{E2}, v_{P1}, v_{P2})) \le V(t,x;u^*) \le V(t,x;(v_{E1}, v_{E2}, v^*_{P1}, v^*_{P2})) \tag{47}$$

for any $(v_{E1}^*, v_{E2}^*, v_{P1}, v_{P2}), (v_{E1}, v_{E2}, v_{P1}^*, v_{P2}^*) \in U$ and all $(t, x) \in [0, T] \times D$. The strategy u^* is here called a *saddle-point feedback strategy*, and (v_{P1}^*, v_{P2}^*) is called an *optimal feedback pursuit strategy.*

IV. COMPUTATION OF FEEDBACK STRATEGIES

Let $\mathscr{D}$ denote the class of all functions $V: [0, T] \times \mathbb{R}^6 \to \mathbb{R}$ such that V is continuous on $[0, T] \times (\bar{D}_0 \cup K)$, $V \in C^{1,2}([0, T) \times D)$, and such that $\partial V/\partial t + L_t(u)V \in L_2([0, T) \times (D \cap A_0))$ for any $u \in U$, where

$$A_0 := \{x: -\pi/2 \leq x_4 \leq \pi/2, -\pi/2 \leq x_5 \leq \pi/2, -\pi \leq x_6 \leq \pi\}. \tag{48}$$

By following the same procedure as in [9], we can find a saddle-point feedback strategy u^* by solving the following problem:

$$\partial V(t,x)/\partial t + L_t(u)V(t,x) = 0, \qquad (t,x) \in [0, T) \times (D \cap A_0), \tag{49}$$

$$V(t,x) = 1, \qquad (t,x) \in [0, T] \times K, \tag{50}$$

$$V(T,x) = 1, \qquad x \in D, \tag{51}$$

$$V(t,x) = 0, \qquad (t,x) \in [0, T] \times B, \tag{52}$$

$$V\left(t, x_1, x_2, x_3, -\frac{\pi}{2} - h_4, x_5, x_6\right) = V\left(t, x_1, x_2, x_3, -\frac{\pi}{2} + h_4, x_5, x_6 - \pi\right),$$

$$V\left(t, x_1, x_2, x_3, \frac{\pi}{2} + h_4, x_5, x_6\right) = V\left(t, x_1, x_2, x_3, \frac{\pi}{2} - h_4, x_5, x_6 - \pi\right),$$

$$\text{for all} \quad (t, x_1, x_2, x_3, x_5, x_6) \in [0, T] \times \mathbb{R}^5 \quad \text{and} \quad 0 \leq h_4 \leq \pi/2; \tag{53}$$

$$V\left(t, x_1, x_2, x_3, x_4, -\frac{\pi}{2} - h_5, x_6\right) = V\left(t, x_1, x_2, x_3, x_4, -\frac{\pi}{2} + h_5, x_6 + \pi\right),$$

$$V\left(t, x_1, x_2, x_3, x_4, \frac{\pi}{2} + h_5, x_6\right) = V\left(t, x_1, x_2, x_3, x_4, \frac{\pi}{2} - h_5, x_6 + \pi\right),$$

$$\text{for all} \quad (t, x_1, x_2, x_3, x_4, x_6) \in [0, T] \times \mathbb{R}^5 \quad \text{and} \quad 0 \leq h_5 \leq \pi/2; \tag{54}$$

$$V(t, x_1, x_2, x_3, x_4, x_5, -\pi) = V(t, x_1, x_2, x_3, x_4, x_5, \pi),$$

$$V(t, x_1, x_2, x_3, x_4, x_5, -\pi - h_6) = V(t, x_1, x_2, x_3, x_4, x_5, \pi - h_6),$$

$$V(t, x_1, x_2, x_3, x_4, x_5, \pi + h_6) = V(t, x_1, x_2, x_3, x_4, x_5, -\pi + h_6),$$

$$\text{for all} \quad (t, x_1, x_2, x_3, x_4, x_5) \in [0, T] \times \mathbb{R}^5 \quad \text{and} \quad 0 \leq h_6 \leq \pi; \tag{55}$$

$$v_{P1}(t,x) = v_{P0} C_{P1}(t,x)/C_P(t,x), \qquad (t,x) \in [0, T) \times D, \tag{56}$$

$$v_{P2}(t,x) = v_{P0} C_{P2}(t,x)/C_P(t,x), \qquad (t,x) \in [0, T) \times D, \tag{57}$$

where

$$C_{P1}(t,x) = x_3\,\partial V(t,x)/\partial x_1 - x_1\,\partial V(t,x)/\partial x_3 + \partial V(t,x)/\partial x_4, \tag{58}$$

$$C_{P2}(t,x) = x_2 \cos x_4\,\partial V(t,x)/\partial x_1 + (-x_1 \cos x_4 + x_3 \sin x_4)\,\partial V(t,x)/\partial x_2$$
$$- x_2 \sin x_4\,\partial V(t,x)/\partial x_3 - \partial V(t,x)/\partial x_6, \tag{59}$$

$$C_P(t,x) = [C_{P1}^2(t,x) + C_{P2}^2(t,x)]^{1/2}; \tag{60}$$

and

$$v_{E1}(t,x) = -v_{E0}(\partial V(t,x)/\partial x_5)/C_E(t,x), \qquad (t,x) \in [0,T) \times D, \tag{61}$$

$$v_{E2}(t,x) = -v_{E0}(\partial V(t,x)/\partial x_6)/C_E(t,x), \qquad (t,x) \in [0,T) \times D, \tag{62}$$

$$C_E(t,x) = [(\partial V(t,x)/\partial x_5)^2 + (\partial V(t,x)/\partial x_6)^2]^{1/2}. \tag{63}$$

Assume that Eqs. (49)–(63) have a solution, denoted here by $(u^*, V(\cdot,\cdot;u^*))$. If $u^* \in U$ and $V(\cdot,\cdot;u^*) \in \mathscr{D}$, then u^* is a saddle-point feedback strategy.

To find a simple approximation to optimal feedback pursuit strategies (v_{P1}^*, v_{P2}^*), we have here solved Eqs. (49)–(55) and (61)–(63), where v_{Pi}, $i = 1, 2$, are given by

$$v_{Pi}(t,x) = \begin{cases} v_{PO}/\sqrt{2} & \text{if} \quad B_i(t,x) \geq v_{PO}/\sqrt{2} \\ B_i(t,x) & \text{if} \quad |B_i(t,x)| < v_{PO}/\sqrt{2}, \\ -v_{PO}/\sqrt{2} & \text{if} \quad B_i(t,x) \leq -v_{PO}/\sqrt{2} \end{cases}$$
$$\text{for} \quad i = 1, 2, \quad (t,x) \in [0,T] \times D, \tag{64}$$

where

$$B_1(t,x) := \Lambda r^{-2}[V_E a_3(x) x_1 - x_3(V_E a_1(x) - V_P)], \tag{65}$$

$$B_2(t,x) := \Lambda r^{-2}[V_E a_2(x) x_1 - x_2(V_E a_1(x) - V_P)]/\cos x_4, \tag{66}$$

Λ is a given positive number, and

$$a_1(x) := \cos x_4 \cos x_5 \cos x_6 + \sin x_4 \sin x_5, \tag{67}$$

$$a_2(x) := \cos x_5 \sin x_6, \tag{68}$$

$$a_3(x) := -\sin x_4 \cos x_5 \cos x_6 + \cos x_4 \sin x_5. \tag{69}$$

Note that B_i, $i = 1, 2$, as given by Eqs. (65)–(66), can be written as

$$B_1(t,x) = -\Lambda\langle \hat{j}_P, d\bar{\sigma}/dt\rangle, \tag{70}$$

$$B_2(t,x) = \Lambda(\cos x_4)^{-1}\langle \hat{k}_P, d\bar{\sigma}/dt\rangle, \tag{71}$$

where

$$d\bar{\sigma}/dt := r^{-2}(\bar{r} \times d\bar{r}/dt), \tag{72}$$

is the line-of-sight rate vector. Here $\bar{a} \times \bar{b}$ denotes the cross-product vector between $\bar{a}$ and $\bar{b}$. Such a version of proportional navigation is applied, for example, in [18] (where the 2-D version is given) and in [19] (where the 3-D version is given).

Assume that Eqs. (49)–(55), (61)–(63), and (64)–(69) have a solution $(u^{PN}, V(\cdot, \cdot; u^{PN}))$, $V(\cdot, \cdot; u^{PN}) \in \mathscr{D}$ and $u^{PN} = (v_{E1}^{PN}, v_{E2}^{PN}, v_{P1}^{PN}, v_{P2}^{PN}) \in U$. Then, it can be shown, [9], that

$$V(t, x; u^{PN}) = P_{t,x}^{u^{PN}}(\{\tau(t, x; u^{PN}) \leq T \quad \text{and} \quad \zeta_{t,x}^{u^{PN}}(\tau(t, x; u^{PN})) \in K\} \cup \{\tau(t, x; u^{PN}) > T\}), \quad (t, x) \in [0, T] \times \mathbb{R}^6. \tag{73}$$

V. A NUMERICAL STUDY

Denote by $\mathbb{R}_h^6$ the following finite-difference grid on $\mathbb{R}^6$:

$$\mathbb{R}_h^6 := \{(ih_1, jh_2, kh_3, lh_4, mh_5, nh_6): i, j, k, l, m, n = 0, \pm 1, \pm 2, \ldots\}. \tag{74}$$

Define $D_{0h} := (D_0 \cup K) \cap A_0 \cap \mathbb{R}_h^6$. Equations (49)–(63), or (49)–(55), (61)–(63), and (64)–(69), have here been solved using an upwind finite-difference method on $[0, T) \times \mathbb{R}_h^6$, described in [9].

Denote by $V^{\Delta,h}(\cdot, \cdot; u^*)$ and $V^{\Delta,h}(\cdot, \cdot; u^{PN})$ the solutions to the finite-difference equations corresponding to Eqs. (49)–(63), or to (49)–(55), (61)–(63), and (64)–(69), respectively.

Define

$$P^{\Delta,h}(t; u) := \sum_{(ih_1, jh_2, kh_3, lh_4, mh_5, nh_6) \in D_{0h}} V^{\Delta,h}(t, ih_1, jh_2, kh_3, lh_4, mh_5, nh_6; u)/N(h), \quad u = u^*, u^{PN}, \tag{75}$$

where $N(h)$ denotes the number of points in D_{0h}.

Computations were carried out using the following set of parameters: $V_E = 300$, $V_P = 900$, $v_{PO} = 30g/(V_P\sqrt{2})$, $v_{EO} = 6g/(V_E\sqrt{2})$, $\sigma_1^2 = \sigma_2^2 = \sigma_3^2 = 9$, $\sigma_4^2 = \sigma_5^2 = \sigma_6^2 = (\pi/200)^2$; and the following cases were computed:

i. $R_0 = 200$, $\rho = 50$, $h_1 = h_2 = h_3 = 50$, $h_4 = h_5 = h_6 = \pi/9$, $T = 1.5$, $\Delta = 0.1$, and $v_0 = 100$. Hence, $N(h) = 105057$.
ii. $R_0 = 200$, $\rho = 200/6$, $h_1 = h_2 = h_3 = 200/6$, $h_4 = h_5 = h_6 = \pi/10$, $T = 1.5$, $\Delta = 0.05$, $v_0 = 100$ and 200. Here, for $v_0 = 100$, $N(h) = 624481$; and for $v_0 = 200$, $N(h) = 508321$.
iii. $R_0 = 600$, $\rho = 150$, $h_1 = h_2 = h_3 = 150$, $h_4 = h_5 = h_6 = \pi/9$, $T = 3$, $\Delta = 0.1$, $v_0 = 100$ and 200. Here, for $v_0 = 100$, $N(h) = 105057$; and for $v_0 = 200$, $N(h) = 81729$.
iv. $R_0 = 600$, $\rho = 100$, $h_1 = h_2 = h_3 = 100$, $h_4 = h_5 = h_6 = \pi/10$, $T = 3$, $\Delta = 0.05$, $v_0 = 200$ and 300. Here, for $v_0 = 200$, $N(h) = 508321$; and for $v_0 = 300$, $N(h) = 411521$.

v. $R_0 = 1600$, $\rho = 400$, $h_1 = h_2 = h_3 = 400$, $h_4 = h_5 = h_6 = \pi/9$, $T = 6$, $\Delta = 0.1$, $v_0 = 200$ and 300. Here, for $v_0 = 200$, $N(h) = 81729$; and for $v_0 = 300$, $N(h) = 70065$.

vi. $R_0 = 1600$, $\rho = 1600/6$, $h_1 = h_2 = h_3 = 1600/6$, $h_4 = h_5 = h_6 = \pi/10$, $T = 6$, $\Delta = 0.05$, $v_0 = 200$ and 300. Here, for $v_0 = 200$, $N(h) = 508321$; and for $v_0 = 300$, $N(h) = 401841$.

vii. $R_0 = 2000$, $\rho = 500$, $h_1 = h_2 = h_3 = 500$, $h_4 = h_5 = h_6 = \pi/9$, $T = 8$, $\Delta = 0.1$, $v_0 = 1$, $v_0 = 100$, 200, and 300. Here, for $v_0 = 1$, $N(h) = 116721$; for $v_0 = 100$, $N(h) = 105057$; for $v_0 = 200$, $N(h) = 81729$; and for $v_0 = 300$, $N(h) = 70065$.

viii. $R_0 = 2000$, $\rho = 2000/6$, $h_1 = h_2 = h_3 = 2000/6$, $h_4 = h_5 = h_6 = \pi/10$, $T = 8$, $\Delta = 0.05$, $v_0 = 200$ and 300. Here, for $v_0 = 200$, $N(h) = 508321$; and for $v_0 = 300$, $N(h) = 392161$.

ix. $R_0 = 2400$, $\rho = 600$, $h_1 = h_2 = h_3 = 600$, $h_4 = h_5 = h_6 = \pi/9$, $T = 8$, $\Delta = 0.1$, $v_0 = 200$ and 300. Here, for $v_0 = 200$, $N(h) = 81729$; and for $v_0 = 300$, $N(h) = 70065$.

x. $R_0 = 2400$, $\rho = 400$, $h_1 = h_2 = h_3 = 400$, $h_4 = h_5 = h_6 = \pi/10$, $T = 8$, $\Delta = 0.05$, and $v_0 = 300$. Here $N(h) = 411521$.

TABLE I. VALUES OF $P^{\Delta,h}(0; u)$, $u = u^*$, u^{PN}, AND ε_P FOR CASES i–x

Case	v_0	$P^{\Delta,h}(0; u^*)$	$P^{\Delta,h}(0; u^{PN})$	ε_P	R_0
i	100	0.236292	0.235679	0.002601	200
ii	100	0.107625	0.107100	0.004902	200
	200	0.124823	0.124478	0.002772	
iii	100	0.255196	0.251970	0.012803	600
	200	0.306189	0.305107	0.003546	
iv	200	0.138177	0.136548	0.011930	600
	300	0.158183	0.157346	0.005319	
v	200	0.373630	0.362684	0.030181	1600
	300	0.390359	0.385415	0.012828	
vi	200	0.182976	0.171979	0.063944	1600
	300	0.212272	0.202327	0.049153	
vii	1	0.316531	0.293646	0.077934	2000
	100	0.341772	0.317280	0.077194	
	200	0.404330	0.383124	0.055350	
	300	0.419988	0.403851	0.039958	
viii	200	0.206117	0.188250	0.094911	2000
	300	0.241455	0.225067	0.072814	
ix	200	0.437695	0.408472	0.071542	2400
	300	0.451370	0.426675	0.057878	
x	300	0.258489	0.233297	0.107983	2400

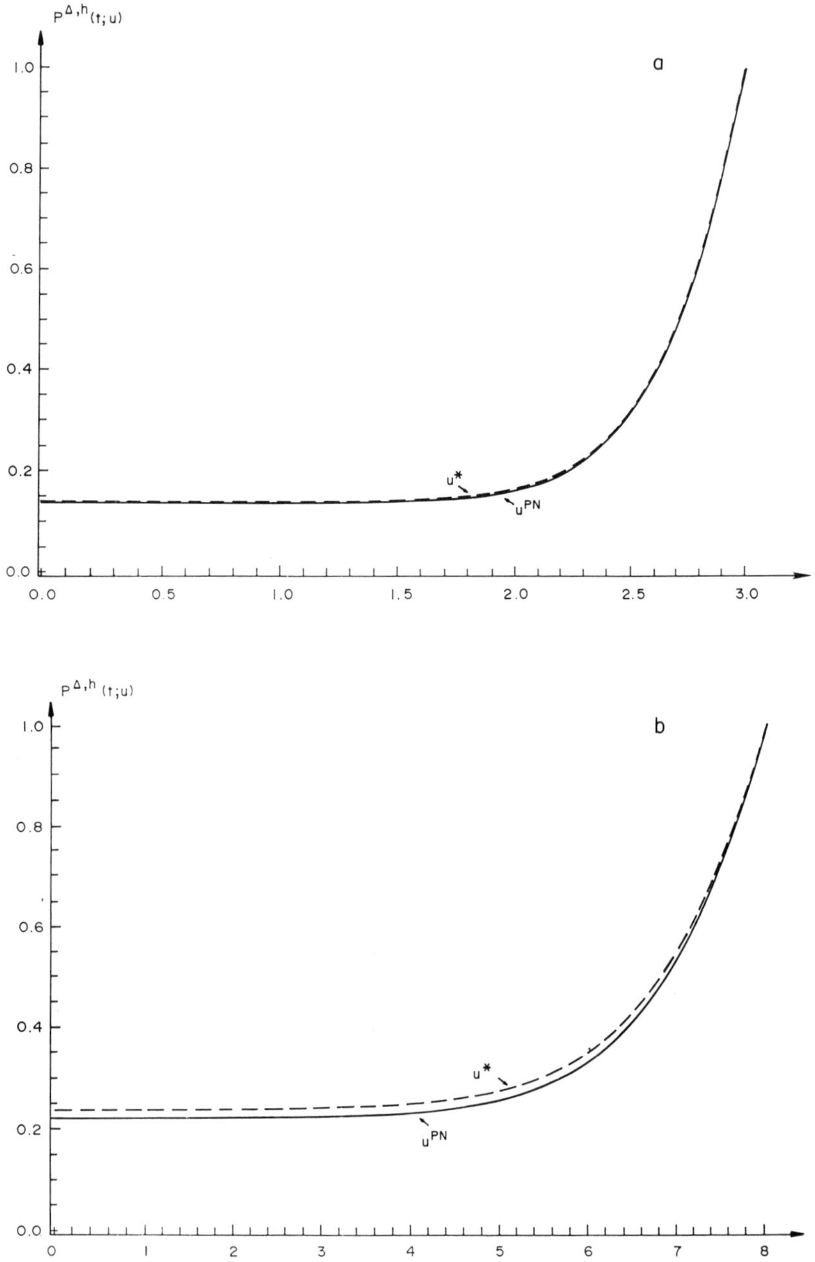

Fig. 1. $P^{\Delta,h}(t,u)$, $u = u^*$, u^{PN}, as functions of t: (a) for case iv, where $v_0 = 200$; (b) for case viii, where $v_0 = 300$; and (c) for case ix, where $v_0 = 300$.

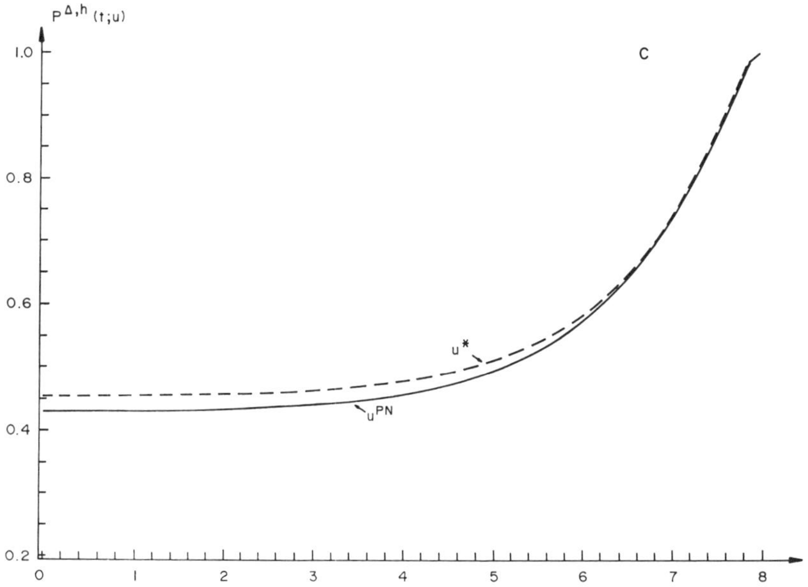

Fig. 1. (*Continued.*)

Some extracts from the numerical results obtained are presented in Table I and Figs. 1a,b, and c. In Table I the number ε_P is defined by

$$\varepsilon_P := [P^{\Delta,h}(0, u^*) - P^{\Delta,h}(0, u^{PN})]/P^{\Delta,h}(0, u^{PN}). \tag{76}$$

The figures represent the typical form of $P^{\Delta,h}(t; u)$, $t \in [0, T]$, $u = u^*, u^{PN}$.

VI. CONCLUSIONS

Define

$$\mu := \max_{0 \le t \le T} (P^{\Delta,h}(t, u^*) - P^{\Delta,h}(t, u^{PN}))/P^{\Delta,h}(t; u^{PN}). \tag{77}$$

The numerical results suggest that $\mu = \varepsilon_P$. The results given in Table I show that for each of the cases in which $R_0 \le 2000$, a value of v_0 can be found such that $\varepsilon_P < 0.05$.

The implementation of the pursuit strategy (v_{P1}^*, v_{P2}^*) consists of two stages. In the first stage, which is a prelaunch stage, Eqs. (49)–(63) are numerically solved, and the values of $(v_{P1}^*(t, x), v_{P2}^*(t, x))$ are stored on the grid $[0, T)_\Delta \times D_{0h}$, where $[0, T)_\Delta := [0, T) \cap \{k\Delta: k = 0, 1, 2, 3, \ldots\}$, and $N\Delta = T$ for some $N > 0$. In the second stage, during the flight of player P, the measured values of $\zeta_{s,x}^u(t)$ are used with some process of interpolation to calculate, from the stored values of $(v^*_{P1}(t,x), v^*_{P2}(t,x))$ on $[0,T)_\Delta \times D_{0h}$, a control law $(v_{P1}(t,\zeta^u_{s,x}(t)), v_{P2}(t,\zeta^u_{s,x}(t)))$. Thus, taking into account that, during the implementation of (v^*_{P1}, v^*_{P2}), only interpolated values thereof are used and not the pure optimal feedback pursuit strategy $\{(v^*_{P1}(t,x), v^*_{P2}(t,x)), (t,x) \in [0,T) \times D\}$, one can consider, for all cases in which $\varepsilon_P < 0.05$, the guidance law $(v^{PN}_{P1}, v^{PN}_{P2})$ to be a good approximation to an optimal feedback pursuit strategy. Furthermore, as R_0 decreases, this approximation improves.

REFERENCES

1. T. MILOH, "A Note on Three-Dimensional Pursuit-Evasion Game with Bounded Curvature," *IEEE Trans. Autom. Control* **AC-27**, 739–741 (1982).
2. N. RAJAN and M. D. ARDEMA, "Interception in Three Dimensions: An Energy Formulation," *J. Guidance, Control Dyn.* **8**, 23–30 (1985).
3. M. D. ARDEMA and N. RAJAN, "Separation of Time Scales in Aircraft Trajectory Optimization," *J. Guidance, Control Dyn.* **8**, 275–278 (1985).
4. M. ARDEMA and N. RAJAN, "Slow and Fast State Variables for Three-Dimensional Flight Dynamics," *J. Guidance, Control Dyn.* **8**, 532–535 (1985).
5. Y. YAVIN and T. MILOH, "Stochastic Two-Target Pursuit–Evasion Differential Games in 3-D," *Optim. Control Appl. Methods* **8**, 311–325 (1987).
6. Y. YAVIN and R. DE VILLIERS, "Stochastic Pursuit–Evasion Differential Games in 3-D," *J. Optim. Theory Appl.* **56**, 345–357 (1988).
7. R. DE VILLIERS, C. J. WRIGHT, and Y. YAVIN, "A Stochastic Pursuit–Evasion Differential Game in 3-D: Optimal Evasion Strategies," *Comput. Math. Appl.* **13**, 623–630 (1987).
8. Y. YAVIN and H. TONSING, "The Game of Two Cars with a Containment Probability as a Cost Function," *Int. J. Syst. Sci.* **19**, 1931–1940 (1988).
9. Y. YAVIN and R. DE VILLIERS, "Proportional Navigation and the Game of Two Cars," Tech. Rep. TWISK 544, NRIMS, CSIR, Pretoria, July 1987.
10. R. ISAACS, "Differential Games," Wiley, New York, 1965.
11. Y. YAVIN and R. DE VILLIERS, "The Game of Two Cars with a Containment Probability as a Cost Function: The Case of Variable Speed," *Comput. Math. Appl.* **18**, 61–67 (1989).
12. Y. YAVIN and R. DE VILLIERS, Proportional Navigation and the Game of Two Cars: The Case of a Pursuer with Variable Speed," *Comput. Math. Appl.* **18**, 69–76 (1989).
13. Y. YAVIN and E. E. JACOBS, "Proportional Navigation and the Game of Two Cars in 3-D: A Stochastic Differential Game," Tech. Rep. TWISK 599, CACDS, CSIR, Pretoria, January 1988.
14. Y. C. HO, A. E. BRYSON, and S. BARON, "Differential Games and Optimal Pursuit–Evasion Strategies," *IEEE Trans. Autom. Control* **AC-10**, 385–389 (1965).
15. A. E. BRYSON and Y. C. HO, "Applied Optimal Control," Blaisdell, Waltham, Massachusetts, 1969.
16. E. KREINDLER, "Optimality of Proportional Navigation," *AIAA J.* **11**, 878–880 (1973).
17. D. W. STROOCK and S. R. S. VARADHAN, "Multidimensional Diffusion Processes," Springer-Verlag, Berlin, 1979.
18. M. GUELMAN, "A Qualitative Study of Proportional Navigation," *IEEE Trans. Aerosp. Electron. Syst.* **AES-7**, 637–643 (1971).
19. K. MORITZ, R. POLIS, and K. H. WELL, "Pursuit–Evasion in Medium-Range Air-Combat Scenarios," *Comput. Math. Appl.* **13**, 167–180 (1987).

PARAMETER IDENTIFICATION IN DISTRIBUTED STRUCTURES

LEONARD MEIROVITCH
MARK A. NORRIS

Department of Engineering Science and Mechanics
Virginia Polytechnic Institute and State University
Blacksburg, Virginia 24061

I. INTRODUCTION

Structures are distributed-parameter systems characterized by parameters that are spatially distributed, such as mass and stiffness. The motion of distributed-parameter structures is governed by partial differential equations, in which the parameters appear in the form of space-dependent functions acting as coefficients. For the most part, the partial differential equations do not admit closed-form solutions, so one must be content with an approximate solution. To obtain an approximate solution, it is necessary to resort to spatial discretization, which amounts to representing the motion of the structure by a finite linear combination of space-dependent admissible functions multiplied by time-dependent generalized coordinates [1]. Certain integrations over the domain of the structure eliminate the dependence on the spatial variables, and the net result is the transformation of the partial differential equations into a set of ordinary differential equations, with the parameters being reflected in the coefficient matrices. The process of obtaining the set of ordinary differential equations is equivalent to obtaining a discrete model whose purpose is to approximate the actual distributed structure. How well the discrete model represents the distributed structure depends on the number and type of admissible functions used in the discretization process. Indeed, the rate of convergence of the approximate solution to the exact solution depends on the number of admissible functions and, perhaps to a larger extent, on the type of admissible functions used [2]. The discretized model can be used to compute a finite number of lower modes of vibration. It is symptomatic of spatial discretization that an even smaller number of computed lower natural frequencies are accurate representations of the actual natural frequencies than the number of degrees of freedom of the discrete model [1]. The preceding discussion pertains to structural modeling on the basis of given distributed parameters. The discrete model can be used to approximate not only the modes of vibration but also the system response. The problem of deriving the response to given excitations when the system characteristics are known, albeit only approximately, can be regarded as a direct problem.

In certain cases, the system parameters are not known, and the object is to infer them from the measured response to known excitations. This represents an inverse problem, more commonly known as parameter identification or parameter estimation. Clearly, in the case of distributed structures, the object is to identify parameter distributions. The implication is that the parameters are distributed nonuniformly because otherwise the problem would be trivial, reducing to the identification of a single number per parameter distribution.

Commonly used discretization procedures, for modeling as well as for parameter identification, are the classical Rayleigh–Ritz method, the finite element method, the Galerkin method, and so on [1]. They all end up characterizing the system parameters by means of matrices such as the mass and stiffness matrices. It is common practice to regard the problem of structural identification as the problem of identifying the coefficient matrices resulting from the discretization process, but this discretization is the very same process that proved incapable of giving wholly accurate eigensolutions. Indeed, it is typical of these modeling techniques that less than half of the computed natural frequencies, and even fewer natural modes, can be accepted as sufficiently accurate [1]. Hence, it is unreasonable to expect that a process identifying parameter matrices can yield more accurate results than those obtained by a corresponding process in mere modeling.

Several factors advocate a cautious approach to parameter identification in distributed structures. In particular, one must interpret and use the results of the identification process judiciously. The mass and stiffness matrices are not unique for a structure, and in fact they do not even represent physical quantities. Indeed, the dimension of the matrices depends on the number of admissible functions used, and the entries of the matrices depend on the nature of the admissible functions. These two factors are related because a wise choice of admissible functions can give superior results with a smaller number of admissible functions. In particular, one must make sure that the admissible functions are such that all the boundary conditions can be satisfied by finite linear combinations of these functions [2]. Mass and stiffness matrices have physical content only when the object is to identify lumped systems [3]. The quantities that have meaning in distributed structures are the mass and stiffness distributions. Perhaps the idea can be best illustrated by using the analogy with the construction of a building, in which the mass and stiffness matrices represent the scaffolding and the mass and stiffness distributions represent the building itself. Hence, an identification process must not have as its goal the identification of the mass and stiffness matrices but the identification of the mass and stiffness distributions [4]. At times, the identification of natural frequencies and modes can serve as an intermediate step toward the identification of parameter distributions [5,6].

Another factor affecting the quality of the parameter identification is the design of the experiment. One must make sure that the actuators and sensors are located at significant points of the structure and that they are in sufficient number. Of course, noisy actuators and sensors can cause difficulties and even lead to instability in the identification process [7].

In this article, the importance of judicious modeling for parameter identification is stressed. The importance of modeling in parameter identification is discussed in [8], but the authors do not identify any of the idiosyncrasies encountered in modeling, which are as crucial to successful parameter identification as they are to successful modeling. In Section II a generic partial differential equation of motion for distributed structures is introduced, and in Section III the differential eigenvalue problem is derived. Section IV is concerned with approximate solutions by means of the classical Rayleigh–Ritz method and the finite element method and provides the background for parameter identification techniques suitable for distributed structures. Sections V and VI present techniques based explicitly on the finite element method and capable of identifying mass and stiffness distributions. Then, in Section VII a Rayleigh–Ritz type parameter identification technique is discussed, which permits the identification of mass and stiffness distributions on the basis of prior knowledge of modal information such as natural frequencies. In Section VIII a procedure for identifying natural frequencies and mode shapes of self-adjoint systems is presented. Finally, in Section IX an inclusion principle is shown to exist in the parameter identification of distributed structures in the same way it exists for Rayleigh–Ritz type modeling. This inclusion principle can be used to demonstrate the convergence characteristics of the identification process.

II. EQUATION OF MOTION

We are concerned with the case in which the motion of a distributed structure is governed by the partial differential equation [1]

$$\mathscr{L}w(P,t) + m(P)\ddot{w}(P,t) = f(P,t), \qquad P \in D \tag{1}$$

where $\mathscr{L}$ is a linear homogeneous differential operator of order $2p$, m the mass density, w the displacement of a nominal point in the spatial position P at time t, f the external force density, and D the domain of extension of the structure.

The solution of Eq. (1) must satisfy the boundary conditions

$$B_i w(P,t) = 0, \qquad i = 1,2,\ldots,p, \qquad P \in S \tag{2}$$

where B_i are linear homogeneous differential operators of maximum order $2p - 1$ and S is the boundary of D.

III. THE DIFFERENTIAL EIGENVALUE PROBLEM

To solve Eq. (1), we must first solve the differential eigenvalue problem

$$\mathscr{L} w(P) = \lambda m(P) w(P), \qquad P \in D \tag{3}$$

where λ is a parameter and w is a function satisfying the boundary conditions derived from Eqs. (2). The solution of the eigenvalue problem consists of a denumerably infinite set of eigenvalues λ_r and associated eigenfunctions $w_r(P)$ $(r = 1, 2, \ldots)$.

To discuss certain properties of the system and its eigensolutions, we must introduce two classes of functions. To this end, we first distinguish between two types of boundary conditions. Boundary conditions of the first type are known as *geometric* and are characterized by operators B_i of order ranging from 0 to $p - 1$. As the name indicates, they reflect geometric conditions at the boundary, such as displacement and slope. Boundary conditions of the second type are called *natural* and are defined by operators B_i of order ranging from 0 to $2p - 1$. Such boundary conditions reflect force or moment balance at the boundary. Functions that are p times differentiable and satisfy the geometric boundary conditions are called *admissible functions*. Functions that are $2p$ times differentiable and satisfy all the boundary conditions are called *comparison functions*.

Next, we consider two comparison functions u and v. Then, if

$$\int_D u \mathscr{L} v \, dD = \int_D v \mathscr{L} u \, dD \tag{4}$$

the operator $\mathscr{L}$ is said to be *self-adjoint*. Whether or not Eq. (4) holds can be ascertained through integrations by parts with due consideration to the boundary conditions. The self-adjointness of $\mathscr{L}$ implies certain mathematical symmetry of the eigenvalue problem, which can be expressed as

$$\int_D u \mathscr{L} v \, dD = [u, v] \tag{5}$$

where $[u, v]$ is an expression symmetric in u and v obtained through integrations by parts and known as an *energy inner product*. The form of the energy inner product can be conveniently illustrated by considering a one-dimensional structure. Then, letting $D: 0 < x < L$ and $S: x = 0, L$, we can write the energy inner product in the general form

$$[u, v] = \int_0^L \sum_{k=0}^{p} a_k \frac{d^k u}{dx^k} \frac{d^k v}{dx^k} dx + \sum_{l=0}^{p-1} b_l \frac{d^l u}{dx^l} \frac{d^l v}{dx^l} \bigg|_0^L \tag{6}$$

where a_k $(k = 0, 1, \ldots, p)$ and b_l $(l = 0, 1, \ldots, p-1)$ are in general functions of x. The mass density m is self-adjoint by definition. Hence, if $\mathscr{L}$ is self-adjoint, then the system is self-adjoint. The eigenvalues of a self-adjoint system are real, and the eigenfunctions are real and orthogonal with respect to m and $\mathscr{L}$. They can be normalized to satisfy

$$\int_D m(P) w_r(P) w_s(P) \, dD = \delta_{rs}, \qquad \int_D w_r(P) \mathscr{L} w_s(P) \, dD = \lambda_r \delta_{rs}, \qquad r, s = 1, 2, \ldots \tag{7a,b}$$

where δ_{rs} is the Kronecker delta. Note that by ascertaining the self-adjointness of a system, one can conclude that the eigenfunctions are orthogonal even when it is not possible to solve the eigenvalue problem to produce the eigenfunctions.

The self-adjointness of the system permits us to conclude that the eigenvalues are real. To infer the sign of the eigenvalues, we must turn once again to the operator $\mathscr{L}$. Indeed, if for any comparison function u,

$$\int_D u \mathscr{L} u \, dD \geq 0 \tag{8}$$

and the equality sign holds only if u is identically zero, then the operator $\mathscr{L}$ is said to be positive definite. The mass density m is positive definite by definition. Hence, if $\mathscr{L}$ is positive definite, then the system is positive definite, and all the eigenvalues are positive. If the equality sign in (8) holds even for $u \neq 0$, then the operator $\mathscr{L}$, and hence the system, is only positive semidefinite, and the eigenvalues are nonnegative [1]. Positive semidefinite systems are characterized by the fact that they can undergo rigid-body motions. In the following, we confine our discussion to self-adjoint systems that are at least positive semidefinite.

The eigenfunctions $w_r (r = 1, 2, \ldots)$ comprise a complete set [1]. This fact permits us to state the expansion theorem: Every function w with continuous $\mathscr{L} w$ and satisfying all the boundary conditions can be expanded in the absolutely and uniformly convergent series

$$w = \sum_{r=1}^{\infty} c_r w_r \tag{9}$$

where the coefficients c_r are given by

$$c_r = \int_D m w w_r \, dD, \qquad r = 1, 2, \ldots \tag{10}$$

The eigenvalue problem requires the solution of a differential equation, where the solution is subject to given boundary conditions. Quite often, it is more convenient to solve the eigenvalue problem by means of an equivalent approach, namely, a variational approach consisting of rendering the value of Rayleigh's quotient stationary. This is particularly true when a closed-form solution of the eigenvalue problem is not possible and the interest lies in an approximate solution. Rayleigh's quotient for a distributed system is defined as

$$R(w) = \frac{[w, w]}{\int_D mw^2 \, dD} \tag{11}$$

where w is a trial function, and we note that $[w, w]$ is a measure of the potential energy and $\int_D mw^2 \, dD$ is a measure of the kinetic energy. Using the expansion theorem, (9), one can show that Rayleigh's quotient has stationary points at the system eigenfunctions and that the stationary values are the system eigenvalues [1]. We would like to point out here that Rayleigh's quotient is defined also when the trial function w is a mere admissible function, as can be concluded from (6).

IV. SOLUTION OF THE EIGENVALUE PROBLEM BY APPROXIMATE METHODS

Closed-form solutions to (1) can be obtained in a few simple cases only, most of them characterized by uniform parameter distributions. For more complex structures, it is necessary to resort to approximation techniques to produce a solution. This amounts to discretizing the partial differential equation in space, so that an approximate solution is obtained by means of a finite set of ordinary differential equations. Common discretization procedures are the classical Rayleigh–Ritz method, the finite element method, and the Galerkin method. The difference between the Rayleigh–Ritz and the Galerkin methods lies in the choice of trial functions. If the Rayleigh–Ritz method employs the variational formulation given by (11), then the trial functions can be merely admissible functions, satisfying the geometric boundary conditions alone. On the other hand, Galerkin's method works with the differential equation (1) and must use comparison functions, satisfying all the boundary conditons. Note that there is no difference between the two methods if the Rayleigh–Ritz method works also with the differential equation. Of course, the Rayleigh–Ritz method is applicable to self-adjoint systems only whereas Galerkin's method can be used for both self-adjoint and nonself-adjoint systems [1]. The finite element method is a variant of the classical Rayleigh–Ritz method, with the main difference between the two being that the finite element method uses local admissible functions and the Rayleigh–Ritz method uses global admissible functions. A brief discussion of the two methods follows.

A. THE CLASSICAL RAYLEIGH–RITZ METHOD

Consider an approximate solution for the displacement $w(P,t)$ as the linear combination

$$w(P,t) \cong \sum_{r=1}^{n} \phi_r(P)q_r(t) = \boldsymbol{\phi}^{\mathrm{T}}(P)\mathbf{q}(t) \tag{12}$$

where $\boldsymbol{\phi}(P) = [\phi_1(P) \quad \phi_2(P) \quad \cdots \quad \phi_n(P)]^{\mathrm{T}}$ is an n-vector global admissible functions and $\mathbf{q}(t) = [q_1(t) \quad q_2(t) \quad \cdots \quad q_n(t)]^{\mathrm{T}}$ is an n-vector of generalized coordinates. We propose to derive first a set of ordinary differential equations to replace the partial differential equation (1). To this end, we want to use Lagrange's equations [1], which can be regarded as an alternative variational principle. This requires the kinetic energy, potential energy, and virtual work. Using (12), we can write the kinetic energy as

$$\begin{aligned} T(t) &= \tfrac{1}{2}\int_D m(P)\dot{w}^2(P,t)\,dD = \tfrac{1}{2}\int_D m(P)[\boldsymbol{\phi}^{\mathrm{T}}(P)\dot{\mathbf{q}}(t)]^{\mathrm{T}}\boldsymbol{\phi}^{\mathrm{T}}(P)\dot{\mathbf{q}}(t)\,dD \\ &= \tfrac{1}{2}\dot{\mathbf{q}}^{\mathrm{T}}(t)M^{(n)}\dot{\mathbf{q}}(t) \end{aligned} \tag{13}$$

where

$$M^{(n)} = \int_D m(P)\boldsymbol{\phi}(P)\boldsymbol{\phi}^{\mathrm{T}}(P)\,dD \tag{14}$$

is an $n \times n$ mass matrix. Similarly, the potential energy can be written in the form

$$\begin{aligned} V(t) &= \tfrac{1}{2}[w(P,t), w(P,t)] = \tfrac{1}{2}[\boldsymbol{\phi}^{\mathrm{T}}(P)\mathbf{q}(t), \boldsymbol{\phi}^{\mathrm{T}}(P)\mathbf{q}(t)] \\ &= \tfrac{1}{2}\mathbf{q}^{\mathrm{T}}(t)K^{(n)}\mathbf{q}(t) \end{aligned} \tag{15}$$

in which

$$K^{(n)} = [\boldsymbol{\phi}(P), \boldsymbol{\phi}^{\mathrm{T}}(P)] \tag{16}$$

is an $n \times n$ stiffness matrix. Finally, the virtual work has the expression

$$\delta W(t) = \int_D f(P,t)\,\delta w(P,t)\,dD = \int_D f(P,t)\boldsymbol{\phi}^{\mathrm{T}}(P)\,\delta\mathbf{q}(t)\,dD = \mathbf{Q}^{\mathrm{T}}(t)\,\delta\mathbf{q}(t) \tag{17}$$

where

$$\mathbf{Q}(t) = \int_D f(P,t)\boldsymbol{\phi}(P)\,dD \tag{18}$$

is an n-vector of generalized forces. Using Lagrange's equations [1], we obtain a set of n ordinary differential equations having the matrix form

$$M^{(n)}\ddot{\mathbf{q}}(t) + K^{(n)}\mathbf{q}(t) = \mathbf{Q}(t) \tag{19}$$

Equation (19) describes a discretized model approximating the actual distributed system.

The eigenvalue problem associated with (19) is

$$K^{(n)}\mathbf{u} = \lambda^{(n)} M^{(n)}\mathbf{u} \tag{20}$$

Its solution consists of n eigenvalues $\lambda_1^{(n)}, \lambda_2^{(n)}, \ldots, \lambda_n^{(n)}$ and n associated eigenvectors $\mathbf{u}_1, \mathbf{u}_2, \ldots, \mathbf{u}_n$. The eigenvectors are orthogonal with respect to $M^{(n)}$ and $K^{(n)}$ and can be normalized to satisfy the orthonormality relations

$$\mathbf{u}_r^{\mathrm{T}} M^{(n)}\mathbf{u}_s = \delta_{rs}, \qquad \mathbf{u}_r^{\mathrm{T}} K^{(n)}\mathbf{u}_s = \lambda_r^{(n)}\,\delta_{rs}, \qquad r,s = 1,2,\ldots,n \tag{21a,b}$$

The computed eigenvalues are approximations to the n lowest actual eigenvalues $\lambda_1, \lambda_2, \ldots, \lambda_n$. Moreover, the eigenvectors can be used to produce the computed eigenfunctions

$$w_r^{(n)}(P) = \boldsymbol{\phi}^{\mathrm{T}}(P)\mathbf{u}_r, \qquad r = 1,2,\ldots,n \tag{22}$$

approximating the n lowest actual eigenfunctions. In view of (21), and recalling definitions (14) and (16), the computed eigenfunctions can be shown to satisfy the orthonormality relations

$$\int_D m(P) w_r^{(n)}(P) w_s^{(n)}(P)\, dD = \delta_{rs}, \qquad [w_r^{(n)}(P), w_s^{(n)}(P)] = \lambda_r^{(n)}\,\delta_{rs},$$

$$r,s = 1,2,\ldots,n \tag{23a,b}$$

How well the computed eigenvalues and eigenfunctions approximate the actual eigenvalues and eigenfunctions depends on the number and nature of the admissible functions.

B. THE FINITE ELEMENT METHOD

As pointed out, the finite element method differs from the classical Rayleigh–Ritz method in the nature of the admissible functions. There is another significant difference between the two methods. Indeed, in the finite element method the generalized coordinates $q_r(t)$ $(r = 1,2,\ldots,n)$ represent actual displacements at given points, whereas in the classical Raleigh–Ritz method they represent abstract quantities. To introduce the ideas involved in the finite element method, we consider a one-dimensional structure, so that $P = x$ in Eq. (1). Moreover, the domain D of the structure is $0 < x < L$, where L is the length. Then, we divide the structure into N subdomains of width $h = L/N$ (Fig. 1), where the subdomains are the finite elements, and denote

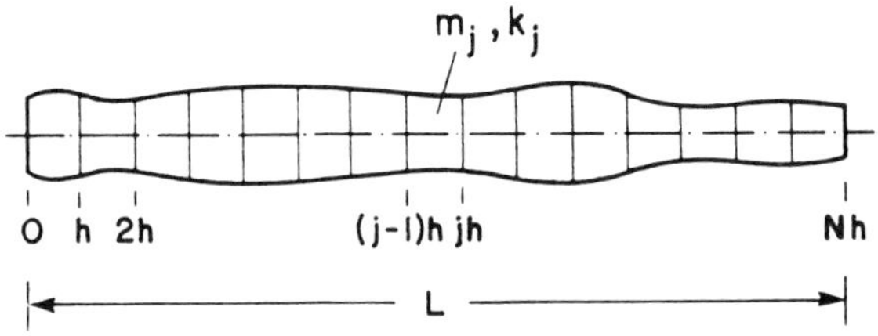

Fig. 1. The finite element model.

by m_j and k_j the "average" values of the mass and stiffness distributions, respectively, over a typical element j ($j = 1, 2, \ldots, N$). The displacement $w(x, t)$ inside the finite element can be expressed in terms of displacements at the boundaries of the element as follows [1]:

$$w(x,t) = \boldsymbol{\phi}^{\mathrm{T}}(x)\mathbf{w}_j(t), \qquad (j-1)h \le x \le jh, \qquad j = 1,2,\ldots,N \tag{24}$$

where $\boldsymbol{\phi}(x)$ is a vector of interpolation functions and $\mathbf{w}_j(t)$ is a vector of "nodal" displacements (Fig. 2). The term *nodal* derives from the fact that in finite element terminology the boundary points are called nodes. If we let the magnitude of the interpolation functions or of their first derivative be equal to either zero or one at the nodes, the nodal coordinates represent the actual coordinates or the actual rotations of the structure at the nodal points.

Following the usual steps [1], we obtain the element mass and stiffness matrices:

$$M_j = \int_{(j-1)h}^{jh} m\boldsymbol{\phi}\boldsymbol{\phi}^{\mathrm{T}}\,dx \cong m_j \int_{(j-1)h}^{jh} \boldsymbol{\phi}\boldsymbol{\phi}^{\mathrm{T}}\,dx = m_j\Phi_M, \qquad j = 1,2,\ldots,N \tag{25a}$$

$$K_j \cong [\boldsymbol{\phi}, \boldsymbol{\phi}^{\mathrm{T}}]_j = k_j\boldsymbol{\phi}_K, \qquad j = 1,2,\ldots,N \tag{25b}$$

where $[\ ,\ ]_j$ represents the energy inner product defined over element j. For details on the use of the interpolation functions entering into the energy inner

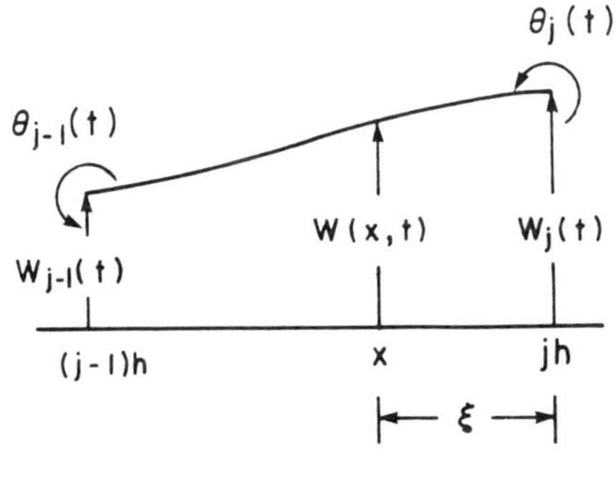

Fig. 2. A typical finite element showing nodal displacements.

product, see [1]. Note that Φ_M and Φ_K are element matrices computed by substituting the given interpolation functions into (25), and they are the same for every element [1].

The global mass and stiffness matrices, M and K, respectively, are obtained by carrying out the so-called assembling process [1], which represents the transition from the individual finite elements to the whole structure. As shown in [1], the equations of motion have the form

$$M\ddot{\mathbf{w}} + K\mathbf{w} = \mathbf{F} \tag{26}$$

The global mass matrix M is obtained through a superposition of element matrices M_j. The superposition is such that the entries in two adjacent matrices corresponding to the shared nodal displacements overlap. The global matrix has the form

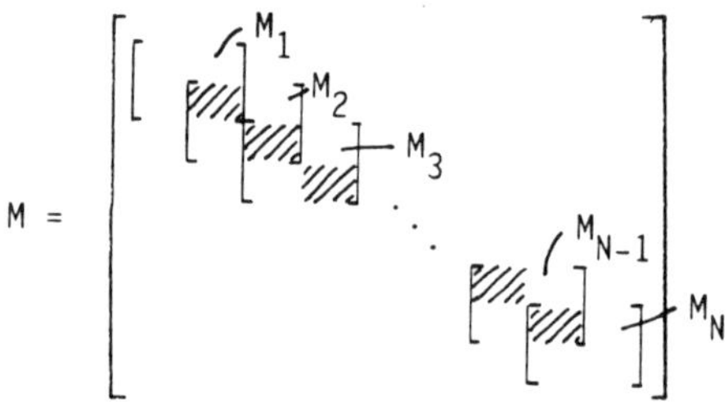

(27)

and it represents the $n \times n$ mass matrix for the whole structure. The overlapping entries, marked by shading in (27), are obtained by adding the corresponding entries in the two adjacent element mass matrices. The $n \times n$ stiffness matrix K has a block-diagonal form similar to that of M.

V. FINITE ELEMENT-BASED PARAMETER IDENTIFICATION

For complex structures, the parameters tend to be complicated functions of the spatial variables. This implies that the use of (1) for identification purposes is not practical, so that an exact parameter identification is not feasible. The inverse problem of identifying the unknown parameters represents a compounded version of the direct or modeling problem, where in the latter the parameters are known. Hence, we should expect at least the same idiosyncracies in parameter identification as those encountered in modeling. As a result, we must choose a suitable number and type of trial functions to construct a discrete model before beginning the parameter identification process.

In this section, we consider a technique for the approximate identification of mass and stiffness distributions in distributed-parameter structures based on the finite element method. The object is to identify "average" values of the mass and stiffness over each finite element, which amounts to physical parameter identification in a finite element sense. This implies that the distributed parameters are identified only approximately, in the same way as the finite element method approximates the behavior of a distributed structure.

The parameter identification process consists of exciting the structure by means of known nodal forces and measuring the response at the nodes. Because the excitation and response are known, (26) can be regarded as a set of simultaneous algebraic equations in the system parameters and can be solved by a least-squares technique. To this end, we introduce the $n \times 2n$ matrix

$$L = [M \mid K] \tag{28}$$

and the $2n$-dimensional vector

$$\mathbf{x}(t) = [\ddot{\mathbf{w}}^{\mathrm{T}}(t) \mid \mathbf{w}^{\mathrm{T}}(t)]^{\mathrm{T}} \tag{29}$$

In terms of this notation, (26) can be rewritten in the form

$$L\mathbf{x}(t) = \mathbf{F}(t) \tag{30}$$

Next, we denote the system parameters as

$$p_r = \begin{cases} m_r, & 1 \leq r \leq N \\ k_{r-N}, & N+1 \leq r \leq 2N \end{cases} \tag{31}$$

and observe that the matrix L can be rewritten as

$$L = \sum_{r=1}^{2N} \frac{\partial L}{\partial p_r} p_r \tag{32}$$

where

$$\frac{\partial L}{\partial p_r} = \begin{cases} \left[\dfrac{\partial M}{\partial m_r} \;\Big|\; 0 \right] = [\Phi'_M \mid 0], & 1 \leq r \leq N \\ \left[0 \;\Big|\; \dfrac{\partial K}{\partial k_{r-N}} \right] = [0 \mid \Phi'_K], & N+1 \leq r \leq 2N \end{cases} \tag{33}$$

in which, from (25a) and (27), Φ'_M is an $n \times n$ matrix with Φ_M occupying the block corresponding to M_r and with zero entries everywhere else. The matrix Φ'_K is defined analogously. Hence, (30) can be expressed explicitly in terms of the system parameters as follows:

$$\sum_{r=1}^{2N} \left[\frac{\partial L}{\partial p_r} \mathbf{x}(t) \right] p_r = \mathbf{F}(t) \tag{34}$$

But, $(\partial L/\partial p_r)\mathbf{x}(t)$ is an n-dimensional vector of the form

$$\frac{\partial L}{\partial p_r} \mathbf{x}(t) = \mathbf{a}_r(t) \tag{35}$$

where

$$\mathbf{a}_r(t) = \Phi'_M \ddot{\mathbf{w}}(t) = \begin{bmatrix} 0 \\ 0 \\ \Phi_M \ddot{\mathbf{w}}_r(t) \\ 0 \\ 0 \end{bmatrix}, \qquad 1 \leq r \leq N \tag{36a}$$

$$\mathbf{a}_r(t) = \Phi'_K \mathbf{w}(t) = \begin{bmatrix} 0 \\ 0 \\ \Phi_K \mathbf{w}_{r-N}(t) \\ 0 \\ 0 \end{bmatrix}, \qquad N + 1 \leq r \leq 2N \tag{36b}$$

Then, introducing the notation

$$A(t) = [\mathbf{a}_1(t) \quad \mathbf{a}_2(t) \quad \cdots \quad \mathbf{a}_{2N}(t)], \qquad \mathbf{p} = [p_1 \quad p_2 \quad \cdots \quad p_{2N}]^{\mathrm{T}} \tag{37a,b}$$

where $A(t)$ is an $n \times 2N$ matrix of coefficients and $\mathbf{p}$ is a $2N$-dimensional vector of parameters, inserting (35) into (34), and considering (37), we obtain

$$A(t)\mathbf{p} = \mathbf{F}(t) \tag{38}$$

which represents the desired equations with the system parameters as unknowns. To extract the system parameters from (38), we consider the sampling times $t = t_k$ $(k = 1, 2, \ldots, m)$ and write

$$A(t_k)\mathbf{p} = \mathbf{F}(t_k), \qquad k = 1, 2, \ldots, m \tag{39}$$

Equations (39) represent a set of $n \cdot m$ algebraic equations and $2N$ unknowns. To solve the equations it is convenient to introduce the notation

$$B = \begin{bmatrix} A(t_1) \\ A(t_2) \\ \vdots \\ A(t_m) \end{bmatrix}, \qquad \mathbf{c} = \begin{bmatrix} \mathbf{F}(t_1) \\ \mathbf{F}(t_2) \\ \vdots \\ \mathbf{F}(t_m) \end{bmatrix} \tag{40a,b}$$

where B is an $n \cdot m \times 2N$ matrix and $\mathbf{c}$ is an $n \cdot m$-dimensional vector, so that (39) can be combined into

$$B\mathbf{p} = \mathbf{c} \tag{41}$$

In general, $n \cdot m > 2N$, so the solution of (41) can be obtained by a least-squares algorithm [9]. The result is

$$\mathbf{p} = B^{\dagger}\mathbf{c} \tag{42}$$

where

$$B^{\dagger} = (B^{\mathrm{T}}B)^{-1}B^{\mathrm{T}} \tag{43}$$

is the pseudoinverse of B, in which B^TB is guaranteed to be nonsingular if B has maximum rank, namely, $2N$.

The equations of motion of a distributed structure free to move in space are linear provided that the rigid-body rotational motion is small. Hence, in the identification process the excitation forces must be such that the rotational motion is not excited significantly.

The parameter identification process works provided the response does not consist of rigid-body motions alone. Indeed, the matrix B in (40a) does not have maximum rank when only rigid-body motions are excited. The stiffness matrix in the case of a distributed structure capable of undergoing rigid-body motions is positive semidefinite. The vector $\mathbf{a}_r(t)(N + 1 < r < 2N)$ in (36b) is orthogonal to the nodal displacement vector $\mathbf{w}(t)$ when the motion is due entirely to rigid-body displacements. Hence, a necessary condition for the matrix B to have maximum rank is that elastic motions participate in the response.

The method is stable in the presence of measurement noise. To determine the effect of noise, the following Numerical Example 1 includes random noise in the nodal forces and in the measurements of the nodal accelerations; the nodal velocities and displacements are obtained by integrating the nodal accelerations in time. The effect of the noise can be reduced by increasing the number of sampling instances m in (40).

Numerical Example 1. We consider a free-free nonuniform beam (Fig. 1) undergoing translational and rotational rigid-body motions in addition to bending vibration. The energy inner product has the form [1]

$$[w, w] = \int_0^L EI(x)\left[\frac{\partial^2 w(x,t)}{\partial x^2}\right]^2 dx \tag{44}$$

where EI is the flexural rigidity. In the finite element model for a beam in bending, the nodal displacements are the transverse displacement and rotation at each node. From (44), we conclude that both the displacement and its first derivative must be continuous over the spatial domain. Suitable interpolation functions are Hermite cubics. In terms of local coordinates (see Fig. 2), the interpolation functions are [1]

$$\begin{aligned} \phi_1 &= 3\xi^2 - 2\xi^3, \qquad & \phi_2 &= \xi^2 - \xi^3 \\ \phi_3 &= 1 - 3\xi^2 + 2\xi^3, \qquad & \phi_4 &= -\xi + 2\xi^2 - \xi^3 \end{aligned} \tag{45}$$

The vector of nodal coordinates in (24) is then

$$\mathbf{w}_j(t) = [w_{j-1}(t)\ h\theta_{j-1}(t)\ w_j(t)\ h\theta_j(t)]^T, \qquad j = 1, 2, \ldots, N \tag{46}$$

where $w_j(t)$ and $\theta_j(t)$ represent translations and rotations, respectively, in which j designates the element number. The nondimensional local coordinate ξ is related to the global coordinate x by $\xi = j - x/h$, as can be concluded from Fig. 2.

To obtain the element mass matrices, we insert the interpolation functions given by (45) into (25a), carry out the integrations, and obtain

$$M_j = \int_{(j-1)h}^{jh} m(x)\boldsymbol{\phi}(x)\boldsymbol{\phi}^{\mathrm{T}}(x)\,dx$$

$$\cong m_j h \int_0^1 \begin{bmatrix} 3\xi^2 - 2\xi^3 \\ \xi^2 - \xi^3 \\ 1 - 3\xi^2 + 2\xi^3 \\ -\xi + 2\xi^2 - \xi^3 \end{bmatrix} \begin{bmatrix} 3\xi^2 - 2\xi^3 \\ \xi^2 - \xi^3 \\ 1 - 3\xi^2 + 2\xi^3 \\ -\xi + 2\xi^2 - \xi^3 \end{bmatrix}^{\mathrm{T}} d\xi$$

$$= \frac{m_j h}{420} \begin{bmatrix} 156 & 22 & 54 & -13 \\ & 4 & 13 & -3 \\ \text{symm} & & 156 & -22 \\ & & & 4 \end{bmatrix} \tag{47}$$

so that

$$\Phi_M = \frac{h}{420} \begin{bmatrix} 156 & 22 & 54 & -13 \\ & 4 & 13 & -3 \\ \text{symm} & & 156 & -22 \\ & & & 4 \end{bmatrix} \tag{48}$$

Similarly, inserting (45) into (25b) and considering (44) yields the element stiffness matrices

$$K_j = \int_{(j-1)h}^{jh} EI(x)\frac{d^2\boldsymbol{\phi}(x)}{dx^2}\frac{d^2\boldsymbol{\phi}^{\mathrm{T}}(x)}{dx^2}\,dx \cong \frac{EI_j}{h^3}\int_0^1 \begin{bmatrix} 6 - 12\xi \\ 2 - 6\xi \\ -6 + 12\xi \\ 4 - 6\xi \end{bmatrix} \begin{bmatrix} 6 - 12\xi \\ 2 - 6\xi \\ -6 + 12\xi \\ 4 - 6\xi \end{bmatrix}^{\mathrm{T}} d\xi$$

$$= k_j \begin{bmatrix} 12 & 6 & -12 & 6 \\ & 4 & -6 & 2 \\ \text{symm} & & 12 & -6 \\ & & & 4 \end{bmatrix} \tag{49}$$

so that

$$\Phi_K = \begin{bmatrix} 12 & 6 & -12 & 6 \\ & 4 & -6 & 2 \\ \text{symm} & & 12 & -6 \\ & & & 4 \end{bmatrix} \tag{50}$$

Note that the stiffness k_j is related to the flexural rigidity of element j according to $k_j = EI_j/h^3$.

As an illustration, we identify a model possessing 15 finite elements, $N = 15$. The model has 16 nodes, and the global mass and stiffness matrices are 32×32. Hence, $n = 32$ in (41). There are 30 parameters p_i $(i = 1, 2, \ldots, 30)$ to be identified. The parameters are the unknown mass and stiffness average values m_j and k_j $(j = 1, 2, \ldots, 15)$ associated with each element.

To construct the matrix $A(t)$, we turn to (36) and (37). The matrix is 32×30, and it is not feasible to give it in full, so we list only the first two and last two columns. From (36), (46), (48), and (50), we can write

$$\mathbf{a}_1(t) = \frac{h}{420}\begin{bmatrix} 156\ddot{w}_0(t) + 22h\ddot{\theta}_0(t) + 54\ddot{w}_1(t) - 13h\ddot{\theta}_1(t) \\ 22\ddot{w}_0(t) + 4h\ddot{\theta}_0(t) + 13\ddot{w}_1(t) - 3h\ddot{\theta}_1(t) \\ 54\ddot{w}_0(t) + 13h\ddot{\theta}_0(t) + 156\ddot{w}_1(t) - 22h\ddot{\theta}_1(t) \\ -13\ddot{w}_0(t) - 3h\ddot{\theta}_0(t) - 22\ddot{w}_1(t) + 4h\ddot{\theta}_1(t) \\ 0 \\ \vdots \\ 0 \end{bmatrix} \tag{51a}$$

$$\mathbf{a}_2(t) = \frac{h}{420}\begin{bmatrix} 0 \\ 0 \\ 156\ddot{w}_1(t) + 22h\ddot{\theta}_1(t) + 54\ddot{w}_2(t) - 13h\ddot{\theta}_2(t) \\ 22\ddot{w}_1(t) + 4h\ddot{\theta}_1(t) + 13\ddot{w}_2(t) - 3h\ddot{\theta}_2(t) \\ 54\ddot{w}_1(t) + 13h\ddot{\theta}_1(t) + 156\ddot{w}_2(t) - 22h\ddot{\theta}_2(t) \\ -13\ddot{w}_1(t) - 3h\ddot{\theta}_1(t) - 22\ddot{w}_2(t) + 4h\ddot{\theta}_2(t) \\ 0 \\ \vdots \\ 0 \end{bmatrix} \tag{51b}$$

$$\vdots$$

$$\mathbf{a}_{29}(t) = \begin{bmatrix} 0 \\ \vdots \\ 0 \\ 12w_{13}(t) + 6h\theta_{13}(t) - 12w_{14}(t) + 6h\theta_{14}(t) \\ 6w_{13}(t) + 4h\theta_{13}(t) - 6w_{14}(t) + 2h\theta_{14}(t) \\ -12w_{13}(t) - 6h\theta_{13}(t) + 12w_{14}(t) - 6h\theta_{14}(t) \\ 6w_{13}(t) + 2h\theta_{13}(t) - 6w_{14}(t) + 4h\theta_{14}(t) \\ 0 \\ 0 \end{bmatrix} \tag{51c}$$

$$\mathbf{a}_{30}(t) = \begin{bmatrix} 0 \\ \vdots \\ 0 \\ 12w_{14}(t) + 6h\theta_{14}(t) - 12w_{15}(t) + 6h\theta_{15}(t) \\ 6w_{14}(t) + 4h\theta_{14}(t) - 6w_{15}(t) + 2h\theta_{15}(t) \\ -12w_{14}(t) - 6h\theta_{14}(t) + 12w_{15}(t) - 6h\theta_{15}(t) \\ 6w_{14}(t) + 2h\theta_{14}(t) - 6w_{15}(t) + 4h\theta_{15}(t) \end{bmatrix} \tag{51d}$$

To excite at least one elastic mode of the beam, a single transverse forcing function given by $f(x,t) = 0.1\,\delta(x - 6h)\cos t$ N (newton) is applied at node 7, where $\delta(x - 6h)$ is a spatial Dirac delta function, so that the rigid-body motions are not excited significantly, although the forcing function has the effect of exciting every mode.

The actual parameters are provided in Table I. The beam has length $L = 15$ m, so that each discrete element has length $h = 1$ m. Gaussian random noise is added to the acceleration measurements and the forcing function to the extent that the noise-to-signal ratio is 2% at one standard deviation. The estimated parameters are shown in Tables II and III for values of m equal to 4 and 8, respectively, at sampling times $t_k = 0.5k$ sec $(k = 1, 2, \ldots, m)$. Also provided in each table is the normalized root-mean-square (RMS) error. The RMS error is normalized by dividing the error in each parameter by the exact

TABLE I. MASS AND STIFFNESS DISTRIBUTIONS OF THE FREE-FREE BEAM

Element number i	Mass distribution $p_i = m_i$ (kg)	Stiffness distribution $p_{i+15} = k_i$ (N/m)
1	8.400	3.300
2	1.600	2.300
3	2.300	1.200
4	4.800	1.300
5	6.300	3.300
6	5.200	4.200
7	7.100	1.800
8	4.200	1.400
9	6.300	4.100
10	1.600	3.600
11	1.100	5.200
12	2.400	3.400
13	3.500	6.600
14	4.600	2.500
15	7.300	5.300

TABLE II. ESTIMATED PARAMETERS FOR FOUR SAMPLING TIMES[a]

Element number i	Mass distribution[b] $p_i = m_i$ (kg)	Stiffness distribution[b] $p_{i+15} = k_i$ (N/m)
1	8.9468	3.4889
2	1.5728	2.3860
3	2.4259	1.2378
4	4.9358	1.3394
5	6.3033	3.3628
6	5.3359	4.2563
7	6.8490	1.7844
8	4.0711	1.3790
9	6.0960	4.0503
10	1.5999	3.5517
11	1.0508	5.1314
12	2.3435	3.3661
13	3.6165	6.5646
14	4.6088	2.4964
15	7.1814	5.3204

[a] Sampling times, $t_k = 0.5k$ sec ($k = 1, 2, 3, 4$).
[b] RMS error, 0.056.

TABLE III. ESTIMATED PARAMETERS FOR EIGHT SAMPLING TIMES[a]

Element number i	Mass distribution[b] $p_i = m_i$ (kg)	Stiffness distribution[b] $p_{i+15} = k_i$ (N/m)
1	8.7153	3.3342
2	1.6093	2.3151
3	2.2972	1.2076
4	4.8362	1.3124
5	6.4140	3.3357
6	5.3101	4.2398
7	6.9578	1.7963
8	4.0427	1.3880
9	6.3078	4.1755
10	1.6465	3.6674
11	1.0563	5.2849
12	2.4603	3.4443
13	3.5955	6.6792
14	4.5489	2.5246
15	7.3629	5.3466

[a] Sampling times, $t_k = 0.5k$ sec ($k = 1, 2, \ldots, 8$).
[b] RMS error, 0.035.

TABLE IV. FIRST TEN NATURAL FREQUENCIES OF THE FREE-FREE BEAM COMPUTED USING THE ACTUAL AND ESTIMATED PARAMETERS

	Natural frequencies		
r	Actual ω_r (rad/s)	Estimated ω_r^* (rad/s)	Error $\omega_r^* - \omega_r$ (rad/s)
1	0.000000	0.000000	0.000000
2	0.000000	0.000000	0.000000
3	0.064455	0.064077	−0.000378
4	0.206939	0.207273	0.000334
5	0.408213	0.408697	0.000484
6	0.719599	0.719890	0.000291
7	1.096452	1.100486	0.004034
8	1.524039	1.530416	0.006377
9	1.999755	2.007110	0.007355
10	2.575960	2.583589	0.007629

value of the parameter. The results show that increasing the number of sampling instances m in (42) reduces the effect of noise. Table IV shows the actual and computed natural frequencies, as well as the error. The results are excellent.

VI. A PERTURBATION TECHNIQUE FOR PARAMETER IDENTIFICATION

We now develop a perturbation approach to the finite-element based identification technique discussed in Section V. The proposed identification process is based on the assumption that there is some *a priori* approximate knowledge of the system parameters and the object is to identify the actual parameters with reasonable accuracy. We refer to the approximate model as "postulated," so that the object is to develop an identification scheme for the actual parameters based on the postulated parameters. Assuming that the difference between the two sets of parameters is small, we consider a perturbation technique in which the postulated parameters represent the unperturbed zero-order solution and the actual parameters the perturbed solution, with the difference between the two sets of parameters playing the role of a perturbation.

The postulated parameters corresponding to the finite element model are denoted by m_{0j} and k_{0j} $(j = 1, 2, \ldots, N)$ and the corresponding actual parameters by m_j and k_j, respectively. Hence, according to the perturbation scheme, we write

$$m_j = m_{0j} + \Delta m_j, \qquad k_j = k_{0j} + \Delta k_j, \qquad j = 1, 2, \ldots, N \tag{52a,b}$$

Similarly, denoting the postulated and actual global mass and stiffness matrices by M_0 and K_0 and M and K, respectively, we can write

$$M = M_0 + \Delta M, \qquad K = K_0 + \Delta K \tag{53a,b}$$

The increments $\Delta m_j, \Delta k_j, \Delta M$, and ΔK in (52) and (53) are assumed to be small. The identification process reduces to the identification of the parameter increments Δm_j and Δk_j ($j = 1, 2, \ldots, N$). The procedure is carried out iteratively, in the sense that the results of the first identification cycle are regarded as improved postulated parameters, not the actual parameters. When ΔM and ΔK reduce to zero, the improved postulated parameters converge to the actual parameters.

The preceding identification process can be carried out conveniently in the frequency domain instead of the time domain, which amounts to exciting the structure harmonically at various frequencies and measuring the frequency response. Letting the harmonic excitation have the form

$$\mathbf{F}(t) = \mathbf{F}^e e^{i\omega^e t}, \qquad e = 1, 2, \ldots, m; \qquad i = \sqrt{-1} \tag{54}$$

where $\mathbf{F}^e$ is a vector of nodal force amplitudes and ω^e is the frequency of excitation, and inserting (54) into the finite element equations of motion, (26), we can write the steady-state response as

$$\mathbf{w}(t) = \mathbf{w}^e e^{i\omega^e t}, \qquad e = 1, 2, \ldots, m \tag{55}$$

where, dividing through by $\exp(i\omega^e t)$, the vector $\mathbf{w}^e$ of nodal displacement amplitudes satisfies the frequency response equations

$$[K - (\omega^e)^2 M]\mathbf{w}^e = \mathbf{F}^e, \qquad e = 1, 2, \ldots, m \tag{56}$$

Quite often, the excitation is contaminated by noise. In this case, (54) must be replaced by

$$\mathbf{F}(t) = (\mathbf{F}^e + \mathbf{V}^e)e^{i(\omega^e + \gamma^e)t}, \qquad e = 1, 2, \ldots, m \tag{57}$$

where $\mathbf{V}^e$ and γ^e are amplitude noise and frequency noise, respectively. Similarly, the response can be written as

$$\mathbf{w}(t) = \mathbf{w}^e e^{i(\omega^e + \gamma^e)t}, \qquad e = 1, 2, \ldots, m \tag{58}$$

and the frequency response equations as

$$[K - (\omega^e + \gamma^e)^2 M]\mathbf{w}^e = \mathbf{F}^e + \mathbf{V}^e, \qquad e = 1, 2, \ldots, m \tag{59}$$

Beginning with the initially postulated parameters, m_{0j} and k_{0j} ($j = 1, 2, \ldots, N$), we first compute the initial global matrices M_0 and K_0 by means of (25) in conjunction with the assembling process indicated by (27). Then, using (55), we compute the response vectors $\mathbf{w}_0^e$ $(e = 1, 2, \ldots, m)$ from the frequency responses

$$[K_0 - (\omega^e)^2 M_0]\mathbf{w}_0^e = \mathbf{F}^e, \quad e = 1, 2, \ldots, m \tag{60}$$

Next, we consider the "perturbed" frequency responses

$$[K_0 + \Delta K - (\omega^e + \gamma^e)^2(M_0 + \Delta M)](\mathbf{w}_0^e + \Delta\mathbf{w}^e) = \mathbf{F}^e + \mathbf{V}^e,$$
$$e = 1, 2, \ldots, m \tag{61}$$

in which

$$\Delta\mathbf{w}^e = \mathbf{w}^e - \mathbf{w}_0^e + \mathbf{W}^e, \qquad e = 1, 2, \ldots, m \tag{62}$$

where $\mathbf{W}^e$ is an n-dimensional vector representing the measurement noise. Note that $\Delta\mathbf{w}^e$ is a first-order perturbation in the response computed by taking the difference between the measured response vector represented by $\mathbf{w}^e + \mathbf{W}^e$ and the corresponding zero-order response vector $\mathbf{w}_0^e$ computed from (60). We regard the measurement noise $\mathbf{W}^e$ and the excitation frequency noise γ^e as small terms of first-order in magnitude. The zero-order terms cancel out by virtue of (60). On the other hand, the first-order terms satisfy the perturbation equations

$$[\Delta K - (\omega^e + \gamma^e)^2\,\Delta M]\mathbf{w}_0^e = \mathbf{h}^e, \qquad e = 1, 2, \ldots, m \tag{63}$$

where

$$\mathbf{h}^e = -[K_0 - (\omega^e + \gamma^e)^2 M_0]\,\Delta\mathbf{w}^e + \mathbf{Y}^e, \qquad e = 1, 2, \ldots, m \tag{64}$$

in which $\mathbf{Y}^e$ is a noise vector given by

$$\mathbf{Y}^e = \mathbf{V}^e - [K_0 - (\omega^e)^2 M_0]\mathbf{W}^e - 2\omega^e\gamma^e M_0\mathbf{w}_0^e, \qquad e = 1, 2, \ldots, m \tag{65}$$

The perturbation in the system parameters is computed by means of (63). To this end, we consider the explicit relations between the perturbation matrices and the parameter perturbations as follows [7]:

$$\Delta M = \sum_{l=1}^{N} \left.\frac{\partial M}{\partial p_l}\right|_{p_j = m_{0j}} \Delta p_l, \qquad \Delta K = \sum_{l=N+1}^{2N} \left.\frac{\partial K}{\partial p_l}\right|_{p_{N+j} = k_{0j}} \Delta p_l,$$
$$j = 1, 2, \ldots, N \tag{66a,b,c}$$

where

$$p_l = \begin{cases} m_l, & 1 \le l \le N \\ k_l, & N + 1 \le l \le 2N \end{cases} \tag{67}$$

are the system parameters. Introducing the $n \times 2N$ matrix

$$G^e = [\mathbf{g}_1^e \quad \mathbf{g}_2^e \quad \cdots \quad \mathbf{g}_{2N}^e] \tag{68}$$

where

$$\mathbf{g}_l^e = \begin{cases} \left[-(\omega^e + \gamma^e)^2 \dfrac{\partial M}{\partial p_l}\bigg|_{p_l = m_l} \right] \mathbf{w}_0^e, & l = 1, 2, \ldots, N \\ \left[\dfrac{\partial K}{\partial p_l}\bigg|_{p_l = k_{l-N}} \right] \mathbf{w}_0^e, & l = N+1, N+2, \ldots, 2N \end{cases} \tag{69}$$

as well as the $2N$-vector of parameter corrections

$$\Delta \mathbf{p} = [\Delta p_1 \quad \Delta p_2 \quad \cdots \quad \Delta p_{2N}]^{\mathrm{T}} \tag{70}$$

we can write (63) in the compact form

$$G^e \Delta \mathbf{p} = \mathbf{h}^e, \qquad e = 1, 2, \ldots, m \tag{71}$$

Equations (71) can be combined into

$$G \Delta \mathbf{p} = \mathbf{h} \tag{72}$$

where

$$G = \begin{bmatrix} G^1 \\ G^2 \\ \vdots \\ G^m \end{bmatrix}, \qquad \mathbf{h} = \begin{bmatrix} \mathbf{h}^1 \\ \mathbf{h}^2 \\ \vdots \\ \mathbf{h}^m \end{bmatrix} \tag{73}$$

and we note that G is an $n \cdot m \times 2N$ matrix and $\mathbf{h}$ is an $n \cdot m$-vector.

Equation (72) forms the basis for the parameter identification algorithm. Because in general $n \cdot m > 2N$, we must obtain the solution of (72) by a least-squares algorithm [9]. The result is

$$\Delta \mathbf{p} = G^{\dagger} \mathbf{h} \tag{74}$$

where

$$G^{\dagger} = (G^{\mathrm{T}} G)^{-1} G^{\mathrm{T}} \tag{75}$$

is the pseudoinverse of G. If G has maximum rank $2N$, then $G^{\mathrm{T}} G$ is guaranteed to be nonsingular.

As pointed out earlier, the algorithm defined by (74) is applied recursively, in the sense that $\Delta \mathbf{p}$ is used to produce improved postulated system parameters. The iteration process converges when $\Delta \mathbf{p}$ reduces to zero.

In practice, implementation of (74) may be difficult because it requires measurements of each nodal displacement. Hence, it is desirable to reformulate (74) so as to permit the use of a reduced number of measurements. This requires that we extend the vector of unknown parameters to include the unmeasured displacement components. We refer to these unmeasured displacement components as "pseudoparameters" because we treat them as parameters for computational purposes.

The response $\mathbf{w}^e$ of the actual system contains unmeasured components. Hence, from (62) it is evident that the corresponding components of the perturbation vector $\Delta\mathbf{w}^e$ are unknown. We consider the case in which $r < m$ displacements are not measured and split (64) into known and unknown quantities as follows:

$$\begin{aligned}\mathbf{h}^e &= -[K_0 - (\omega^e + \gamma^e)^2 M_0] I_{n-r} \Delta\mathbf{w}^e_{n-r} \\ &\quad - [K_0 - (\omega^e + \gamma^e)^2 M_0] I_r \Delta\mathbf{w}^e_r + \mathbf{Y}^e \\ &= D^e \Delta\mathbf{w}^e_{n-r} + E^e \Delta\mathbf{w}^e_r + \mathbf{Y}^e \end{aligned} \tag{76}$$

where I_{n-r} and I_r are $n \times (n - r)$ and $n \times r$ rectangular matrices, respectively, and we note that I_{n-r} and I_r have entries equal to either 0 or 1; the entries are placed so as to permit separation of the measured and unmeasured displacement components. Moreover,

$$D^e = -[K_0 - (\omega^e + \gamma^e)^2 M_0] I_{n-r} \tag{77a}$$

$$E^e = -[K_0 - (\omega^e + \gamma^e)^2 M_0] I_r \tag{77b}$$

are $n \times (n - r)$ and $n \times r$ coefficient matrices, respectively. The vectors $\Delta\mathbf{w}^e_{n-r}$ and $\Delta\mathbf{w}^e_r$ contain the known and unknown perturbations in the responses, respectively. In addition, the vector $\Delta\mathbf{w}^e_{n-r}$ includes measurement noise as in (62) where the n-dimensional vectors are replaced by $(n - r)$-dimensional vectors. Hence, reformulating (71), we have

$$H^e \begin{bmatrix} \Delta\mathbf{p} \\ \hline \Delta\mathbf{w}^e_r \end{bmatrix} = \mathbf{d}^e, \qquad e = 1, 2, \ldots, m \tag{78}$$

where H^e is an $n \times (2N + r)$ matrix given by

$$H^e = [G^e \mid E^e] \tag{79}$$

and $\mathbf{d}^e$ is an n-dimensional vector given by

$$\mathbf{d}^e = D^e \Delta\mathbf{w}^e_{n-r} + \mathbf{Y}^e \tag{80}$$

Note that a new vector of pseudoparameters $\Delta\mathbf{w}^e_r$ is generated at each sampling frequency ω^e $(e = 1, 2, \ldots, m)$. To extract the system parameter corrections from (78), we consider m different harmonic excitations ω^e and write

$$H = \begin{bmatrix} G^1 & E^1 & 0 & 0 & \cdots & 0 \\ G^2 & 0 & E^2 & 0 & \cdots & 0 \\ \vdots & & & & & \\ G^m & 0 & 0 & 0 & \cdots & E^m \end{bmatrix}, \qquad \mathbf{d} = \begin{bmatrix} \mathbf{d}^1 \\ \mathbf{d}^2 \\ \vdots \\ \mathbf{d}^m \end{bmatrix} \tag{81}$$

where H is an $n \cdot m \times (2N + r \cdot m)$ matrix and $\mathbf{d}$ is an $n \cdot m$-dimensional vector, so that (78) can be combined into

$$H\,\Delta\mathbf{p}^* = \mathbf{d} \tag{82}$$

where

$$\Delta\mathbf{p}^* = [\Delta\mathbf{p}^{\mathrm{T}} \quad (\Delta\mathbf{w}_r^1)^{\mathrm{T}} \quad (\Delta\mathbf{w}_r^2)^{\mathrm{T}} \quad \cdots \quad (\Delta\mathbf{w}_r^m)^{\mathrm{T}}]^{\mathrm{T}} \tag{83}$$

The number m of sampling frequencies must satisfy $m \geq 2N/(n - r)$. When the inequality holds, the solution of (82) can be obtained by a least-squares algorithm, or

$$\Delta\mathbf{p}^* = (H^{\mathrm{T}}H)^{-1}H^{\mathrm{T}}\,\mathbf{d} \tag{84}$$

where $H^{\mathrm{T}}H$ is nonsingular when H has maximum rank $2N + r \cdot m$. Hence, with unmeasured displacement components, the identification process consists of using (84) recursively until $\Delta\mathbf{p}^*$ reduces to zero, at which point the postulated parameters converge to the actual parameters.

Numerical Example 2. To illustrate the perturbation technique, we consider an undamped cantilever beam undergoing bending vibration. Both the deterministic and stochastic problems are investigated. The stochastic problem is examined by adding Gaussian random noise to the amplitude and frequency of excitation in the perturbed frequency response given by (61) and to the sensor measurements in (62).

The finite element formulation is as in Numerical Example 1, except that the boundary conditions differ. For this example, we consider a model possessing six finite elements, $N = 6$. The model has six nodes and $n = 12$ degrees of freedom, so that 12 parameters p_i $(i = 1, 2, \ldots, 12)$ are to be identified. The parameters are the unknown element mass and stiffness distributions m_j and k_j $(j = 1, 2, \ldots, 6)$. The structural properties of the beam are illustrated in Fig. 1, except that in this example the left end is clamped. The element mass and stiffness matrices are given by (47) and (49), and the global matrices are assembled as shown in (27). Note that, to account for the fact that the displacement and slope are zero at the clamped end, we must delete the first two rows and columns from the assembled matrices [1].

For the deterministic problem, we have $\mathbf{V}^e = \mathbf{0}$, $\gamma^e = 0$, and $\mathbf{W}^e = \mathbf{0}$ in (78). We consider two cases. In the first case the full array of measurements is available ($r = 0$), and in the second case only one sensor measuring a transverse displacement is available ($r = 11$). To satisfy the condition $m \geq 2N/(n - r)$, in Case 1 we choose $m = 1$ and in Case 2 we choose $m = 12$. The beam is excited harmonically by an actuator applying a transverse load at the free end.

The actual and postulated parameters are provided in Table V. The $m = 12$ sampling frequencies range from 0.5 to 6.0 rad/sec in increments of 0.5 rad/sec. In Case 1, only the first test frequency is used. The beam has length $L = 6$ m, so each finite element has length $h = 1$ m. Figures 3a,b show plots of the normalized RMS error for each case. The RMS error is normalized as in Numerical Example 1. The results indicate that the net effect of having access

TABLE V. VALUES OF ACTUAL AND POSTULATED PARAMETERS FOR CASES 1 AND 2

Actual			Postulated		
Parameter	Case 1	Case 2	Parameter	Case 1	Case 2
m_1 (kg)	0.92	0.8990	m_{01} (kg)	0.90	0.8600
m_2 (kg)	1.28	1.0520	m_{02} (kg)	1.15	1.0100
m_3 (kg)	1.17	1.1490	m_{03} (kg)	1.20	1.1300
m_4 (kg)	0.63	0.4520	m_{04} (kg)	0.50	0.4400
m_5 (kg)	1.11	1.0040	m_{05} (kg)	1.20	0.9800
m_6 (kg)	0.98	0.9010	m_{06} (kg)	0.90	0.9000
k_1 (N/m)	1.38	1.0420	k_{01} (N/m)	1.30	1.0000
k_2 (N/m)	0.68	0.7480	k_{02} (N/m)	0.60	0.7100
k_3 (N/m)	1.24	1.1980	k_{03} (N/m)	1.10	1.1700
k_4 (N/m)	0.56	0.5520	k_{04} (N/m)	0.50	0.5400
k_5 (N/m)	0.76	1.1010	k_{05} (N/m)	0.90	1.0800
k_6 (N/m)	1.12	0.9010	k_{06} (N/m)	1.20	0.9000

to the full array of measurements is a process that is less sensitive to perturbations in the parameters. Indeed, Figures 3a,b show that when all the nodal displacements are measured, the permissible initial RMS error is 12%; and when only one nodal displacement is measured, the permissible initial RMS error drops to 3%. Indeed, if a single measurement is used, then the algorithm cannot converge when the initial RMS error exceeds 3%. Note

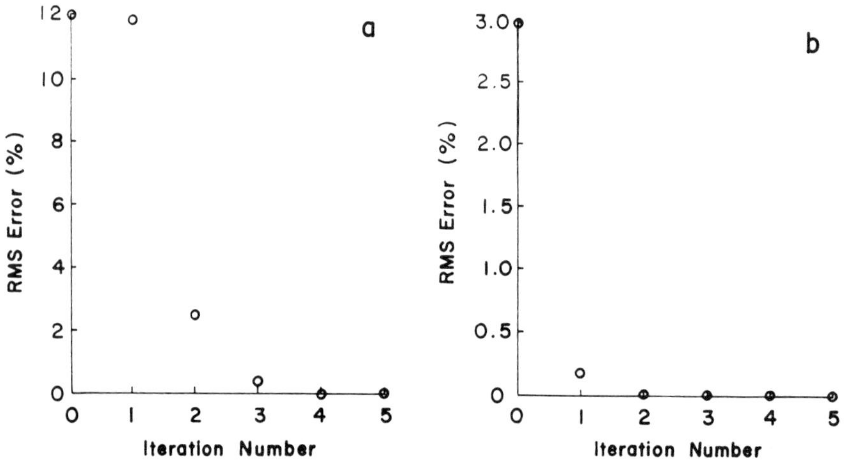

Fig. 3. Normalized permissible RMS error for (a) the case in which all nodal measurements are available (deterministic problem) and for (b) the case in which a single nodal measurement is available (deterministic problem).

that the RMS error in both cases reduces to zero, so that the postulated parameters converge to the actual parameters shown in Table V. The convergence is achieved in five iteration steps.

For the stochastic problem, we consider the same cases as in the deterministic problem, except that zero-mean Gaussian random noise is included in the input excitations given by (57) and in the perturbation in the responses given by (62). One implication of this is that $E[\mathbf{V}^e] = \mathbf{0}$, $E[\gamma^e] = 0$, and $E[\mathbf{W}^e] = \mathbf{0}$ $(e = 1, 2, \ldots, m)$. The noise-to-signal ratios in the sensor measurements were 1% and 0.01% at one standard deviation for Cases 1 and 2, respectively. The amplitude and frequency of the excitation had equivalent noise-to-signal ratios of 0.5% and 0.0005% at one standard deviation for

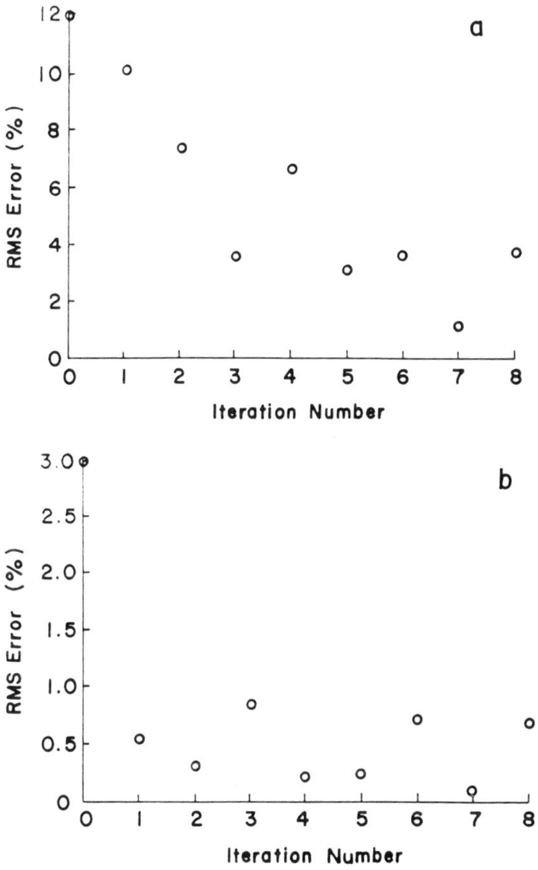

Fig. 4. Normalized permissible RMS error for (a) the case in which all nodal measurements are available (stochastic problem) and for (b) the case in which a single nodal measurement is available (stochastic problem).

Cases 1 and 2, respectively. Figures 4a,b show plots of the normalized permissible RMS error for each case. The results indicate that the noise affects convergence, and Case 2 is highly sensitive to noise. As in the deterministic case, the algorithm does not converge for higher values at the initial RMS error, so that Case 2 is more sensitive to initial RMS errors than Case 1.

VII. A RAYLEIGH–RITZ TYPE PARAMETER IDENTIFICATION

In the preceding two sections, the parameters were identified in a finite element sense, that is, in the sense that the structure was divided into finite elements and the parameter distributions were approximated by assuming uniform values over the elements equal to the average values over the elements. Then, the average values of the parameters for each element were identified on the basis of known excitation and response at the nodal points. In this section, we consider an identification approach more akin to the classical Rayleigh–Ritz method than to the finite element method. Indeed, here we represent the parameter distributions as linear combinations of known global functions multiplied by undetermined coefficients. The parameter identification reduces to the identification of the undetermined coefficients.

Let us assume that accurate representations of the mass and stiffness distributions are given by [4]

$$m(P) = \sum_{r=1}^{g} \alpha_r m_r(P), \qquad k(P) = \sum_{r=1}^{h} \beta_r k_r(P) \tag{85a,b}$$

where $m_r(P)$ and $k_r(P)$ are functions from complete sets, and α_r and β_r are undetermined coefficients playing the role of unknown parameters in the identification process. The functions $m_r(P)$ and $k_r(P)$ can be global or local functions. Inserting (85) into (14) and (16), one can show that the coefficient matrices in (19) can be written in the form [4]

$$M^{(n)} = \sum_{r=1}^{g} \alpha_r M_r^{(n)}, \qquad K^{(n)} = \sum_{r=1}^{h} \beta_r K_r^{(n)} \tag{86a,b}$$

where

$$M_r^{(n)} = \int_D m_r(P)\boldsymbol{\phi}(P)\boldsymbol{\phi}^{\mathrm{T}}(P)\,dD, \qquad K_r^{(n)} = [\boldsymbol{\phi}(P), \boldsymbol{\phi}^{\mathrm{T}}(P)]_r \tag{87a,b}$$

One must proceed with caution, however, because (12) and (85) represent approximations to the displacement profile and distributed parameters, respectively. Indeed, the discretized model given by (19) was obtained as an approximate solution to (1). Moreover, the discretized representation given by (19) is not unique because the dimension of the mass and stiffness matrices and the value of their entries depend on the number and type of admissible functions used in (87). In fact, the accuracy of the discretized model depends on the number and type of admissible functions used [2], and these two factors affect, in turn, the accuracy of the estimated parameters in the identification process.

We now present an iterative procedure in which the parameter distributions are updated using a set of natural frequencies either measured directly from the frequency response or identified from the measured transient response of the distributed structure. In the next section, we present a method for identifying the natural frequencies from the transient response of the system. In the ensuing discussion, we refer to the natural frequencies of the distributed structure as measured, whether they were measured directly or identified. We adopt an incremental approach in which a vector $\boldsymbol{\omega} = [\omega_1 \quad \omega_2 \quad \cdots \quad \omega_f]^{\mathrm{T}}$ of f measured natural frequencies of the actual distributed structure is used to update a parameter vector given by $\mathbf{p} = [\alpha_1 \quad \alpha_2 \quad \cdots \quad \alpha_g \quad \beta_1 \quad \beta_2 \quad \cdots \quad \beta_h]^{\mathrm{T}}$. The iteration process is based on the incremental relations

$$\Delta\boldsymbol{\omega} = \boldsymbol{\omega} - \boldsymbol{\omega}^{(n)}, \qquad \Delta\boldsymbol{\omega} = \left[\frac{\partial \omega_i}{\partial p_j}\right]\Delta\mathbf{p}, \qquad \Delta\mathbf{p} = \mathbf{p} - \mathbf{p}_0 \qquad \text{(88a,b,c)}$$

To begin the parameter identification, we postulate a parameter vector $\mathbf{p}_0$, compute the corresponding mass and stiffness matrices using (86) and (87), and solve for the associated natural frequencies $\boldsymbol{\omega}^{(n)} = [\sqrt{\lambda_1^{(n)}} \quad \sqrt{\lambda_2^{(n)}} \quad \cdots \quad \sqrt{\lambda_f^{(n)}}]^{\mathrm{T}}$ using (20). Then, we use the measurement vector $\boldsymbol{\omega}$ to compute $\Delta\boldsymbol{\omega}$ by using (88a). Replacing $\lambda_i^{(n)}$ by $(\omega_i^{(n)})^2$ in the ith solution of the eigenvalue problem (20), taking partial derivatives with respect to the system parameters p_j $(j = 1, 2, \ldots, g + h)$, premultiplying the result by $\mathbf{u}_i^{\mathrm{T}}$, and invoking the orthogonality conditions (21), we can show that the Jacobian matrix in (88b) has the following entries:

$$\frac{\partial \omega_i}{\partial p_j} = \frac{1}{2\omega_i^{(n)}}\left[\mathbf{u}_i^{\mathrm{T}}\frac{\partial K^{(n)}}{\partial p_j}\mathbf{u}_i - (\omega_i^{(n)})^2\mathbf{u}_i^{\mathrm{T}}\frac{\partial M^{(n)}}{\partial p_j}\mathbf{u}_i\right],$$
$$i = 1, 2, \ldots, f, \qquad j = 1, 2, \ldots, g + h \qquad (89)$$

where the entries of the mass and stiffness sensitivity matrices are given by

$$\begin{aligned} &\frac{\partial M^{(n)}}{\partial p_j} = M_j^{(n)}, \qquad \frac{\partial K^{(n)}}{\partial p_j} = 0, \qquad j = 1, 2, \ldots, g \\ &\frac{\partial M^{(n)}}{\partial p_j} = 0, \qquad \frac{\partial K^{(n)}}{\partial p_j} = K_j^{(n)}, \qquad j = g + 1, g + 2, \ldots, g + h \end{aligned} \qquad (90)$$

Then the increment $\Delta\mathbf{p}$ can be computed by means of (88b). For the case in which the number f of measured natural frequencies is greater than the number of parameter $g + h$, a least-squares solution of (88b) yields

$$\Delta\mathbf{p} = \left[\frac{\partial \omega_i}{\partial p_j}\right]^{\dagger}\Delta\mathbf{w} \qquad (91)$$

where

$$\left[\frac{\partial \omega_i}{\partial p_j}\right]^{\dagger} = \left(\left[\frac{\partial \omega_i}{\partial p_j}\right]^{\mathrm{T}}\left[\frac{\partial \omega_i}{\partial p_j}\right]\right)^{-1}\left[\frac{\partial \omega_i}{\partial p_j}\right]^{\mathrm{T}} \tag{92}$$

is the pseudoinverse of $[\partial\omega_i/\partial p_j]$. Finally, from (88c), we obtain the improved parameter vector

$$\mathbf{p} = \mathbf{p}_0 + \Delta\mathbf{p} \tag{93}$$

The procedure is repeated using (88a), (89), (91), and (93) until convergence is achieved.

Numerical Example 3. As an illustration, we consider a rod in axial vibration with a spring of stiffness k attached to the free end, as shown in Fig. 5. In this case, the stiffness operator $\mathscr{L}$ in (1) has order 2 ($p = 1$) and is given by

$$\mathscr{L} = -\frac{\partial}{\partial x}\left[EA(x)\frac{\partial}{\partial x}\right] \tag{94}$$

where $EA(x)$ is the axial stiffness. The boundary conditions are given by

$$B_1 = 1 \quad \text{at} \quad x = 0, \qquad B_1 = EA\frac{\partial}{\partial x} + k \quad \text{at} \quad x = L \tag{95}$$

Moreover, the energy inner product in (15) has the form

$$[u, u] = \int_0^L EA\left(\frac{\partial u}{\partial x}\right)^2 dx + ku^2(L, t) \tag{96}$$

The mass and stiffness distributions for the actual model are given by

$$m(x) = \frac{6}{5}m\left[1 - \frac{1}{2}\left(\frac{x}{L}\right)^2\right], \qquad EA(x) = \frac{6}{5}EA\left[1 - \frac{1}{2}\left(\frac{x}{L}\right)^2\right] \tag{97a,b}$$

We consider the case in which the distributions are known with unknown scaling, so that $g = h = 1$ and $m_1(x) = \frac{6}{5}[1 - \frac{1}{2}(x^2/L)]$, $k_1(x) = \frac{6}{5}[1 - \frac{1}{2}(x^2/L)]$ in (85). Hence, the problem reduces to identifying three parameters: m, EA, and k. Moreover, because free vibration data are used, to identify the

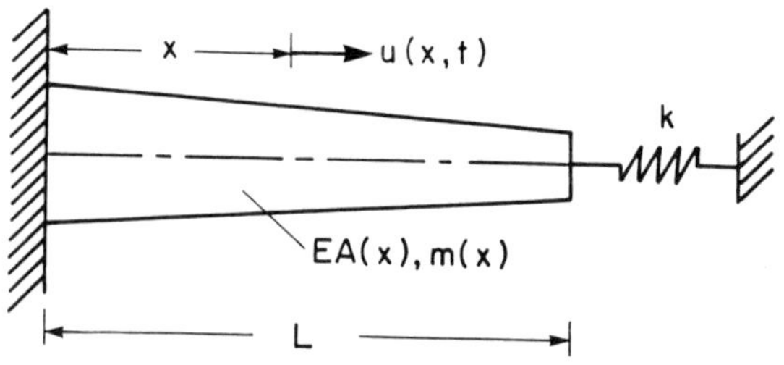

Fig. 5. Rod in axial vibration with a spring attached to the free end.

parameters uniquely, one of the parameters must be known. For convenience, we chose $m = 1$ kg/m.

An added objcctive is to show that accurate modeling has a direct influence on the accuracy of the identification results. The system does not have a closed-form solution so we must resort to spatial discretization. To this end, we consider two sets of trial functions $\phi_r(P)$ $(r = 1, 2, \ldots, n)$ to be used in (12). The first consists of the admissible functions

$$\phi_r(x) = \sin\frac{(2r-1)\pi x}{2L}, \qquad r = 1, 2, \ldots, n \tag{98}$$

We note that these functions satisfy the geometric boundary condition $u = 0$ at $x = 0$. They represent the eigenfunctions for a related problem; that is, they are the eigenfunctions of a uniform rod with no spring at the free end. The second set of trial functions consists of the functions

$$\phi_r(x) = \sin\frac{r\pi x}{2L}, \qquad r = 1, 2, \ldots, n \tag{99}$$

These functions are also admissible functions, and they represent quasi-comparison functions for this example [2]. Note that a finite linear combination of the quasi-comparison functions can satisfy the natural boundary condition at $x = L$, whereas the first set of admissible functions can satisfy the natural boundary condition only when n approaches infinity.

To refine the system parameters EA and k, we used the first three natural frequencies from the actual model, so that $f = 3$ in (89). As an initially postulated model, we used the parameters $EA = 1.5$ N and $k = 1.5$ N/m, whereas the actual model parameters are $EA = 1$ N and $k = 1$ N/m. To check the algorithm, several other cases involving various initially postulated parameters were tested. The results are not presented here, but for reasonable starting values the identification results were insensitive to the initially postulated parameters, and the algorithm converged within five iterations. In addition to using ordinary admissible functions and quasi-comparison functions for modeling, we used various numbers of degrees of freedom. Table VI displays the results. As expected, the identified parameters improve as the number n of degrees of freedom increases. Indeed, as the number n of admissible functions increases, the model becomes more representative of the actual system, resulting in improved identified parameters. The model with the admissible functions can predict the value of EA very well, but the identification of the parameter k is rather poor because a finite number of admissible functions cannot satisfy the natural boundary condition. On the other hand, the parameter identification based on the model using quasi-comparison functions is extremely good for $n > 4$: Both parameters are identified exactly.

TABLE VI. IDENTIFIED PARAMETERS USING ADMISSIBLE FUNCTIONS (AF) AND QUASI-COMPARISON FUNCTIONS (QCF) FOR DIFFERENT DEGREES OF FREEDOM

	AF			QCF		
n	EA	k	RMS error (%)	EA	k	RMS error (%)
4	1.0016	0.91705	5.87	0.98809	1.0564	4.08
5	1.0010	0.93335	4.71	0.99996	0.99977	0.02
6	1.0008	0.94474	3.91	0.99996	0.99984	0.01
7	1.0006	0.95286	3.33	0.99999	0.99987	0.01
8	1.0005	0.95208	2.89	1.00000	1.00000	0.00

VIII. MODAL IDENTIFICATION OF SELF-ADJOINT SYSTEMS

Earlier in this article, we identified distributed physical parameters of a structure using the system response in the time domain and in the frequency domain. In addition, we presented a Rayleigh–Ritz type parameter identification technique in which parameter distributions were identified using measured natural frequencies from the actual structure. In this section, we present an algorithm for identifying modal parameters of a distributed structure, such as natural frequencies, using the free response.

Consider the free response of a distributed structure. The equation of motion is obtained from (1) by setting $f(P, t) = 0$. The eigenfunctions are obtained by solving (3). They comprise a complete set, so the motion of the distributed structure can be expressed as

$$w(P, t) = \sum_{r=1}^{\infty} w_r(P)\eta_r(t) \tag{100}$$

where $w_r(P)$ are the system eigenfunctions and $\eta_r(t)$ $(r = 1, 2, \ldots)$ are modal coordinates. Introducing (100) into (1), multiplying the result by $w_s(P)$, integrating over the domain of the system, and considering (7), we obtain the modal equations of motion

$$\ddot{\eta}_r(t) + \omega_r^2 \eta_r(t) = 0, \qquad r = 1, 2, \ldots \tag{101}$$

The modal coordinates $\eta_r(t)$ $(r = 1, 2, \ldots)$ are independent, and hence uncorrelated, so that

$$\langle \eta_r(t), \eta_s(t) \rangle = \lim_{T \to \infty} \frac{1}{T} \int_0^T \eta_r(t)\eta_s(t)\, dt = Q_r\, \delta_{rs} \tag{102}$$

where $\langle \ , \ \rangle$ represents a temporal inner product and Q_r $(r = 1, 2, \ldots)$ are positive constants. Moreover, the modal velocities are also uncorrelated, so that

$$\langle \dot{\eta}_r(t), \dot{\eta}_s(t) \rangle = \lim_{T \to \infty} \frac{1}{T} \int_0^T \dot{\eta}_r(t) \dot{\eta}_s(t)\, dt = \omega_r^2 Q_r \delta_{rs} \tag{103}$$

The objective is to identify the natural frequencies ω_r $(r = 1, 2, \ldots)$ from the free response. To this end, we define a pseudo-Rayleigh quotient in the form [6]

$$R(\phi(P)) = \frac{\langle \dot{q}(t), \dot{q}(t) \rangle}{\langle q(t), q(t) \rangle} \tag{104}$$

where

$$q(t) = \int_D \phi(P) w(P, t)\, dD \tag{105}$$

in which $\phi(P)$ is a trial function in the form of an admissible function. We consider expressing the admissible function $\phi(P)$ as a linear combination of the eigenfunctions of the form

$$\phi(P) = \sum_{r=1}^{\infty} a_r m(P) w_r(P) \tag{106}$$

Introducing (100) and (106) into (105) and recalling the orthonormality relations (7a), inserting the result into (104) and considering (102) and (103), we obtain

$$R(a_1, a_2, \ldots) = \frac{\Sigma_{r=1}^{\infty} a_r^2 Q_r \omega_r^2}{\Sigma_{r=1}^{\infty} a_r^2 Q_r} \tag{107}$$

To determine the stationary values of the pseudo-Rayleigh quotient, we write

$$\frac{\partial R}{\partial a_s} = \frac{2 a_s Q_s (\omega_s^2 - R)}{\Sigma_{r=1}^{\infty} a_r^2 Q_r} = 0, \qquad s = 1, 2, \ldots \tag{108}$$

From (108), we conclude that the pseudo-Rayleigh quotient has stationary values for

$$a_r = 0, \qquad r = 1, 2, \ldots, \qquad r \neq s \tag{109}$$

In view of (106) and (109), we observe that stationary values of the pseudo-Rayleigh quotient occur when the trial function $\phi(P)$ is proportional to an eigenfunction multiplied by the mass density. Moreover, the stationary values are

$$R = \omega_s^2, \qquad s = 1, 2, \ldots \tag{110}$$

Hence, the pseudo-Rayleigh quotient and the ordinary Rayleigh quotient (11) possess the same stationary values, namely, the system eigenvalues.

Our interest lies in identifying the natural frequencies and the associated modes of vibration from the system response. In practice, it is possible to identify only a finite number of natural frequencies and associated modes of vibration. To this end, we express the trial function $\phi(P)$ as a finite linear combination of the admissible function $\phi_r(P)$ as follows:

$$\phi(P) = \sum_{r=1}^{m} c_r \phi_r(P) \tag{111}$$

where c_r are undetermined coefficients. Introducing (111) into (105), we have

$$q(t) = \sum_{r=1}^{m} c_r q_r(t), \qquad q_r(t) = \int_D \phi_r(P) w(P, t)\, dD \tag{112a,b}$$

Inserting (112a) into (104), we obtain

$$R(c_1, c_2, \ldots, c_m) = \frac{\sum_{r=1}^{m} \sum_{s=1}^{m} k_{rs}^{(m)} c_r c_s}{\sum_{r=1}^{m} \sum_{s=1}^{m} m_{rs}^{(m)} c_r c_s} \tag{113}$$

where

$$m_{rs}^{(m)} = m_{sr}^{(m)} = \langle q_r(t), q_s(t) \rangle, \qquad r, s = 1, 2, \ldots, m \tag{114a}$$

$$k_{rs}^{(m)} = k_{sr}^{(m)} = \langle \dot{q}_r(t), \dot{q}_s(t) \rangle, \qquad r, s = 1, 2, \ldots, m \tag{114b}$$

Determination of the stationary values of Rayleigh's quotient (113) can be carried out by solving the algebraic eigenvalue problem given by (20) with $n = m$, where $M^{(m)}$ and $K^{(m)}$ have entries $[m_{rs}^{(m)}]$ and $[k_{rs}^{(m)}]$ given by (114a) and (114b), respectively. The solution represents the mth-order approximation to the stationary values of the pseudo-Rayleigh quotient (104). The mth-order approximate eigenfunctions can be computed using (22) with $n = m$. The identified eigenvalues and eigenfunctions represent the mth-order approximation to the eigenvalues and eigenfunctions of the actual system, in the same way that the solution to (20), in conjunction with (22), represents the nth-order approximation to (3).

IX. AN INCLUSION PRINCIPLE FOR PARAMETER IDENTIFICATION

In modeling a distributed structure by a discrete model, the differential eigenvalue problem (3) is approximated by the algebraic eigenvalue problem (20). Convergence of the solution of the algebraic eigenvalue problem to the actual solution of the differential eigenvalue problem can be verified by means of the inclusion principle [1]. In this section, we show that an inclusion principle also exists for parameter identification. An attractive feature of the Rayleigh–Ritz method is that by increasing the number n of degrees of freedom the previously calculated mass and stiffness coefficients remain unaffected, so one must only calculate one additional row (or column) to obtain the updated mass and stiffness matrices. Hence, for an $(n + 1)$-degree-of-freedom discretized model, the mass and stiffness matrices have the form

$$M^{(n+1)} = \begin{bmatrix} & & x \\ & M^{(n)} & x \\ x & x & x \end{bmatrix}, \qquad K^{(n+1)} = \begin{bmatrix} & & x \\ & K^{(n)} & x \\ x & x & x \end{bmatrix} \tag{115}$$

The eigenvalue problem associated with discrete models described by matrices of the type (115) is given by (20). The inclusion principle [1] states that the relationship between the eigenvalues $\lambda_r^{(n)}$ $(r = 1, 2, \ldots, n)$ of the n-degree-of-freedom model and the eigenvalues $\lambda_r^{(n+1)}$ $(r = 1, 2, \ldots, n + 1)$ of the $(n + 1)$-degree-of-freedom model is given by

$$\lambda_1^{(n+1)} \leq \lambda_1^{(n)} \leq \lambda_2^{(n+1)} \leq \lambda_2^{(n)} \leq \cdots \leq \lambda_n^{(n)} \leq \lambda_{n+1}^{(n+1)} \tag{116}$$

As the number of degrees of freedom in the discretized model is increased, the approximate eigenvalues decrease monotonically and approach the actual eigenvalues of the system asymptotically from above [1].

Next, we consider the pseudo-Rayleigh quotient (104) for the distributed structure. The stationary values of this quotient were shown to be identical to those of the ordinary Rayleigh quotient (11). Proof of this was based on (105), which requires distributed measurements; that is, $w(P, t)$ must be known. In practice, however, only a finite number of modal parameters are to be identified, and distributed measurements may not be available. Instead of the actual eigenvalues, approximate stationary values of the pseudo-Rayleigh quotient can be obtained by determining the stationary values of the quotient given by (113).

In modeling, convergence of the solution of the discrete model to the exact solution can be enhanced by increasing the number of admissible functions in the solution as long as the set of admissible functions is complete in energy and the natural boundary conditions can be satisfied with a finite number of terms in the solution [2]. Moreover, when the addition of an admissible function produces mass and stiffness matrices, as illustrated by (115), the eigenvalues satisfy the inclusion principle. The resulting matrices $M^{(m)}$ and $K^{(m)}$, with identified elements given by (114a) and (b), respectively, possess the same attractive features as those obtained by the Rayleigh–Ritz method because the modal identification technique is based on a pseudo-Rayleigh quotient. Hence, the eigenvalues obtained using (113) also act as approximations to the eigenvalues of the actual system and satisfy the inclusion principle as well. This implies that by increasing the number m of admissible functions in (111), (113), and (114), the identified eigenvalues approach the actual eigenvalues monotonically from above.

Numerical Example 4. To illustrate the inclusion principle in parameter identification, we consider the rod in axial vibration described in Numerical Example 3. To identify the natural frequencies from the free response, it was necessary to simulate the response of the actual system. The model for this purpose was obtained by the Rayleigh–Ritz method using $n = 8$ admissible functions in (12), (14), and (16). The admissible functions used in the discretization were the quasi-comparison functions described by (99). Different order models, defined by $m = 4$, 5, 6, and 7 in (112) and (114), were identified using the free response. The free response was computed using the modal equations (101) in which only the first eight modes were used to compute the response given by (100). The model was subjected to an initial impulse of magnitude 1 N sec acting at $x = L$. The eigenfunctions in (100) were computed using (20) and (22) with $n = 8$. In addition, the coordinates $q_r(t)$, $\dot{q}_r(t)$ $(r = 1, 2, \ldots, m)$ in (114) were computed using (112b). To identify the natural frequencies, the eigenvalue problem given by (20) was solved; the results are presented in Table VII. We observe that, as the order of the identified model increases, the estimated natural frequencies decrease monotonically and approach the actual natural frequencies asymptotically from above. Moreover, the computed eigenvalues satisfy the inclusion principle, as stated by inequalities (116).

TABLE VII. IDENTIFIED NATURAL FREQUENCIES FOR DIFFERENT DEGREES OF FREEDOM

Identified natural frequencies (rad/s)				Natural frequencies of discrete model (rad/s)
$m = 4$	$m = 5$	$m = 6$	$m = 7$	
2.388	2.250	2.249	2.228	2.210
15.083	5.255	5.223	5.133	5.083
21.886	17.165	8.822	8.173	8.087
57.160	23.860	17.198	12.860	11.148
	63.161	23.918	17.308	14.237
		63.351	24.155	17.535
			64.156	24.388
				64.946

X. SUMMARY

Parameter identification in distributed structures is usually based on discretized models defined by mass and stiffness matrices. Mass and stiffness matrices, however, have physical meaning only in the case of lumped systems. For distributed structures, the physical characteristics are described by mass and stiffness distributions and not matrices. Moreover, mass and stiffness matrices are not unique for a given structure, and their dimensions and entries depend on the number and type of the trial functions used in the modeling process. Hence, the object of a parameter identification technique must be to identify mass and stiffness distributions and not mass and stiffness matrices, although such matrices can serve as useful tools in the identification process.

Parameter identification in distributed structures should be approached with caution. Indeed, the process represents a compounded version of the modeling problem in structures, so we must expect at the very least the same idiosyncracies encountered in parameter identification as those encountered in modeling. Sections IV, V, and VI are devoted to methods for the identification of distributed parameters in structures. The methods are illustrated in Numerical Examples 1 and 2. Moreover, a Rayleigh–Ritz type parameter identification technique is discussed in Section VII, in which the parameter distributions are expressed as series of global functions multiplied by unknown coefficients, with the coefficients playing the role of parameters. Numerical Example 3 indicates that the choice of the model can greatly affect the results of the parameter identification process. Indeed, the results show that the number and type of admissible functions is at least as important in parameter identification as it is in modeling. A wise choice of the number and type of the admissible functions can greatly improve the results of the parameter identification process. An identification technique suitable for distributed structures in which the identified quantities are natural frequencies rather than parameter distributions is discussed in Section VIII. Finally, in Section IX it is demonstrated that an inclusion principle exists in the identification of distributed structures, in the same way as it exists in modeling.

REFERENCES

1. L. MEIROVITCH, "Computational Methods in Structural Dynamics," Sijthoff & Noordhoff, Netherlands, 1980.
2. L. MEIROVITCH and M. K. KWAK, "Some Thoughts on the Convergence of the Classical Rayleigh–Ritz Method and the Finite Element Method," *AIAA/ASME/ASCE/AHS 29th Struct. Dyn. Mater. Conf., Williamsburg, Va.* (1988).
3. P. CARAVANI, M. L. WATSON, and W. T. THOMSON, "Recursive Least-Squares Identification of Structural Parameters," *J. Appl. Mech.* 135–140 (1977).

4. L. MEIROVITCH and M. A. NORRIS, "Parameter Identification in Distributed Spacecraft Structures," *J. Astronaut. Sci.* **32**, 341–353 (1986).
5. H. BARUH and L. MEIROVITCH, "Parameter Identification in Distributed Systems," *J. Sound Vib.* **101**, 551–564 (1985).
6. M. A. NORRIS and L. M. SILVERBERG, "Modal Identification of Self-Adjoint Distributed-Parameter Systems," *23rd Annu. Tech. Meet. Soc. Eng. Sci., Buffalo, N.Y.* (1986); (to appear). *Earthquake Eng. Struct. Dyn.* **18**, 633–642 (1989).
7. L. MEIROVITCH and M. A. NORRIS, "A Perturbation Technique for Parameter Identification," *Appl. Math. Modell.* **12**, 167–174 (1988).
8. E. DENMAN, T. HASSELMAN, C. T. SUN, J. N. JUANG, J. L. JUNKINS, F. UDWADIA, V. VENKAYYA, and M. KAMAT, "Identification of Large Space Structures on Orbit," AFRPL TR-86-054 Final Rep., September 1986.
9. J. L. JUNKINS, "Optimal Estimation of Dynamical Systems," Sijthoff & Noordhoff, Netherlands 1978.

COMBINED STRUCTURAL AND CONTROL OPTIMIZATION: A STEEPEST DESCENTS APPROACH

DAVID F. MILLER

Department of Mathematics and Statistics
Wright State University
Dayton, Ohio 45435

I. INTRODUCTION

A. MOTIVATION FOR COMBINED STRUCTURAL AND CONTROL OPTIMIZATION

The optimal control of dynamic systems has been intensively studied for many years, and a highly developed and useful mathematical theory exists today. The typical control problem involves the determination of inputs that drive a dynamic system so as to minimize a measure of its performance such as optimal signal tracking or total energy minimization. In the separate field of structural optimization, which has also been extensively developed, the typical concern is the minimization of structural weight or maximization of stiffness subject to constraints on strength and other performance characteristics. Traditionally, control and structural engineers have enjoyed little interaction. For example, in aeronautics, aircraft structures have conventionally been essentially determined prior to the addition of working control designs.

Could the simultaneous consideration of the control and structural design processes yield more efficient and superior performing, more "totally optimal" engineering systems? Strong motivation for combining structural and control design has come from the aerospace community. In the years ahead, the deployment and routine operation of large structures in space will become a reality. Because of their enormous size and the high cost of transporting construction materials into earth orbit, many will be highly articulated, built-up structures comprised largely of trusslike elements joined to form a lightweight superstructure. This superstructure will provide for the attachment and required spatial separation of mission-related functional components. Such highly flexible structures will not be static even in their weightless environment; they will inevitably be vulnerable to dynamic excitation from a variety of sources, such as the accelerations due to slewing and pointing maneuvers, thermal transients, and the operation of onboard mechanical devices such as coolers and generators.

Large space structure design provides challenges for both structural and control engineers. The structural engineer is concerned primarily with minimizing the structure's weight while satisfying strength, stiffness, and other mission-related requirements. In contrast to this, the control engineer is primarily concerned with inputting forces to eliminate unwanted motions (vibrations), maintain structural shape and alignment, and effect changes in position and orientation. Because of high construction and deployment costs, and because extensive on-orbit structural modifications will be impossible, it is imperative that space structures be as well designed as possible prior to launch. The need for such totally optimal space systems suggests that all engineering design processes should be integrated, particularly the structural and control design processes.

B. RECENT LITERATURE

Considerable attention has recently been focused on the possibility of simultaneously optimizing structural and control designs for structural systems [1–18]. A precise formulation of this concept was provided by Hale *et al.* [3,4]. They proposed the simultaneous minimization, in structural parameters and control variables, of a single optimization criterion containing measures of both structural and control performance: the sum of structural mass and the quadratic performance index of the linear regulator optimal control problem. System dynamics were permitted to depend explicitly upon structural parameters, a key idea in this and all other related formulations. Using techniques from the calculus of variations, the authors derived the necessary conditions for minimizing this criterion subject to the dynamics satisfying fixed initial and terminal conditions. The proposed solution of these conditions alternated two-point boundary value problem solutions for fixed structural parameter values, with quasi-Newton parameter updates. The general methodology of iterating separately in control and parameter space has been adopted by several other investigators.

Messac and Turner [6] studied the fixed end-point linear regulator problem in modal space for parameter dependent structural systems. They also alternated control and structural parameter updates. Linear regulator theory provides the optimal control for each choice of structural parameters. Minimization in structural parameters is accomplished by using a gradient projection optimization. Bodden and Junkins [9,10] presented an eigenspace optimization approach to the dual structural/control design problem. Based on a continuation procedure, it permits the minimization of a performance measure that is a general function of a structural parameter vector and the corresponding system eigenvalues and eigenvectors. Constraints are imposed that are also explicit functions of these three quantities.

Salama *et al.* [13] considered the simultaneous minimization, in structural and control variables, of the sum of structural mass and the infinite horizon linear regulator quadratic control cost. They showed that this combined structural and control optimization problem possesses a very special form. Optimal controls are always determined through the solution of specified algebraic Riccati equations, so the problem reduces to a minimization over the structural variables alone. They observe that the derivatives (with respect to structural parameters) of the Riccati equation solutions satisfy Lyapunov equations. The Newton–Raphson (second-order) algorithm proposed for the solution of the Kuhn–Tucker optimality conditions centers about these derivatives.

Onoda and Haftka [16] examined the minimization, in structural parameters and control variables, of the sum of structural mass and a certain measure of control effort. They imposed a total displacement constraint and presented a nested optimization technique for iterating between structural and control variables. Rao *et al.* [17] formulated the combined structural and control design problem as a multiobjective optimization problem. They considered four separate performance measures–structural mass, controlled system energy, weighted control gain norm, and effective damping response time—and attempted to minimize them simultaneously subject to constraints on structural parameters and system closed-loop damping ratios. They employed a cooperative game theory approach, based upon the minimization of a super criterion, to find a best Pareto-optimal solution.

C. OVERVIEW

The purpose of this article is to develop a particular combined structural and control design concept (see [11,12]) and apply it to the vibration suppression problem for structural systems. Specifically, we present an alternative algorithm for solving the problem formulated in [13] as described. Given an initial structural design, the objective of our optimization is to reduce both the mass and the vibrational energy at the same time. Constraints are imposed on structural parameters by restricting system natural frequencies and the sizes of structural elements. Control is provided by the optimal feedback gains of linear regulator theory. Optimization in the structural parameters is accomplished by using gradient projection and penalty function techniques, thus avoiding the need for costly second-derivative computations.

The optimization strategy developed is applied to the 10-bar cantilevered truss of [14]. Simulations are performed by linking finite element, control, and structural parameter optimization programs into a single, integrated package for the purpose of updating models, computing structural derivatives, and determining optimal controls and structural parameter improvements. The analysis is formulated and conducted in a general finite element setting and hence is applicable in theory to flexible system models of high dimension.

II. A SPECIFIC COMBINED STRUCTURAL AND CONTROL OPTIMIZATION PROBLEM

A. THE MODEL

Large space structures are by nature distributed parameter (continuous) systems with multiple inputs (controls) and a continuum of outputs (point displacements). From a practical standpoint, experience gained from past analyses of various successful aerospace systems suggests that finite element models are most useful in describing these structures. The linear differential equations resulting from a finite element analysis are particularly attractive from a control theoretic point of view because the full power of Pontryagin's maximum principle and the linear regulator theory can be brought to bear on control system design. The finite element model also provides a convenient framework for the application of powerful structural optimization techniques.

With this in mind, we consider a dynamical system governed by

$$M(\xi)\ddot{r} + C(\xi)\dot{r} + K(\xi)r = B_0(\xi)u, \qquad r(0) = r_0, \qquad \dot{r}(0) = \dot{r}_0 \tag{1}$$

where r is an $n \times 1$ vector of physical coordinates (nodal displacements), ξ is a $p \times 1$ vector of structural parameters, u is an $m \times 1$ control vector, and $M(\xi)$, $C(\xi)$, $K(\xi)$, and $B_0(\xi)$ are the mass, damping, stiffness, and control influence matrices, respectively, of appropriate dimensions. We assume, as usual, that $M(\xi)$ is symmetric, positive definite and that $K(\xi)$ is symmetric, positive semidefinite. Formulated in the state space, system (1) becomes

$$\begin{aligned} \dot{x} &= A(\xi)x + B(\xi)u \\ x(0) &= x_0(\xi) \end{aligned} \tag{2}$$

where

$$A = \left[\begin{array}{c|c} 0 & I \\ \hline -M^{-1}K & -M^{-1}C \end{array}\right], \qquad B = \begin{bmatrix} 0 \\ M^{-1}B_0 \end{bmatrix}, \qquad \text{and } x = \begin{bmatrix} r \\ \dot{r} \end{bmatrix} \tag{3}$$

As in (3), the vector ξ is often suppressed for notational convenience. The explicit dependence of x_0 on ξ is discussed in Section V.

Consider the minimization of

$$F(\xi, u) = q_1 W(\xi) + \tfrac{1}{2} q_2 \int_0^\infty [x^T Q(\xi) x + u^T R(\xi) u] \, dt \tag{4}$$

subject to constraints

$$g_j(\xi) \geq G_j, \qquad j = 1, 2, \ldots, l. \tag{5}$$

In (4), $W(\xi)$ measures selected aspects of the static structure underlying (1) (e.g., total mass); and the integral, the performance measure of the linear regulator optimal control problem, measures aspects of the structure's controlled motion (e.g., total energy). Thus, roughly speaking, (4) is the weighted sum of mass and total energy. Structural constraints (5) are imposed on geometry, element sizes, material properties, natural frequencies, and so on. The weighting matrices $Q(\xi)$ and $R(\xi)$ are assumed positive semidefinite and positive definite, respectively, $q_1 > 0$ and $q_2 > 0$ are scalar weights, the $g_j(\xi)$ are functions of ξ, and the G_j are constants. The minimization is to take place simultaneously in ξ and u.

For fixed ξ, let $P = P(\xi)$ be the solution of the matrix Riccati equation

$$A^T P + PA + Q - PBR^{-1}B^T P = 0 \tag{6}$$

and let

$$u(\xi) = -R^{-1}(\xi) B^T(\xi) P(\xi) x \tag{7}$$

be the corresponding optimal control from linear regulator theory. Thus, for fixed ξ, $u(\xi)$ in (7) minimizes, without constraints (5), the integral term in (4). If (ξ^*, u^*) minimizes F, subject to the constraints (5), then fixing $\xi = \xi^*$ in (4), one can easily see (see [13]) that u^* can be taken to be the optimal control $u(\xi^*)$ defined through (7). To see this, reason as follows. If (ξ^*, u^*) minimizes F subject to (5), then u^* minimizes the integral in (4) with ξ fixed at ξ^* in (2). If not, then there exists $\hat{u}$ that makes the integral smaller for $\xi = \xi^*$, contradicting the optimality of (ξ^*, u^*). But if u^* minimizes the integral, since $u(\xi^*)$ from (7) is also a minimizer, we can choose $u^* = u(\xi^*)$. In particular, we need only consider the controls $u(\xi)$ in (7). For these controls, by standard optimal control theory,

$$\tfrac{1}{2} q_2 \int_0^\infty [x^T Q(\xi) x + u^T R(\xi) u] \, dt = \tfrac{1}{2} q_2 x_0^T(\xi) P(\xi) x_0(\xi) \tag{8}$$

for given $x_0(\xi)$. Thus, the minimization of F reduces to minimizing, in ξ alone,

$$J(\xi) = F(\xi, u(\xi)) = q_1 W(\xi) + \tfrac{1}{2} q_2 x_0^{\mathrm{T}}(\xi) P(\xi) x_0(\xi) \tag{9}$$

for given initial condition $x_0(\xi)$.

B. PROBLEM SOLUTION

To solve the optimization problem of the preceding section, sensitivities of J in (9) to changes in the parameter vector ξ are needed. Thus, to minimize J numerically, ∇J is required. A computation shows that if R is symmetric, an assumption we now impose, then

$$J_{\xi_i} = \frac{\partial J}{\partial \xi_i} = q_1 W_{\xi_i} + \frac{1}{2} q_2 x_0^{\mathrm{T}} P_{\xi_i} x_0 + q_2 x_0^{\mathrm{T}} P x_{0,\xi_i} \tag{10}$$

where P_{ξ_i} satisfies the Lyapunov equation

$$\begin{aligned}[][A^{\mathrm{T}} - PBR^{-1}B^{\mathrm{T}}]P_{\xi_i} + P_{\xi_i}[A^{\mathrm{T}} - PBR^{-1}B^{\mathrm{T}}]^{\mathrm{T}} \\ + [A_{\xi_i}^{\mathrm{T}} P + PA_{\xi_i} - P(BR^{-1}B^{\mathrm{T}})_{\xi_i} P + Q_{\xi_i}] = 0.\end{aligned} \tag{11}$$

Equation (11) is derived by differentiating (6) with respect to the components of ξ. Here x_{0,ξ_i} denotes $\dfrac{\partial}{\partial \xi_i} x_0(\xi)$. Note that $(x_{0,\xi_i}^{\mathrm{T}} P x_0)^{\mathrm{T}} = x_0^{\mathrm{T}} P x_{0,\xi_i}$ since P is symmetric.

To minimize J subject to (5), [13] proposes an iterative solution of the appropriate Kuhn–Tucker optimality conditions. [In [13], $x_0(\xi) \equiv x_0$ is independent of ξ.] These conditions are

$$J_{\xi_i} + \Sigma_j \mu_j g_{j,\xi_i} = 0, \qquad \mu_j g_j = 0 \qquad i = 1, 2, \ldots, p, \qquad j = 1, 2, \ldots, l. \tag{12}$$

Here $g_{j,\xi_i} = (\partial/\partial \xi_i) g_j$ and the μ_j are unknown multipliers. Reference [13] proposes the solution of (12) via the recursive algorithm (Newton's method):

$$\left[\begin{array}{c|c} J_{\xi\xi} + \Sigma_j \mu_j g_{j,\xi\xi} & g_{j,\xi} \\ \hline \mu_j g_{j,\xi} & g_j \end{array}\right]_k \begin{bmatrix} \Delta \xi^k \\ \Delta \mu^k \end{bmatrix} = -\left[\begin{array}{c} J_\xi + \Sigma_j \mu_j g_{j,\xi} \\ \hline \mu_j g_j \end{array}\right]_k \tag{13}$$

$$\begin{bmatrix} \xi^{k+1} \\ \mu^{k+1} \end{bmatrix} = \begin{bmatrix} \xi^k \\ \mu^k \end{bmatrix} + \begin{bmatrix} \Delta \xi^k \\ \Delta \mu^k \end{bmatrix}. \tag{14}$$

The linear system (13) is solved repeatedly, and ξ^k and μ^k are updated according to (14) and iterated to convergence yielding solutions ξ^* and μ^* to (12). Here $g_{j,\xi} = \nabla g_j^{\mathrm{T}}$, and $J_{\xi\xi}$ and $g_{j,\xi\xi}$ are the Hessian matrices of J and g_j, respectively. Note that the solution of (13) requires calculation of the mixed partial derivatives $J_{\xi_i\xi_j}$. From (10), $J_{\xi_i\xi_j}$ depends on $P_{\xi_i\xi_j}$. Differentiating (11), one sees that $P_{\xi_i \xi_j}$ satisfies a Lyapunov equation involving mixed partials of A, B, Q, and R.

To avoid the expense of computing second derivatives of P, J and the g_j (especially for high-order systems), we explore here the use of the method of steepest descents to minimize J. When constraints are present, the augmented function

$$\hat{J}(\xi) = q_1 W(\xi) + \tfrac{1}{2} q_2 x_0^{\mathrm{T}}(\xi) P(\xi) x_0(\xi) + \Sigma_j p_j(\xi)[g_j(\xi) - G_j]^2 \tag{15}$$

is minimized. Here the penalty multiplier $p_j(\xi)$ is given by

$$p_j(\xi) = \begin{cases} 0 & \text{if} \quad g_j(\xi) \geq G_j \\ p & \text{if} \quad g_j(\xi) < G_j \end{cases} \tag{16}$$

$p > 0$ a chosen constant.

The theory of mathematical programming guarantees (under appropriate technical assumptions) that as $p \to \infty$, the corresponding ξ values minimizing $\hat{J}$ in (15) converge to a value ξ^*, which minimizes J in (9) subject to the constraints (5). If constraints such as $\omega_j(\xi) \geq \bar{\omega}_j$ are imposed ($\bar{\omega}_j > 0$ constant) on the open-loop frequencies $\omega_j(\xi)$ of system (2), analytical derivatives $\omega_{j,\xi_i}(\xi)$ must be computed to determine $\nabla\hat{J} = (\hat{J}_{\xi_1}, \hat{J}_{\xi_2}, \ldots, \hat{J}_{\xi_p})^{\mathrm{T}}$. As is well known [15],

$$\frac{\partial}{\partial \xi_i} \omega_j^2 = 2\omega_j \omega_{j,\xi_i} = \frac{1}{\phi_j^{\mathrm{T}} M \phi_j} [\phi_j^{\mathrm{T}} (K_{\xi_i} - \omega_j^2 M_{\xi_i}) \phi_j] \tag{17}$$

where the $\omega_j^2 = \lambda_j$ and corresponding vectors ϕ_j are solutions of the eigenvalue problem

$$K\phi_j = \lambda_j M \phi_j. \tag{18}$$

If simple magnitude constraints $\xi_j \geq \bar{\xi}_j$ are imposed, $J(\xi)$ in (9) can be minimized straightforwardly by using the gradient projection technique.

III. THE NUMERICAL ALGORITHM

We now present a practical methodology for minimizing $\hat{J}$ in (15). In subsequent sections, we discuss the application of this strategy to a problem in vibration suppression for structural systems. In particular, we propose to minimize $\hat{J}$, for given initial vector ξ^0, by employing $-\nabla\hat{J}$ to generate a sequence $\xi^1, \xi^2, \ldots$ with $\hat{J}(\xi^{k+1}) < \hat{J}(\xi^k)$ and hopefully $\hat{J}(\xi^k) \to \hat{J}(\xi^*)$. The minimization of $\hat{J}$ is accomplished by linking three computer programs: (1) a finite element program, (2) an optimal control program, and (3) an optimization/driver program. Program (1) is employed to construct models in the form (2) for given parameter vectors ξ. Program (2) solves (6) for P and evaluates $x_0^T P x_0$. Program (3) computes $\nabla \hat{J}$ by computing derivatives of A, B, Q, and R and then solving (11). This program also computes derivatives of the g_j as needed and coordinates the use of programs (1) and (2) in implementing the steepest descents optimization. The derivatives of A, B, Q, and R depend on the derivatives of M, K, and B_0. For the 10-bar truss model, to be discussed in the next sections, these later derivatives are constant. For general finite element models, derivatives can be computed either explicitly, by taking advantage of special structure in the models considered, or numerically, using finite difference approximations. The specific general computational strategy adopted here is outlined in Fig. 1. The optimization algorithm begins with a given baseline design ξ^0 ($k = 0$ in Fig. 1). The finite element program is called with $\xi = \xi^0$ to construct the model (2). The optimal control program is then called to solve (6) for $P(\xi^0)$ and hence to compute $\hat{J}(\xi^0)$. The optimization program is called to step in parameter space to an updated vector ξ^1. This is accomplished as follows.

The components of ξ^0 are incremented sequentially, and calls to the finite element program permit finite difference approximations of the derivatives of A, B, Q, and R; for example, $\partial/\partial\xi_1 \, A(\xi^0) \approx (1/2h)[A(\xi^0 + he_1) - A(\xi^0 - he_1)]$, $e_1 = (1, 0, 0, \ldots, 0)^T$. Constraint derivatives g_{j,ξ_i} are also approximated as needed. The vector $\nabla \hat{J}(\xi^0)$ is assembled, and a candidate ξ_h^1 for ξ^1 is computed according to the general parameter space update formula

$$\xi_h^{k+1} = \xi^k - h \frac{\nabla \hat{J}(\xi^k)}{\|\nabla \hat{J}(\xi^k)\|}. \tag{19}$$

With $\xi = \xi_h^1$, a new model (2) is constructed, $P(\xi_h^1)$ is determined, and $\hat{J}(\xi_h^1)$ is calculated. If $\hat{J}(\xi_h^1) < \hat{J}(\xi^0)$, we set $\xi^1 = \xi_h^1$ and proceed to determine ξ^2. If $\hat{J}(\xi_h^1) \geq \hat{J}(\xi^0)$, we repeatedly halve h (at most a preset number of times) until the reverse inequality is satisfied. We then set $\xi^1 = \xi_h^1$. To determine ξ^2, we repeat the steps just outlined with ξ^1 and ξ_h^1 replacing ξ^0 and ξ_h^0, respectively. Repeated looping using (19) generates the sequence ξ^1, $\xi^2, \ldots$ with $\hat{J}(\xi^0) > \hat{J}(\xi^1) > \hat{J}(\xi^2) > \cdots$. The algorithm terminates when the optimality check

$$\left| \frac{\hat{J}(\xi^k) - \hat{J}(\xi^{k+1})}{\hat{J}(\xi^k)} \right| < \varepsilon \tag{20}$$

is satisfied, where $\varepsilon > 0$ is a prescribed tolerance. Upon termination, we set $\xi^* = \xi^{k+1}$.

Note that this algorithm is suboptimal in the sense that we do not minimize $\hat{J}(\xi_h^{k+1})$ as a function of h to determine a "best" vector ξ^{k+1} at each iteration. The reason is that extensive experimentation has shown that each function evaluation $\hat{J}(\xi_h^{k+1})$ is roughly 1 to 2 times as expensive computationally as a gradient $\nabla \hat{J}(\xi_h^{k+1})$ computation, given that $\hat{J}(\xi_h^{k+1})$ is known. This is due to

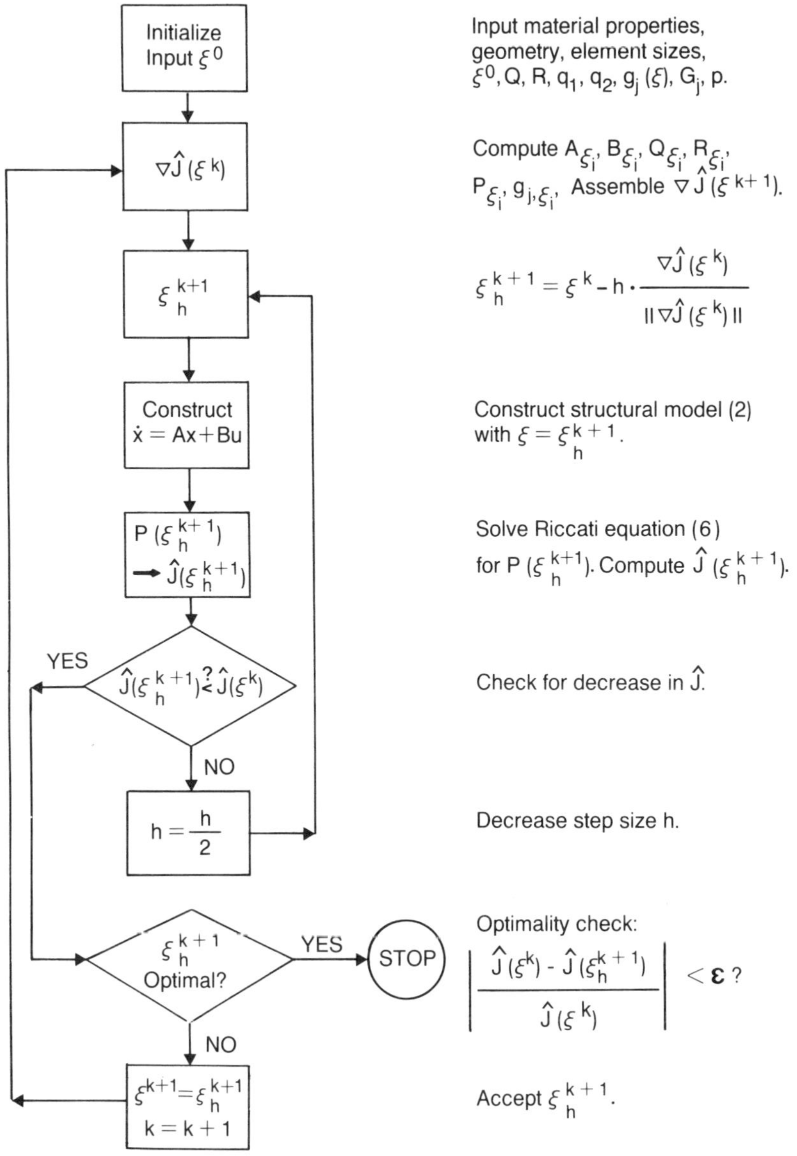

Fig. 1. Numerical algorithm for minimizing $\hat{J}(\xi)$, where $\hat{J}(\xi) = q_1 W(\xi) + \frac{1}{2} q_2 x_0^{\mathrm{T}}(\xi) P(\xi) x_0(\xi) + \Sigma_j p_j(\xi)[g_j(\xi) - G_j]^2$.

the time required to solve (6) for $P(\xi_h^{k+1})$. Thus, since repeated computation of $\hat{J}(\xi_h^{k+1})$ would be required to minimize this quantity in h, we elect to set $\xi = \xi_h^{k+1}$ once $\hat{J}(\xi_h^{k+1}) < \hat{J}(\xi^k)$. Additionally, experimentation has shown that small changes in ξ can effect large changes in $\partial/\partial\xi_i x_0^T(\xi)P(\xi)x_0(\xi)$. For these reasons, it is computationally advantageous to compute $\nabla\hat{J}$ often, while accepting a suboptimal h value at each iteration.

IV. THE 10-BAR TRUSS

In this section we present a 16-state model of a controlled structural system; in Section V we will discuss the application of the algorithm of Section III to this model and analyze detailed simulation results.

To this end, consider the 2-dimensional 10–bar cantilevered truss of Fig. 2. Base nodes 5 and 6 are held fixed, while nodes 1–4 are free. A finite element model (1) is employed to describe the in-plane dynamics of this structure. For simplicity, it is assumed that $C = 0$; that is, no natural internal damping is present. The variables r_1–r_8 measure the relative x and y (horizontal and vertical) displacements of nodes 1–4 from their equilibrium positions (e.g., r_5 and r_6 are the x and y displacements of node 3). The truss is assumed to be constructed of aluminum with the following physical dimensions and material properties (see [12]): length, 100 in.; base width, 36 in.; tip width, 24 in.; modulus of elasticity, 10^7 lb/in.^{2}; and weight density, 0.1 lb/in.^{3} In addition, a nonstructural mass of 1.29 lb sec^2/in. is assumed present at each of the nodes 1–4. (In all cases considered, the nonstructural mass is much greater than the structural mass.)

We consider motion (vibration) control for this prototype truss structure. Force actuators are assumed located at nodes 1–4. The parameter vector $\xi = (\xi_1, \xi_2, \ldots, \xi_{10})^T$ is chosen with ξ_i measuring the cross-sectional area of bar i of the truss, $i = 1, 2, \ldots, 10$. For symmetry, we assume that $\xi_1 = \xi_3$,

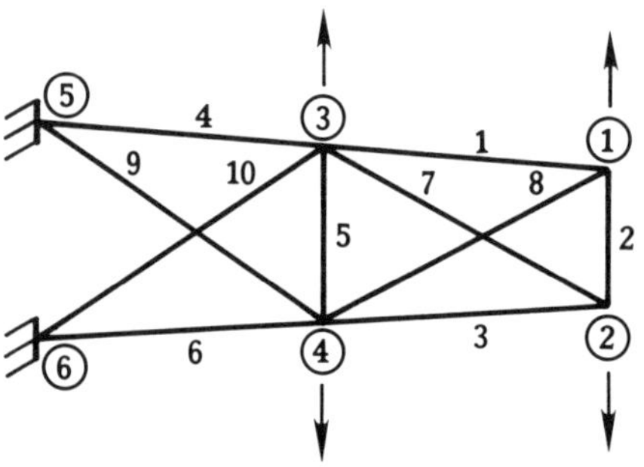

Fig. 2. 10-Bar cantilevered truss.

$\xi_4 = \xi_6$, $\xi_7 = \xi_8$, and $\xi_9 = \xi_{10}$. We characterize an initial (baseline) design ξ^0 by setting $\xi_i^0 = 0.1$ in.^{2} for all i. Excluding nonstructural mass, the resulting truss weighs 4.88 lb.

We consider the numerical solution of the combined structural and control optimization problem, as discussed in Sections II and III, for the 10-bar truss. The control objective is the suppression of structural vibrations resulting from initial excitations x_0. We attempt to minimize J in (9) by minimizing $\hat{J}$ in (15) (omit the penalty terms when constraints are absent). The function $W(\xi)$ is always taken to be the mass of the truss specified by the vector ξ, excluding the nonstructural mass. The function $x_0^{\mathrm{T}} P x_0$ is determined by Q and R. From a structural dynamicist's point of view, natural choices for Q and R are (see [14])

$$Q(\xi) = \begin{bmatrix} K(\xi) & 0 \\ 0 & M(\xi) \end{bmatrix} \quad \text{and} \quad R(\xi) = B_0^{\mathrm{T}}(\xi) K(\xi)^{-1} B_0(\xi). \tag{21}$$

With these choices, $x_0^{\mathrm{T}} P x_0$ in (9) provides a measure of total system strain, kinetic and control energies. We employ the matrices in (21) in this study. Loosely speaking then, given a baseline truss design ξ^0, the goal of optimization here is to identify a less massive design ξ^* with reduced total controlled system energy content.

V. SIMULATION PRELIMINARIES

We now begin our discussion of simulation results for the 10-bar truss. Concisely, our problem is to minimize J in (9) subject to (5) (via the minimization of $\hat{J}$) with Q and R as in (21) and $\xi_i^0 = 0.1$ for all i. In the optimization algorithm, we select h in (19) satisfying $0.01 \leq h \leq 0.1$, and set $\varepsilon = 0.005$ in (20).

A. INITIAL CONDITIONS

We consider two initial conditions (structural excitations) $x_0 = [r(0) \quad \dot{r}(0)]^{\mathrm{T}}$, denoted $x_0^1(\xi)$ and $x_0^2(\xi)$. In both cases, the displacements $r_i(0)$ are set equal to the equilibrium displacements observed in the truss when statically loaded at nodes 1–4. We set the velocities $\dot{r}_i(0) = 0$ for all i. Since structural characteristics and hence static displacements depend upon ξ, so does $x_0 = x_0(\xi)$. Specifically, (1) $x_0 = x_0^1(\xi)$ is determined when a 10,000-lb force is applied (upward) at nodes 1–4, and (2) $x_0 = x_0^2(\xi)$ is determined when the forces at nodes 3 and 4 in (1) are reversed (applied downward). If the truss is viewed as a cantilevered beam, x_0^1 and x_0^2 are chosen to excite modes 1 and 2, respectively.

B. q_1, q_2 SELECTION

Since J is the weighted sum of structural mass and energy, noncommensurate quantities, a question arises as to the physical meaning of its minimization. In this study, we are concerned not with providing a precise interpretation of J but with using J to achieve the earlier stated goal of reducing W and $x_0^T P x_0$ simultaneously. We accomplish this by selecting q_1 and q_2 appropriately. The comparison of masses W for various truss designs is unambiguous. As for the energy terms, $x_0^T P x_0$ measures the total system energy developed in response to the initial excitation x_0. We can meaningfully compare system energies in various truss designs only if we measure their dynamic responses under the same loading conditions. It is important therefore to permit x_0 to depend on ξ. Indeed, as is seen in [12], optimization with x_0 independent of ξ can lead to erroneous conclusions. (It should be remarked that it was recognized early in the combined structural and control optimization literature that optima depend on initial conditions and that initial conditions constitute derived information, that is, they are derived from applied disturbances. This fact motivated the authors of [2–4], [6,7] to consider the problem of fixed end-point maneuvers. Thus, they posed the optimization problem directly in terms of mission requirements rather than derived characteristics, which, as in the case of settling after maneuvers, will vary as the structure is varied. It seems likely, however, that optimal designs for fixed end-point problems also vary with specific chosen end-point conditions.)

For the examples considered, $x_0^T P x_0$ is between 3 and 4 orders of magnitude greater than W. For a balanced minimization of these terms then, the choices for q_1 and q_2 are clearly important. Factoring q_2 out of J, we can assume that $q_2 = 1$ ($J = q_2[(q_1/q_2)W + \frac{1}{2}x_0^T P x_0]$) since only the ratio q_1/q_2 determines ξ^*. As expected, experimentation reveals that in general, for large q_1 values, the minimization of W dominates the minimization of J. Decreases in W are accompanied by increases in $x_0^T P x_0$. All bar thicknesses decrease, whereas node 1–4 initial vertical displacements increase. Conversely, for small q_1 values, $x_0^T P x_0$ decreases whereas W increases. Correspondingly, bar thicknesses increase leading to decreased initial nodal displacements.

VI. SIMULATION RESULTS

Data for the specific simulation results discussed here are recorded in Table I. In each case, optimal ξ_i values are listed along with percentage decreases in W and $x_0^T P x_0$. These changes are measured with respect to the corresponding W and $x_0^T P x_0$ values for the baseline design $\xi_i^0 = 0.1$, all i, excited with the same initial condition x_0^1 or x_0^2. Minimal and maximal system open- and closed-loop frequencies (in rad/sec) are included in Table I, and the choices of initial conditions and constraints are indicated. Constraints on the ξ_i and $\omega_1(\xi)$, the fundamental truss open-loop frequency, are considered. The "optimal" q_1 values listed in Table I were selected roughly as those that permitted reasonable simultaneous unconstrained reductions of both W and $x_0^T P x_0$ for given excitation $x_0(\xi)$ (see Cases I and II, Table I). These selections were made somewhat subjectively. Exhaustive searches over the possible q_1 values were prohibited by the associated high computational costs. (Unfortunately, optimal q_1 values usually change with each example considered and determining them represents an additional computational expense.) The data listed in Table I give an indication of the degree of design improvement possible through this analysis. A discussion of each of the cases follows.

A. CASES I AND II

Cases I and II present the unconstrained minimization of J for the initial conditions $x_0^1(\xi)$ and $x_0^2(\xi)$, respectively. Note the differences in the optimal ξ_i values for these cases. (To prevent any ξ_i from being driven to zero, lower bounds $\xi_i \geq 0.0001$ were imposed in all computations.) These data demonstrate graphically the dependence of ξ^* on the initial data x_0 (i.e., the loading that produces x_0). This point bears emphasizing. Unlike the optimal feedback control for the linear regulator problem, which is independent of initial conditions, in general, for the minimization of J, ξ^* varies with x_0.

Constraints are imposed in Cases III–VII. It should be remarked that for the constrained minimization problems considered in this study, the effectiveness of $\hat{J}$ as an optimization criterion was disappointing. In theory, ξ^* can be determined by letting the penalty constant $p \to \infty$. In practice however, as p increases, one finds it increasingly difficult to complete successful steps (ones that reduce $\hat{J}$) away from ξ^0. Thus, one attempts to choose an "optimal" $p > 0$, one that is sufficiently large that the constraints are approximately satisfied and, at the same time, one that enables the steepest descents algorithm to select a sequence ξ^k with $\hat{J}(\xi^k)$ decreasing. Although this strategy can be made to work here, the selection of p is a time-consuming and frustrating process. Fortunately, as described later, one is usually able to bypass $\hat{J}$ and minimize J directly.

B. CASES III AND IV

In cases III and IV, constraints $0.05 \leq \xi_i \leq 0.15$ are imposed. In these cases, J is most easily minimized by projecting ∇J onto the tangent subspace of the

TABLE I. OPTIMIZATION RESULTS FOR THE 10-BAR TRUSS

CASE	BASELINE		I	II	III
x_0	$x_0^1(\xi)$	$x_0^2(\xi)$	$x_0^1(\xi)$	$x_0^2(\xi)$	$x_0^1(\xi)$
q_1			3850	1500	3850
Constraints			None	None	$.05 \leq \xi_i \leq .15$
$\xi_1 = \xi_3$		.1	.05274	.07829	.05254
ξ_2		.1	.01104	.08312	.05000
$\xi_4 = \xi_6$		.1	.18586	.14654	.15000
ξ_5		.1	.00010	.07893	.05000
$\xi_7 = \xi_8$		.1	.06076	.08112	.06657
$\xi_9 = \xi_{10}$		.1	.08367	.00835	.08860
Decrease in $W(\xi)$			15.7%	24%	15.6%
Decrease in $x_0^T(\xi)P(\xi)x_0(\xi)$			24%	32%	15.1%
Decrease in $J(\xi)$			18.8%	26%	15.4%
Min. Open Loop Frequency (Rad/Sec)		21.6	23.5	13.8	22.6
Max. Open Loop Frequency		275	237	253	231
Min. Closed Loop Frequency		21.2	23	13.5	22.1
Max. Closed Loop Frequency		257	237	236	229
Initial Node 1 Displacement (Inches)	18.9	10.0	15.8	5.8	17.1
Maximum Node 1 Actuator Input (Pounds Force)	7900	4300	7500	5800	7800

IV	V	VI	VII	VIII	IX
$x_0^2(\xi)$	$x_0^1(\xi)$	$x_0^2(\xi)$	$x_0^1(\xi)$	$x_0^1(\xi)$	$x_0^1(\xi)$
1500	3850	1500	Min W p=.0005	3850	3850
$.05 \leq \xi_i \leq .15$	$\omega_1 \leq 22.9$	$\omega_1 \geq 20.0$	$\omega_1 = 21.6$	$\xi_i^0 = .05$	$\xi_i^0 = .15$
.07587	.09374	.08197	.05499	.05453	.06475
.05087	.09757	.08629	.07792	.00433	.06366
.15000	.12284	.14425	.14666	.18527	.18690
.05000	.09697	.08289	.07244	.00010	.04228
.08050	.09384	.08444	.05680	.05973	.06573
.05000	.09746	.02682	.05701	.07877	.08644
17%	-1%	18%	23%	17.3%	6%
20.8%	16.3%	26.8%	-5%	22%	30%
18.2%	5.5%	20.5%		19%	14.9%
22.4	23.0	20.0			
246	271	258			
21.9	22.5	19.6			
243	256	241			
8.5	16.8	7.8			
4500	8000	5200			

feasible region determined by the active constraints. (As a practical matter, the ξ_i are observed to increase or decrease monotonically as the minimization proceeds so that once ξ_i reaches 0.05 or 0.15, it remains there.) The excessively small ξ_i values of Cases I and II are now absent (see Table I), though still impressive reductions in mass and energy are observed.

C. CASES V, VI, AND VII

In Cases V and VI, the constraints $\omega_1(\xi) \leq 22.9$ rad/sec (3.64 Hz) and $\omega_1(\xi) \geq 20.0$ rad/sec (3.18 Hz), respectively, were imposed. The baseline design $\xi_i^0 \equiv 0.1$ has $\omega_1(\xi^0) = 21.6$ rad/sec (3.44 Hz). For these case, $\hat{J}$ was minimized with $g_1(\xi) = -\omega_1(\xi)$ and $g_1(\xi) = \omega_1(\xi)$, and $G_1 = -22.9$ and $G_1 = 20.0$, respectively. First consider Case VI, for which $x_0 = x_0^2(\xi)$. For this case, it was possible to reduce $\hat{J}$ significantly, but as previously remarked, locating an optimal p value was time-consuming, and the repeated solution of (18) added to the computational expense. Observing that, in Case II, $\omega_1(\xi)$ decreases monotonically as the algorithm proceeds, to minimize J, one is led to the alternative strategy of simply proceeding with steps in the direction $-\nabla J$ until $\omega_1(\xi)$ decreases to 20.0. The resulting ξ^* is then accepted as the optimal design. This strategy works very well, producing the results in Table I. Significant reductions in mass and energy are observed, comparable to those achieved by minimization of $\hat{J}$.

If the constraint $\omega_1(\xi) \geq 20.0$ of Case VI is considered and $\hat{J}$ is minimized with $x_0 = x_0^1(\xi)$, interestingly, the constraint is always satisfied because the frequency $\omega_1(\xi)$ increases monotonically as the optimization proceeds. The results of this minimization are therefore identical to those of Case I. It appears that $x_0^1(\xi)$ opposes the reduction of the fundamental frequency. [Indeed, when the hard constraint $\omega_1(\xi) = 20.0$ is imposed and $\hat{J}$ is minimized with $x_0 = x_0^1(\xi)$, W decreases 15% but $x_0^T P x_0$ increases roughly 20%!] Case V considers the minimization of J with $x_0 = x_0^1(\xi)$ subject to the constraint $\omega_1(\xi) \leq 22.9$. Taking advantage of the monotonicity of $\omega_1(\xi)$ noted earlier, J can be effectively minimized directly by simply stopping the minimization in Case I when $\omega_1(\xi) \leq 22.9$ is violated. As seen from Table I, the minimization of J results in a 16.3% reduction in $x_0^T P x_0$, accompanied by a 1% increase in W. (Both W and $x_0^T P x_0$ could be decreased by selecting a "better" q_1 value though $x_0^T P x_0$ would not decrease as significantly.)

Before considering Cases V and VI, an attempt was made to minimize J subject to the hard constraint $\omega_1(\xi) = 21.6$ ($g_1 = \omega_1 \geq 21.6$ and $g_2 = -\omega_1 \geq -21.6$). Experimentation demonstrated that it was not possible to reduce J at all (since $\hat{J}$ could not be reduced) except in the special case $q_1 = 1$ and $q_2 = 0$ (i.e., minimize $W(\xi)$ alone). For this one case the penalty function approach worked very well, reducing W a significant 23%. This is Case VII in Table I. (When the resulting optimized truss is controlled with initial condition $x_0^1(\xi)$, however, the energy term $x_0^T P x_0$ increases by 5% over the baseline value.)

At this point, it is interesting to compare the results presented here with those of Salama *et al.* [13]. In their paper, as discussed earlier, Newton's method was employed to minimize J with constraints for a segmented (3 segments) cantilevered beam, ξ_i measuring the cross-sectional area of segment i. The beam's fundamental frequency ω_1 was constrained to remain constant at its baseline value determined when all segments had equal cross-sectional areas. The weighting matrices were chosen to be identities. Three minimization problems were considered: (1) Minimize $W(\xi)$ alone; (2) minimize $J(\xi)$ with x_0 equal to the baseline beam's first vibrational mode; (3) minimize $J(\xi)$ with x_0 equal to the baseline beam's second mode. In all cases, optimal ξ^* values were identical, specifying a beam tapered from base to tip. The dependence of ξ^* on x_0 was not observed. The authors note that the frequency constraint appears to numerically dominate the optimization.

In the cases examined here, ξ^* definitely does depend on x_0. A general trend toward tapering the truss from base to tip, which is expected intuitively, is also present. Outside bar thicknesses $\xi_4 = \xi_6$ exceed $\xi_1 = \xi_3$ consistently. Inside bar thicknesses $\xi_9 = \xi_{10}$ exceed $\xi_7 = \xi_8$ in Cases I, III, and V, whereas the opposite is true for Cases II, IV, and VI. Presumably, these latter differences can be attributed to the torquing effect of x_0^2. Bars 2 and 5 are approximately equal in all cases, except Case I. The 10–bar truss possesses a richer geometry than the segmented beam. In particular, load paths for distributing forces are more complicated. It is not surprising, therefore, that truss optimizations produce results that are less clear cut than those for the cantilevered beam. Indeed, the results of this section suggest that conclusions drawn from the solution of the combined structural and control problem may be ambiguous due to the dependence of ξ^* on x_0. An additional complication is that the ξ^* located by minimizing J may represent only local minima. The data from Cases VIII and IX in Table I address this concern.

D. CASES VIII AND IX

In Case VIII, J with $q_1 = 3850$ is minimized without constraints using $x_0 = x_0^1$ and $\xi_i^0 = 0.05$ for all i. In case IX, $\xi_i^0 \equiv 0.15$. Comparing the results with Case I, we discover essentially the same optimal parameter vectors in Case I. Thus, the existence of local minima does not appear to be a cause for concern here. The differences observed in the ξ^* vectors in the three cases are most likely due to the algorithm's stopping criterion, since near optimality the decreases in J are very slight at each successful step.

This evidence suggests that, in practice, the combined structural and control problem is quite complicated. The payoffs obtainable, as seen in Table I, seem unmistakable however.

VII. CONTROLLED SYSTEM RESPONSE

The uncontrolled response of the baseline truss to the excitation $x_0 = x_0^1(\xi)$ is graphed in Fig. 3a. Vertical displacements of node 1 from its equilibrium position are plotted versus time. (Recall that for convenience we have set $C = 0$ so that no internal damping is present.) Node 1 oscillates with a frequency of about 3.44 Hz, the truss's fundamental frequency, so that x_0^1 essentially excites only the first mode. Figure 3b shows the controlled response of the baseline truss when $x_0 = x_0^1$ and control is provided by (7) and Q and R given by (21). Actuator inputs at node 1 are graphed in Fig. 3c. Clearly the weighting matrix choices in (21) ensure effective control. Truss vibrations are arrested smoothly and rapidly. (It is interesting to note that for all cases considered, closed-loop frequencies are very close to corresponding open-loop frequencies; that is, feedback controllers primarily add system damping. See Table I.)

Plots of node 1 displacements and actuator inputs for Cases I–IX are qualitatively all very similar to Figs. 3b,c. Initial node 1 displacements (see Table I) differ because $x_0(\xi)$ depends on ξ. Note that initial displacements for the optimized structures are less than the corresponding baseline values. The same is true for nodes 2, 3, and 4. Reduced initial displacements account, at least in part, for reduced $x_0^T P x_0$ values. Figures 4a–d give node 1 displacements and control inputs for Cases III and VI. Although initial node 1 displacements for excitations $x_0^1(\xi)$ exceed those for $x_0^2(\xi)$ in Cases I–VI, settling times are approximately equal in all cases (about 0.4 sec). Maximum actuator inputs at node 1 are also compared in Table I.

For Case VII, with $x_0 = x_0^1$, plots of node 1 displacements and actuator inputs are again essentially identical to Figs. 3b,c, the major difference being that initial node 1 displacement has increased from 18.9 to 19.2 in., and maximum actuator input has decreased from 7900 to 7500 lb. Thus, the controlled dynamic response of the optimized truss is essentially equivalent to that of the baseline truss. This strongly suggests that if one's major concern is the minimization of structural mass, structural optimization on mass alone may well result in a design with largely unchanged controlled dynamic response characteristics. Such an optimization is much easier computationally than the minimization of J. Furthermore, it accommodates imposed constraints nicely, whereas J does not.

The dynamic response plots discussed reveal that the matrices in (21)

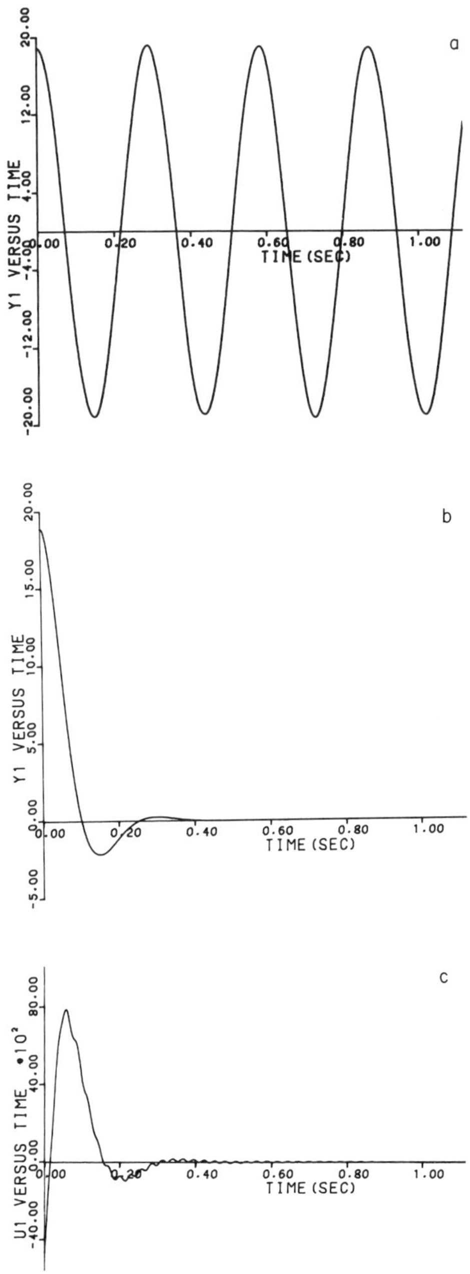

Fig. 3. (a) Uncontrolled node 1 displacements: $\xi_i = 0.1$, all i, $x_0 = x_0^1$. (b) Controlled node 1 displacements: $\xi_i = 0.1$, all i, $x_0 = x_0^1$. (c) Actuator inputs at node 1: $\xi_i = 0.1$, all i, $x_0 = x_0^1$.

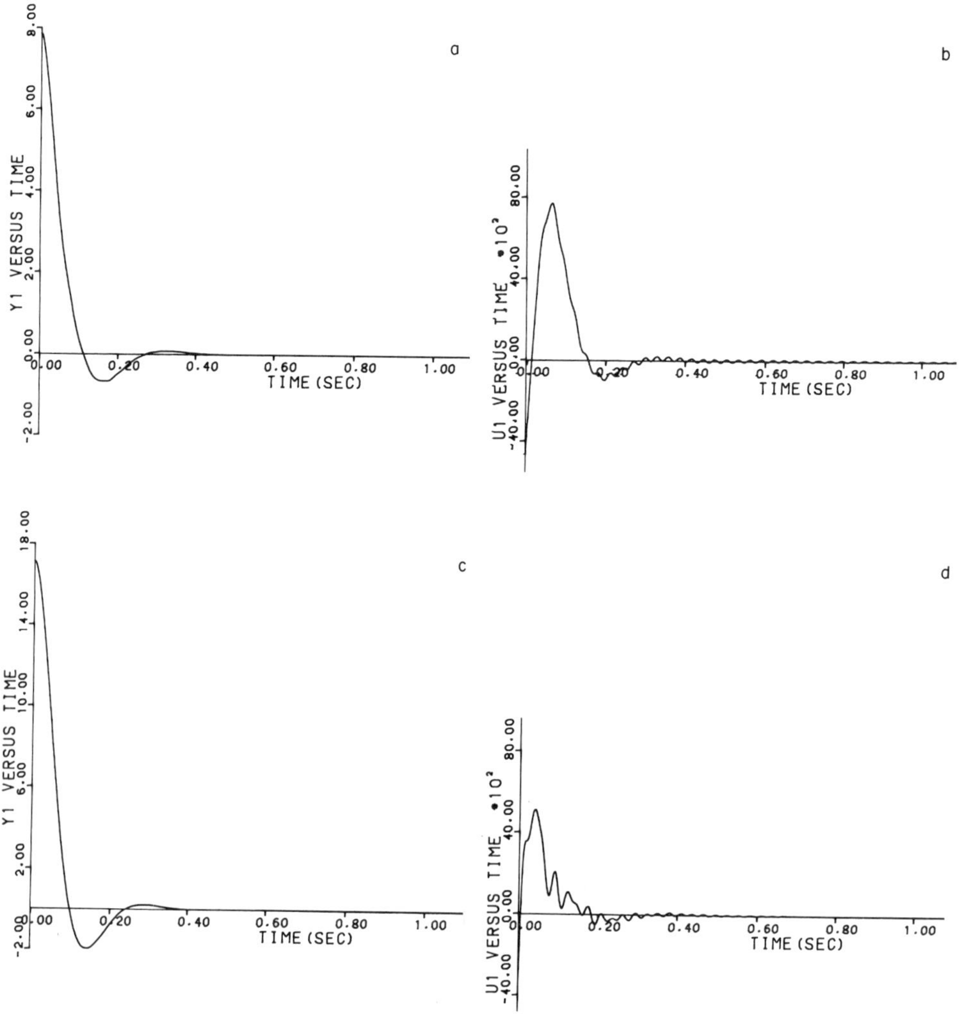

Fig. 4. (a) Node 1 displacements, Case III: $0.05 \leq \xi_i \leq 0.15$, $x_0 = x_0^1$. (b) Actuator inputs, Case III: $0.05 \leq \xi_i \leq 0.15$, $x_0 = x_0^1$. (c) Node 1 displacements, Case VI: $\omega_1(\xi) \geq 20.0$, $x_0 = x_0^2$. (d) Actuator inputs, Case VI: $\omega_1(\xi) \geq 20.0$, $x_0 = x_0^2$.

provide effective truss control that is essentially independent of the combined structural and control optimization process. Interestingly, it is shown in [11] that if the optimization algorithm is applied to Cases I–IX with $Q = 1000 \cdot \mathrm{I}$ and $R = I$ (I an identity matrix), data strikingly similar to those listed in Table I result. Furthermore, corresponding dynamic response plots are practically identical to those described.

VIII. FURTHER OPTIMIZATION RESULTS

In this section, we briefly consider further aspects of the combined structural and control optimization problem. More thorough discussions are found in [11]. We first investigate the effectiveness of optimal truss designs determined through x_0^1 in damping out the excitation x_0^2 (and vice versa). Data for Cases X and XII in Table II were generated by exciting the optimal truss designs of Cases I and III with $x_0 = x_0^2(\xi)$. In Cases XI and XIII, the trusses of Cases II and IV were excited with $x_0 = x_0^1(\xi)$. In Table II, changes in W and $x_0^{\mathrm{T}} P x_0$ are again measured with respect to the baseline ($\xi_i \equiv 0.1$) design. For Cases X–XIII, changes in W are of course the same as those shown in Table I for corresponding designs. The values of $x_0^{\mathrm{T}} P x_0$ have increased significantly, however. For example, when the truss of Case I is excited by x_0^1, $x_0^{\mathrm{T}} P x_0$ decreases 24%. When the same truss is excited by x_0^2, $x_0^{\mathrm{T}} P x_0$ decreases only 4.6%. In Cases XI and XII, $x_0^{\mathrm{T}} P x_0$ actually exceeds its baseline values. These data clearly illustrate that a truss design that is optimal for one initial condition may represent, from an energy standpoint, a much poorer design for other initial excitations. Plots of node 1 displacements and actuator inputs for Cases X–XIII are qualitatively quite similar to Figs. 3b,c. Basically, only changes in initial displacements and maximum actuator inputs, respectively, are observed.

In Cases XIV and XV, the optimal ξ_i values from Cases III and IV are averaged for each i. It is hoped that the single resulting truss design will give rise to significant reductions in both mass and system energy developed when the truss is excited by either x_0^1 or x_0^2. The $x_0^{\mathrm{T}} P x_0$ values for these cases show a marked improvement over the corresponding data for Cases XII and XIII. These reductions are not as large as those observed in Cases III and IV, however. Reductions in W are comparable in all cases. The data suggest that the averaged ξ_i values will produce favorable reductions in $x_0^{\mathrm{T}} P x_0$ for any excitation x_0 that is a linear combination of x_0^1 and x_0^2. This further suggests that if one can identify a finite collection of fundamental excitations x_0^i that generate an envelope of expected system excitations, an averaging scheme applied to individually optimal designs, like the one employed here, may give rise to a single satisfactory improved design. Natural candidates for fundamental excitations x_0^i are truss mode shapes. One is concerned, however, that as the class of expected excitations grows, the averaging of designs may altogether eliminate reductions in energy realized with individual excitations x_0^i.

Now consider structural excitations resulting from sharp blows delivered to the structure by external agents (e.g., meteorite collisions or shuttle-docking impacts). As is customary, we model these excitations as impulse forces $\alpha \cdot \delta(t)$ (delta function with magnitude $\alpha > 0$) applied to the structure. Such forces give rise to initial conditions x_0 containing zero displacements and nonzero

TABLE II. OPTIMAL $x_0^2(\xi)$ DESIGN EXCITED BY $x_0^1(\xi)$ (AND VICE VERSA); AVERAGED DESIGNS; IMPULSE EXCITATION

CASE	X	XI	XII
x_0	$x_0^2(\xi)$	$x_0^1(\xi)$	$x_0^2(\xi)$
	(Case I)	(Case II)	(Case III)
$\xi_1 = \xi_3$	.05274	.07829	.05254
ξ_2	.01104	.08312	.05000
$\xi_4 = \xi_6$	.18586	.14654	.15000
ξ_5	.00010	.07893	.05000
$\xi_7 = \xi_8$	.06076	.08112	.06657
$\xi_9 = \xi_{10}$	.08367	.00835	.08860
Decrease in $W(\xi)$	15.7%	23.9%	15.6%
Decrease in $x_0^T(\xi)P(\xi)x_0(\xi)$	4.6%	-392%	- 3.9%
Min. Open Loop Frequency (Rad/Sec)	23.5	13.8	22.6
Max. Open Loop Frequency	237	253	231
Min. Closed Loop Frequency	23	13.5	22.1
Max. Closed Loop Frequency	237	236	229
Initial Node 1 Displacement (Inches)	9.3	42.0	9.97
Max. Node 1 Actuator Input (Pounds Force)	4700	6400	4600

instantaneous velocities. In the 10-bar truss, if $\alpha \cdot \delta(t)$ acts in the upward direction at node 3 for example, $x_0 = B[0 \quad 0 \quad \alpha \quad 0]^T$. Note that again $x_0 = x_0(\xi)$ depends on ξ through $B = B(\xi)$. With respect to minimizing J, these initial conditions are very attractive because they are easy to calculate. Observe that to determine x_0 in Section VI, it was necessary to solve the static displacement equations $Kr_0 = B_0 f$, where $f = [f_1 \quad f_2 \quad f_3 \quad f_4]^T$ and f_i is the force (loading) acting at node i.

XIII	XIV	XV	XVI	XVII
$x_0^1(\xi)$	$x_0^1(\xi)$	$x_0^2(\xi)$	$\alpha\cdot\delta(t)$ at Node 3 $\alpha = 6{,}000$	$\alpha\cdot\delta(t)$ at Node 2 $\alpha = 2{,}000$
(Case IV)	(Avg of Cases III and IV)			
.07587	.06421	.06421	.07786	.07365
.05087	.05043	.05043	.07702	.10931
.15000	.15000	.15000	.09186	.16625
.05000	.05000	.05000	.14348	.07401
.08050	.07354	.07354	.03515	.07229
.05000	.06930	.06930	.14128	.05048
17.0%	16.3%	16.3%	9.6%	11.6%
1.2%	12.1%	10.0%	9.0%	6.8%
22.4	22.8	22.8	19.3	22.7
246	238	238	285	273
21.9	22.3	22.3	18.9	22.2
243	235	235	278	264
17.8	17.0	9.1		
7700	7700	4400		

As in Section VI, when initial conditions $x_0(\xi)$ are determined by impulse forces, the combined structural and control optimization problem is nicely behaved. Data for two sample cases are given in Table II. In Case XVI, an impulse force with $\alpha = 6000$ is applied at node 3, and J is minimized without constraints. The q_1 value producing the best simultaneous reduction of W and $x_0^T P x_0$ is $q_1 = 15{,}000$. For this case, W, $x_0^T P x_0$, and J all decrease roughly 9% from their corresponding baseline values (determined by exciting the $\xi_i^0 \equiv 0.1$

truss with the same impulse force). In Case XVII, $\alpha \cdot \delta(t)$ with $\alpha = 2000$ is applied at node 2. Here the optimal q_1 value is $q_1 = 4000$ and $W, x_0^T P x_0$, and J decrease 11.6%, 6.8%, and 8.8%, respectively. Note that the percentage decreases in performance are smaller here than in Cases I and II. This is probably due to the fact that $\alpha \cdot \delta(t)$ excites higher system modes than do x_0^1 or x_0^2. Further evidence of this is recorded in Figs. 5a,b, in which node 1 displacements and actuator inputs for Case XVI are plotted. Observe the higher frequency transients in both figures.

IX. CONCLUSION

This article has presented an applications-oriented strategy for solving a problem in combined structural and control optimization for flexible systems. The strategy centers on the gradient-based optimization of a cost functional depending on structural parameters alone. The need for costly second-derivative calculations is thereby eliminated. A practical optimization algorithm was outlined, its application based on linking finite element, optimal control, and gradient optimization software. Posed in this general setting, the algorithm applies straightforwardly to any structure with available finite element model.

The combined optimization problem for the 10-bar truss was solved for several cases. Initial loadings exciting first and second truss modes were considered. Significant simultaneous reductions in mass and energy were recorded. Two specific undesirable characteristics of the optimization problem were observed: (1) Optimal truss designs were directly dependent on selected initial conditions, and (2) the use of penalty functions to satisfy imposed constraints proved unsatisfactory numerically. Favorable characteristics observed included: (1) Eigenvalue monotonicity eliminated the need for penalty functions when fundamental frequency constraints were imposed; (2) bothersome local minima were absent; (3) dynamic response plots revealed effective control in all optimized models; and (4) the averaging of structural designs, each optimal for a member of a class of fundamental excitations, showed promise in reducing the effects of problem initial condition dependence.

The analysis presented here has shown that the application of gradient searches to solve the combined structural and control optimization problem is feasible for structures described by general finite element models, however, numerically, the algorithm requires significant amounts of computer time (typically 7–15 CPU minutes on an IBM 3010 were required for each of the cases considered here). For high-dimensional systems, the algorithm will surely require the computational power of supercomputers, but its perfor-

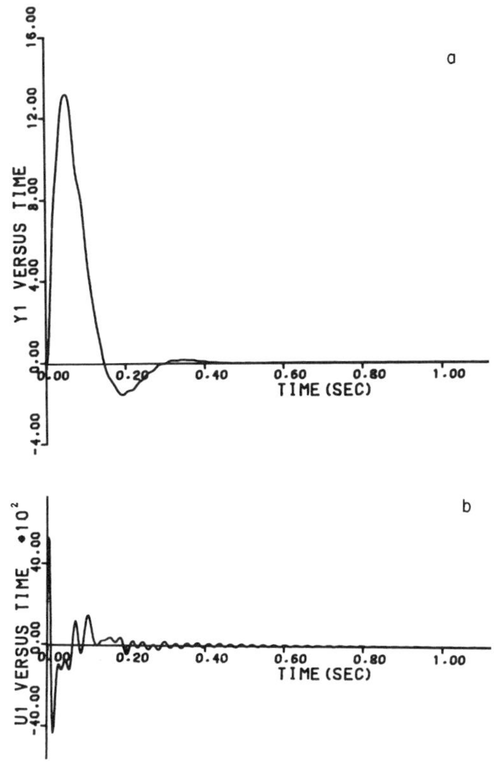

Fig. 5. (a) Node 1 displacements, Case XVI: $\alpha \cdot \delta(t)$ exerted at node 3, $\alpha = 6{,}000$. (b) Actuator inputs, Case XVI: $\alpha \cdot \delta(t)$ exerted at node 3, $\alpha = 6{,}000$.

mance should be satisfactory. The major problem for the analysis lies then in the very nature of the problem itself: the fact that optimal designs are initial condition dependent. If few modes participate in a system's dynamic response to expected excitations, it seems likely that useful results can be generated by this technique. If many modes participate, however, the outcome seems less certain.

ACKNOWLEDGMENTS

The research for this article was sponsored by the Flight Dynamics Laboratory, Wright-Patterson Air Force Base, Dayton, Ohio, under Contract No. F33615-84-C-3217. Portions of the article are adapted from an earlier paper [12], with permission of the American Institute of Aeronautics and Astronautics.

REFERENCES

1. A. K. AMOS and W. L. HALLAUER, Jr. (eds.), *Proc 2nd AFOSR/NASA Forum Space Struct., Washington, D.C.* (1984).
2. A. L. HALE and R. J. LISOWSKI, "Optimal Simultaneous Structural and Control Design of Maneuvering Flexible Spacecraft", *Proc. 4th VPI SU/AIAA Symp. Dyn. Control Large Struct., Blacksburg, Va.* (1983).
3. A. L. HALE, R. J. LISOWSKI, and W. E. DAHL, "Optimizing Both the Structure and the Control of Maneuvering Flexible Spacecraft," *AAS/AIAA Astrodyn. Conf., Lake Placid, N.Y.*, AIAA Pap. No. 83-377 (1983).
4. A. L. HALE, R. J. LISOWSKI, and W. E. DAHL, "Optimal Simultaneous Structural and Control Design of Maneuvering Flexible Spacecraft," *J. Guidance, Control Dyn.* **8**, 86–93 (1984).
5. R. J. LISOWSKI and A. L. HALE, "Optimal Design for Single Axis Rotational Maneuvers of a Flexible Structure", *J. Astronaut. Sci.* **33**, 179–196 (1985).
6. A. MESSAC and J. TURNER, "Dual Structural-Control Optimization of Large Space Structures," *AIAA Dyn. Spec. Conf., Palm Springs, Calif.* (1984).
7. A. MESSAC and J. TURNER, "Optimal Minimum-Mass Structural-Control Design for Large Space Structures," *AIAA Dyn. Spec. Conf., Palm Springs, Calif.* (1984).
8. J. L. JUNKINS, D. S. BODDEN, and M. P. KAMAT, "An Eigenvalue Optimization Approach For Feedback Control of Flexible Structures," *Proc. Southeast. Conf. Theor. Appl. Mech. XII*, **2**, 303–308 (1984).
9. D. S. BODDEN and J. L. JUNKINS, "Eigenvalue Optimization Algorithms for Structural/Controller Design Iterations," *Am. Control. Conf., San Diego, Calif.* (1984).
10. D. S. BODDEN and J. L. JUNKINS, "Eigenvalue Optimization Algorithms for Structure/Controller Design Iterations," *J. Guidance, Control, Dyn.* **8**, 697–706 (1985).
11. D. F. MILLER and J. SHIM, "Combined Structural and Control Optimization for Flexible Systems Using Gradient Based Searches," *AIAA 24th Aerosp. Sci. Meet., Reno, Nev.*, AIAA Pap. No. 86–0178 (1986).
12. D. F. MILLER and J. SHIM, "Gradient-Based Combined Structural and Control Optimization," *J. Guidance, Control, Dyn.* **10**, 291–298 (1987).
13. M. SALAMA, M. HAMIDI, and L. DEMSETZ, "Optimization of Controlled Structures," *Proc. Workshop Identif. Control Flexible Space Struct., San Diego, Calif.* (1984).
14. V. B. VENKAYYA and V. A. TISCHLER, "Frequency Control and Its Effect on the Dynamic Response of Flexible Structures," *AIAA J.* **23**, 1768–1774 (1985).
15. R. L. FOX and M. P. KAPOOR, "Rates of Change of Eigenvalues and Eigenvectors," *AIAA J.* **6**, 2426–2429 (1968).
16. J. ONODA and R. T. HAFTKA, "An Approach to Structure/Control Simultaneous Optimization for Large Flexible Structures," *AIAA J.* **25**, 1133–1138 (1987).
17. S. S. RAO, V. B. VENKAYYA, and N. S. KHOT, "Game Theory Approach for the Integrated Design of Structures and Controls," *AIAA J.* **26**, 463–469 (1988).
18. N. S. KHOT, H. ÖZ, R. V. GRANDHI, F. E. EASTSTEP, and V. B. VENKAYYA, "Optimal Structural Design with Control Gain Norm Constraint," *AIAA J.* **26**, 604–611 (1988).

AN ASYMPTOTIC PERTURBATION METHOD FOR NONLINEAR OPTIMAL CONTROL PROBLEMS

ROGER C. THOMPSON

Department of Aerospace Engineering
The Pennsylvania State University
University Park, Pennsylvania 16802

JOHN L. JUNKINS

Department of Aerospace Engineering
Texas A&M University
College Station, Texas 77843

I. INTRODUCTION

The problems encountered in many fields of modern mechanics are often described by a coupled set of nonlinear differential equations that represent a specific physical system. Nonlinear terms may arise from the particular choice of coordinates chosen to describe the behavior of a system, or they may be an intrinsic part of the problem to be examined. Inherently nonlinear problems are by far the most difficult systems to solve; although the nonlinearities can be transformed, they cannot be eliminated simply by a judicious choice of variables. Initial value problems can often be solved by direct integration, either in closed form or by numerical methods. Conversely, a two-point boundary value problem (TPBVP) has boundary conditions specified at two distinct values of the independent variable. A TPBVP is considered solved if one set of missing initial or final conditions is determined such that the specified conditions at the other end of the interval result from the ensuing initial value problem. For a small subset of problems encountered in practice, analytic, closed-form solutions of the TPBVP can be obtained. However, this fortuitous situation is rare, so numerical methods are most commonly used for obtaining solutions.

Paralleling the development of digital computers, several numerical techniques have been established for solving TPBVPs. Of the available methods, a few have gained widespread popularity. Examples of commonly used algorithms are several finite difference methods [1,2], the method of complementary functions [2,3], the method of adjoints [2,3], quasilinearization [4,5], and the method of particular solutions [6,7]. Each method has advantages and disadvantages for various types of TPBVPs; no single method is universally applicable for all problems, and it is often difficult, a priori, to predict which method will prove most effective on a new unsolved problem.

The classical perturbation method is an entirely analytical procedure for producing approximate solutions of ordinary differential equations (ODE). It is most commonly applied to initial value problems, and the solutions sought are often nonlinear periodic oscillations, so care must be taken to eliminate secular terms that are characteristic of the basic perturbation approach. As all users of this method are well aware, the algebra and calculus required to generate even a second-order perturbation expansion for a scalar differential equation can be considerable. For large systems of coupled nonlinear equations, determining an analytical solution by perturbation methods is impractical.

As is evident in [8–10], it is indeed rare that third- or higher-order perturbation solutions can be carried to completion for initial value problems. The most common perturbation method, the straightforward expansion, has received little treatment in the literature for solving TPBVPs. Indeed, in a landmark textbook on indirect methods for solving TPBVPs [2], the power series approximation approach is mentioned only in the context of traditional applications that seek an algebraic form for each term in the series: The authors chose instead to use the term *perturbation techniques* to describe another imbedding procedure that is more widely known as *continuation* [11]. Although the relationship between the power series expansion and variational perturbation methods has also been explored [12], the approach was purely analytical.

The motivation supporting the present development of the asymptotic perturbation method is to establish the sequence of linear differential equations underlying perturbation solutions of optimal control problems and extend recently developed methods to solve these equations. The solution process takes full advantage of available analytical and numerical methods for efficient and accurate computation of the matrix exponential and integrals involving matrix exponentials. Each order of the perturbation expansion is shown to be governed by a nonhomogeneous ODE. The generally nonintegrable nonhomogeneous terms can be represented at each order by a finite Fourier series; we then calculate particular solutions in terms of matrix exponentials and the Fourier coefficients, using a recently established matrix exponential identity [see 18]. Since the analytical integrations characteristic of the perturbation approach have been replaced by algebraic and numerical operations, which can be automated, we can carry the perturbation expansions to high order, even for systems of moderate dimensionality.

The asymptotic perturbation method is a quasianalytical approach that is broadly applicable to many nonlinear TPBVPs. Although developed as a means for solving open-loop optimal control problems, the perturbation method we present applies to a broad class of constant coefficient systems of differential equations. The numerical examples presented in this chapter arose in the context of optimal control of dynamical systems.

II. OPTIMAL CONTROL FORMULATION

In this section, we establish the form of the TPBVP for open-loop control of systems described by the nonlinear differential equation

$$\ddot{\mathbf{x}} = \Gamma\dot{\mathbf{x}} + \Lambda\mathbf{x} = \mathbf{B}\mathbf{u} + \mathbf{f}(\mathbf{x}, \dot{\mathbf{x}}, \mathbf{u}, \dot{\mathbf{u}}, t) \tag{1}$$

with boundary conditions

$$\mathbf{x}(t_0) = \mathbf{x}_0 \qquad \dot{\mathbf{x}}(t_0) = \dot{\mathbf{x}}_0 \qquad \mathbf{u}(t_0) = \mathbf{u}_0 \qquad \dot{\mathbf{u}}(t_0) = \dot{\mathbf{u}}_0$$

$$\mathbf{x}(t_f) = \mathbf{x}_f \qquad \dot{\mathbf{x}}(t_f) = \dot{\mathbf{x}}_f \qquad \mathbf{u}(t_f) = \mathbf{u}_f \qquad \dot{\mathbf{u}}(t_f) = \dot{\mathbf{u}}_f$$

where $\mathbf{x}$ is an $n \times 1$ vector of modal coordinates, Γ is a diagonal matrix of damping coefficients, $\mathbf{B}$ is the control influence matrix, $\mathbf{u}$ is an $m \times 1$ vector of control inputs, $\mathbf{f}$ is a vector function containing all nonlinear terms, and the overdots denote differentiation with respect to time. The form of Eq. (1) is based on the assumption that the linear part of the equations of motion have been rendered uncoupled by a linear modal transformation to reduce the complexity of the control formulation. Furthermore, we assume that the n coordinates constitute the subset of the complete modal coordinate set that is to be explicitly considered in the determination of the control. For example, consider a problem described by a set of N discrete configuration coordinates. After we complete the modal transformation, we obtain a set of N modal coordinates; these are usually ordered according to increasing linearized system eigenvalues. In the modal truncation approach, we select the first n modal coordinates and neglect the higher modal coordinates to obtain the n corresponding transformed differential equations as our reduced-order system in the form of Eq. (1). This decoupling and approximate order reduction procedure is entirely arbitrary, though some order reduction process is invariably required to apply this approach to very high order systems. For systems of moderate dimensionality, one may be successful in controlling all of the system coordinates; however, this restrictive view is not necessary and is in fact a hindrance to progress which can otherwise be achieved when applying these approaches to practical problems.

Forming the augmented state vector of the system coordinates, controls, and their first time derivatives, we find the state space form of the system differential equation to be

$$\dot{\mathbf{z}} = F\mathbf{z} + DH + \rho \tag{2}$$

where

$$\mathbf{z} = \mathrm{col}(\mathbf{x}, \dot{\mathbf{x}}, \mathbf{u}, \dot{\mathbf{u}}), \qquad \tilde{n} \times 1$$

$$F = \begin{bmatrix} 0 & I & 0 & 0 \\ -\Lambda & -\Gamma & B & 0 \\ 0 & 0 & 0 & I \\ 0 & 0 & 0 & 0 \end{bmatrix}, \qquad \tilde{n} \times \tilde{n}$$

$$D = \begin{bmatrix} 0 \\ 0 \\ 0 \\ I \end{bmatrix}, \qquad \tilde{n} \times m$$

$$\mathbf{U} = \ddot{\mathbf{u}}, \qquad m \times 1$$

$$\rho = \mathrm{col}(0, \mathbf{f}, 0, 0), \qquad \tilde{n} \times 1$$

and where I is an identity matrix, 0 is a null matrix or vector, and $\tilde{n} = 2(n + m)$.

Including the control and control rates in the augmented state vector enables us to penalize large control accelerations in the design of the optimal control inputs. This makes both the controls and the resulting trajectories smooth and continuous, and permits the imposition of initial and final boundary conditions on the control as well as the state variables. We usually [13,14] elect to set the control and the control derivatives to zero at the initial and final times to avoid the jerk in acceleration and the associated excitation of the structural vibrations. We find that selection of performance weights allows a degree of shaping of the on/off initial and final control profiles. We seek the optimal control that drives Eq. (2) such that the following performance index is minimized:

$$J = \frac{1}{2}\mathbf{z}^{\mathrm{T}}S\mathbf{z}\big|_{t_0} + \frac{1}{2}\int_{t_0}^{t_f} (\mathbf{z}^{\mathrm{T}}Q\mathbf{z} + \mathbf{U}^{\mathrm{T}}R\mathbf{U})\,dt \tag{3}$$

where R and S are positive definite weight matrices, and Q is a positive semidefinite weight matrix ($Q = 0$ is not excluded). It is clear that the matrix Q

can be used to weight not only the relative emphasis on position and velocity errors but also the controls and the control derivatives.

The Hamiltonian, formed from the system given by Eq. (2) and the integrand of Eq. (3), is defined as

$$H = \tfrac{1}{2}(\mathbf{z}^{\mathrm{T}}Q\mathbf{z} + \mathbf{U}^{\mathrm{T}}R\mathbf{U}) + \lambda^{\mathrm{T}}(F\mathbf{z} + D\mathbf{U} + \rho) \tag{4}$$

where λ is an $\tilde{n}$ vector of Lagrange multipliers. Pontryagin's necessary conditions [15] for determining the optimal control are expressed in terms of the Hamiltonian as

$$\dot{\mathbf{z}} = \frac{\partial H}{\partial \lambda} = F\mathbf{z} + D\mathbf{U} + \rho \tag{5}$$

$$\dot{\lambda} = -\frac{\partial H}{\partial \mathbf{z}} = -Q\mathbf{z} - F^{\mathrm{T}}\lambda - \left[\frac{\partial \rho}{\partial \mathbf{z}}\right]^{\mathrm{T}} \lambda \tag{6}$$

$$\mathbf{0} = -\frac{\partial H}{\partial \mathbf{U}} = R\mathbf{U} + D^{\mathrm{T}}\lambda \tag{7}$$

with the boundary condition

$$\lambda(t_{\mathrm{f}}) = S\mathbf{z}(t_{\mathrm{f}}) \tag{8}$$

Solving Eq. (7) for **U** and substituting into Eq. (5) reduces the optimal control problem to an equivalent and well-posed coupled system of $2\tilde{n}$ nonlinear differential equations. Combining the state (**z**) and costate (λ) vectors into an augmented state/costate vector **X**, the differential equations governing the optimal problem may be recast in the following form:

$$\dot{\mathbf{X}} = A\mathbf{X} + \varepsilon\mathbf{d}(\mathbf{X}) \tag{9}$$

where

$$\mathbf{X} = \mathrm{col}(\mathbf{z}, \lambda), \qquad 2\tilde{n} \times 1$$

$$A = \begin{bmatrix} F & -DR^{-1}D^{\mathrm{T}} \\ -Q & -F^{\mathrm{T}} \end{bmatrix}, \qquad 2\tilde{n} \times 2\tilde{n}$$

$$\mathbf{d}(\mathbf{X}) = \begin{Bmatrix} \rho \\ -\left[\dfrac{\partial \rho}{\partial \mathbf{z}}\right]^{\mathrm{T}} \lambda \end{Bmatrix}, \qquad 2\tilde{n} \times 1$$

The parameter ε can be thought of as a small dimensionless bookkeeping parameter, but as we shall see, it is not necessary that ε be infinitesimal to obtain accurate convergence. If a small parameter does not naturally appear in the first-derived equations, then ε can be introduced by simply multiplying and dividing the nonlinear terms by a scale factor.

The boundary conditions on the augmented state/costate system of Eq. (9) can be expressed in the general form,

$$\text{initial:} \quad T_0\mathbf{X}(t_0) = \beta_0, \qquad \text{final:} \quad T_f\mathbf{X}(t_f) = \beta_f \tag{10}$$

where T_0 and T_f are $\tilde{n} \times 2\tilde{n}$ matrices. If the boundary conditions are expessed directly on the initial and final state variables, then these matrices will be sparsely populated with ones and zeroes that select the state/costate coordinates for which the boundary conditions are known.

Now we address the two-point boundary value problem posed by finding the solution to Eq. (9) subject to the boundary conditions of Eq. (10). The development of the perturbation method begins in the next section with the derivation of the sequence of differential equations that governs each order of the perturbation expansion. Subsequent sections develop the analytical and numerical methods used to solve this sequence of differential equations.

III. AN ASYMPTOTIC PERTURBATION METHOD: THE PEDESTRIAN EXPANSION

For the weakly nonlinear ODE, we assume that the solution can be represented by a power series in ε [16]. Mathematically, we write the solution $\mathbf{X}(t)$ in the form

$$\mathbf{X}(t) = \mathbf{X}_0(t) + \varepsilon\mathbf{X}_1(t) + \varepsilon^2\mathbf{X}_2(t) + \varepsilon^3\mathbf{X}_3(t) + \cdots \tag{11}$$

Substituting this assumed form of the solution into Eq. (9), we are led to an equation of the form

$$\begin{aligned}\dot{\mathbf{X}}_0(t) + \varepsilon\dot{\mathbf{X}}_1(t) + \varepsilon^2\dot{\mathbf{X}}_2(t) + O(\varepsilon^3) = A\mathbf{X}_0(t) &+ \varepsilon[A\mathbf{X}_1(t) + \mathbf{d}_1(\mathbf{X}_0)] \\ &+ \varepsilon^2[A\mathbf{X}_2(t) + \mathbf{d}_2(\mathbf{X}_0, \mathbf{X}_1)] + O(\varepsilon^3)\end{aligned} \tag{12}$$

where the nonlinear terms have been expanded as a power series in ε and the dependence of each term upon $\mathbf{X}_i(t)$ at each order is indicated. Since we seek a solution valid for all values of ε, we equate terms with like powers of ε in Eq. (12) and are led directly to the sequence of linear differential equations:

$$\dot{\mathbf{X}}_0 = A\mathbf{X}_0 \tag{13a}$$

$$\dot{\mathbf{X}}_1 = A\mathbf{X}_1 + \mathbf{d}_1(\mathbf{X}_0) \tag{13b}$$

$$\dot{\mathbf{X}}_2 = A\mathbf{X}_2 + \mathbf{d}_2(\mathbf{X}_0, \mathbf{X}_1) \tag{13c}$$

where for illustrative purposes, we show only the equations through order ε^2. We note that the order can be extended in principle to higher orders if the algebra and computations are feasible and if necessary to achieve satisfactory convergence. The boundary conditions on the expansion variables $\mathbf{X}_i$ are

$$\text{initial:} \quad T_0\mathbf{X}_0(t_0) = \beta_0, \qquad \text{final:} \quad T_f\mathbf{X}_0(t_f) = \beta_f \tag{14a}$$

$$\text{initial:} \quad T_0\mathbf{X}_i(t_0) = \mathbf{0}, \qquad \text{final:} \quad T_f\mathbf{X}_i(t_f) = \mathbf{0}, \qquad i = 1, 2, 3, \ldots \tag{14b}$$

We note that since T_0 and T_f are $\tilde{n} \times 2\tilde{n}$ matrices, there are $\tilde{n}$ elements of the augmented state/costate vector, usually the initial and final costates $\lambda(t_0)$ and $\lambda(t_f)$, that are unspecified at the initial and final times. We know from Pontryagin's necessary conditions that $\lambda_i(t_f) = S\mathbf{z}(\tilde{t_f})$, and as we establish in Section V, this provides enough information to determine the missing initial or final costates. Since we have applied the state and control boundary conditions to the zeroth order solution in Eq. (14a), it is evident the boundary conditions of Eq. (14b) follow because Eq. (11) must satisfy the initial and final boundary conditions. The fact that the constants of integration associated with solving Eqs. (13b) and (13c) and the higher-order solutions must be determined so that $\mathbf{X}_i(t_0)$ and $\mathbf{X}_i(t_f)$ vanish is important for a subtle reason: The two-point boundary conditions dominate the solutions near the boundaries and indirectly enhance the convergence. Since this is a finite time problem, if these boundary conditions are enforced, we can only experience divergence interior to the solution interval $\{t_0, t_f\}$. The point here is that secular terms are not necessarily catastrophic *vis-à-vis* validity of the solution for finite-time two-point boundary value problems as they are when we seek the more usual initial value solutions valid over infinite time intervals.

Thus the straightforward expansion yields a well-posed sequence of linear differential equations; in the ideal application, the zeroth order solution provides a solution that satisfies the initial and final conditions, and the subsequent higher-order solutions provide a sequence of successively smaller corrections. Of course, as in classical perturbation methods for initial value problems, it is not possible to guarantee convergence *a priori*, but this usually does not prevent practical progress. As developed later, we have indeed established a quasianalytical procedure that leads to high-order perturbation solutions for a large family of nonlinear control problems.

IV. SOLUTION OF THE NONHOMOGENEOUS EQUATIONS

In this section, we construct an algorithm we subsequently use to solve the sequence of ODEs given in Eqs. (13). We begin with the general integral form of the solution and then develop a quasianalytical method for constructing the solution. The general solution of a typical first-order matrix differential equation in the sequence of Eqs. (13) is [17]

$$\mathbf{X}_i(t) = \mathbf{e}^{At}[\mathbf{X}_i(0) + \int_0^t \mathbf{e}^{A\tau}\mathbf{d}_i(\tau)d\tau] \qquad \text{for} \qquad i = 1, 2, \ldots \tag{15}$$

where we have set $t_0 = 0$, and it is clear that $\mathbf{X}_0(t) = \mathbf{e}^{At}\mathbf{X}_0(0)$, and $\mathbf{e}^{At}$ denotes the matrix exponential. Although Eqs. (15) provide a formal solution, actually carrying through the algebra and evaluating the integrals is often a formidable task. In the most general circumstances the integrals may be analytically impossible and numerical integration may be necessary. On the other hand, if the forcing terms $\mathbf{d}_i(t)$ can be accurately approximated by elementary functions of time, then we can easily complete the integration process using an augmented matrix exponential identity due to Van Loan [18].

We choose to approximate each element of $\mathbf{d}_i(t)$ by a finite Fourier series of the form

$$f(t) = b_0 + \sum_{i=1}^{r} \{a_i \sin i\omega_0 t + b_i \cos i\omega_0 t\} \tag{16}$$

We can calculate the coefficients from k samples of the elements of $\mathbf{d}_i(t)$ by any discrete Fourier transform algorithm. We elect to be explicit here and indicate the calculation of the coefficients by a conventional least-squares procedure. Using Eq. (16) to approximate the jth element of $\mathbf{d}_i(t)$ leads to the linear system of algebraic equations

$$L\mathbf{c}_j = \tilde{\mathbf{d}}_j \tag{17}$$

where

$$L = \begin{bmatrix} 1 & 0 & 1 & 0 & 1 & \cdots & 0 & 1 \\ 1 & s(\tau_1) & c(\tau_1) & s(2\tau_1) & c(2\tau_1) & \cdots & s(r\tau_1) & c(r\tau_1) \\ 1 & s(\tau_2) & c(\tau_2) & s(2\tau_2) & c(2\tau_2) & \cdots & s(r\tau_2) & c(r\tau_2) \\ \vdots & & & & & & & \\ 1 & s(\tau_k) & c(\tau_k) & s(2\tau_k) & c(2\tau_k) & \cdots & s(r\tau_k) & c(r\tau_k) \end{bmatrix}, \quad c \equiv \cos, \quad s \equiv \sin$$

$$\mathbf{c}_j = [b_{0j} \quad a_{1j} \quad b_{1j} \quad a_{2j} \quad b_{2j} \quad a_{3j} \quad b_{3j} \quad \cdots \quad a_{rj} \quad b_{rj}]^{\mathrm{T}}$$

$$\tilde{\mathbf{d}}_j = [\mathbf{d}_i^j(0) \quad \mathbf{d}_i^j(\Delta t) \quad \mathbf{d}_i^j(2\,\Delta t) \quad \cdots \quad \mathbf{d}_i^j(k\,\Delta t)]^{\mathrm{T}},$$

$$\Delta t = t_{\mathrm{f}}/k, \qquad \tau_l = l\omega_0\,\Delta t, \qquad \omega_0 = 2\pi/t_{\mathrm{f}}$$

and the notation $\mathbf{d}_i^j(k\,\Delta t)$ indicates the jth element of $\mathbf{d}_i(t)$ evaluated at time $t = k\,\Delta t$. The coefficients can then be computed by least-square inversion of Eq. (17), indicated formally as

$$\mathbf{c}_j = (L^{\mathrm{T}}L)^{-1}L^{\mathrm{T}}\tilde{\mathbf{d}}_j \tag{18}$$

Notice that with appropriate sample points (symmetric about $\tau = \pi$), $L^{\mathrm{T}}L$ is diagonal, and the inverse is trivial owing to the orthogonality of sine and cosine. It is also evident that adoption of fixed sample times leads to economies because the least-square operator becomes invariant, even if discrete orthogonality is not enforced. Proceeding element-by-element through the ith forcing term $\mathbf{d}_i(t)$, we can use as many terms in Eq. (16) as necessary to obtain arbitrarily accurate Fourier approximations.

As can be verified by expansion, the Fourier approximation of the forcing function can be expressed as the matrix exponential

$$\mathbf{d}_j(t) = G_i \mathbf{e}^{\Omega t} \mathbf{g}_0 \tag{19}$$

where

$$G_i = [\mathbf{g}_1 \quad \mathbf{g}_2 \quad \mathbf{g}_3 \quad \cdots \quad \mathbf{g}_s], \qquad s = 2\tilde{n}$$

$$\mathbf{g}_j = [b_{0j} \quad \omega_0 a_{1j} \quad b_{1j} \quad 2\omega_0 a_{2j} \quad b_{2j} \quad \cdots \quad r\omega_0 a_{rj} \quad b_{rj}]^{\mathrm{T}}, \qquad j = 1, 2, 3, \ldots, s$$

$$\mathbf{g}_0 = [1 \quad 0 \quad 1 \quad 0 \quad 1 \quad \cdots \quad 0 \quad 1], \qquad (2r+1) \times 1$$

$$\mathbf{\Omega} = \text{block diagonal}[0, \mathbf{\Omega}_1, \mathbf{\Omega}_2, \mathbf{\Omega}_3, \ldots, \mathbf{\Omega}_r], \qquad (2r+1) \times (2r+1)$$

$$\mathbf{\Omega}_l = \begin{bmatrix} 0 & 1 \\ -(l\omega_0)^2 & 0 \end{bmatrix}, \qquad l = 1, 2, 3, \ldots, r$$

We now have the nonhomogeneous term represented by a continuous function of time given in exponential form. Consequently, we can make use of the results of Eq. (18) to directly carry out the integration in Eq. (15) by using a matrix exponential calculation. Briefly, it is shown in [18] that if we introduce the augmented matrix Y_i defined as

$$Y_i(t) = \begin{bmatrix} A & G_i \\ 0 & \Omega \end{bmatrix} \tag{20}$$

then the matrix exponential of Y_i is

$$\mathbf{e}^{Y_i t} = \begin{bmatrix} \mathbf{e}^{At} & \mathbf{e}^{At} \displaystyle\int_0^t \mathbf{e}^{-A\tau} G_i \mathbf{e}^{\Omega\tau} \, d\tau \\ 0 & \mathbf{e}^{\Omega\tau} \end{bmatrix} \equiv \begin{bmatrix} \Phi_1(t) & \Phi_{2i}(t) \\ & \Phi_3(t) \end{bmatrix} \tag{21}$$

where we have introduced a shorthand notation for the three nonzero submatrices of the matrix exponential:

$$\Phi_1(t) = \mathbf{e}^{At} \tag{22a}$$

$$\Phi_{2i}(t) = \mathbf{e}^{At} \int_0^t \mathbf{e}^{-A\tau} G_i \mathbf{e}^{\Omega\tau} \, d\tau \tag{22b}$$

$$\Phi_{3i}(t) = G_i \mathbf{e}^{\Omega\tau} \tag{22c}$$

Observe that we can make direct use of the submatrices of the matrix exponential to write the solution of Eq. (15) as

$$\mathbf{X}_i(t) = \Phi_1(t)\mathbf{X}_i(0) + \Phi_{2i}(t)\mathbf{g}_0 \tag{23}$$

where we note that $\mathbf{\Phi}_{2i}(t)$ is numerically different for each expansion variable, as is indicated by the subscript i in Eqs. (21)–(23).

The numerical algorithm just presented may appear very cumbersome; however, it is primarily the bookkeeping and associated notation that are complicated. In practice, the procedure is quite simple to implement with only a modest computer programming effort. Because the matrices A and Ω are constant for a given problem and specified sample times, respectively, and the elements of G_i are computed by simple matrix multiplications, it is evident that assembly of the matrix of Eq. (20) can be easily accomplished. Calculating the matrix exponential consumes most of the computational burden. However, there are several excellent algorithms for computing the matrix exponential [19].

V. DETERMINATION OF THE INITIAL COSTATES

In Section IV, we developed the form of the solution, Eq. (23), for each order of the power series expansion. However, no solution can be calculated until the missing initial or final conditions are determined. By virtue of the boundary conditions in Eq. (8) and the boundary conditions specified in the problem statement of Eq. (1), the complete set of costate conditions is known only at $t = t_f$. The state transition matrix defined in Eq. (21) can always be used to define the relationship between the state vector at any time relative to the initial state of the system. Because the only unknown terms in this relationship are the initial costates, there is an explicit, algebraic equation that can be used to calculate the missing initial conditions.

Evaluating Eq. (23) at $t = t_f$ and recalling the boundary conditions from Eq. (14), we find that

$$\mathbf{X}_i(t_f) = \begin{Bmatrix} \mathbf{z}_i(t_f) \\ S\mathbf{z}_i(t_f) \end{Bmatrix} = \Phi_1(t_f)\begin{Bmatrix} \mathbf{z}_i(0) \\ \lambda_i(0) \end{Bmatrix} + \Phi_{2i}(t_f)\mathbf{g}_0 \tag{24}$$

It proves useful to write the state transition matrix $\Phi_1(t_f)$ in partitioned form and also to partition the last term in Eq. (24). Therefore, we define the partitions of each term to be

$$\Phi_1(t_f) = \begin{bmatrix} \phi_1^{11}(t_f) & \phi_1^{12}(t_f) \\ \phi_1^{21}(t_f) & \phi_1^{22}(t_f) \end{bmatrix} \tag{25a}$$

$$\Phi_{2i}(t_f)\mathbf{g}_0 = \begin{Bmatrix} \Psi_{1i}(t_f) \\ \Psi_{2i}(t_f) \end{Bmatrix} \tag{25b}$$

Substituting Eq. (25) into Eq. (24) yields two coupled algebraic equations,

$$\mathbf{z}_i(t_f) = \phi_1^{11}(t_f)\mathbf{z}_i(0) + \phi_1^{12}(t_f)\lambda_i(0) + \Psi_{1i}(t_f) \tag{26}$$

$$S\mathbf{z}_i(t_f) = \phi_1^{21}(t_f)\mathbf{z}_i(0) + \phi_1^{22}(t_f)\lambda_i(0) + \Psi_{2i}(t_f) \tag{27}$$

in which $\lambda_i(0)$ is the only unknown.

Multiplying Eq. (26) by the positive definite matrix S, combining this with Eq. (27), and collecting terms yields

$$[\phi_1^{22}(t_f) - S\phi_1^{12}(t_f)]\lambda_i(0) = [S\phi_1^{11}(t_f) - \phi_1^{21}(t_f)]\mathbf{z}(0) + S\Psi_{1i}(t_f) - \Psi_{2i}(t_f) \tag{28}$$

which can easily be solved for the initial costates using any appropirate algorithm. Now that all of the initial conditions of $\mathbf{X}_i$ are known, Eq. (23) can be used to produce the solution of the expansion variable at any time in the interval $0 \leq t \leq t_f$.

VI. RECURSIVE SOLUTION OF THE STATE/COSTATE TRAJECTORIES

Once the solution for a given expansion variable is found, we then proceed to the next higher order. However, to produce the Fourier series approximation of the nonhomogeneous term in the next higher order requires that we sample the trajectory of the current order at fixed intervals of time (Δt) throughout the maneuver. Evaluating the matrix exponential indicated in Eq. (21) at each interval would prove to be too costly and time-consuming in terms of computational effort. An alternative procedure is to develop a recursive formula for calculating the state trajectories whereby the matrix exponential is evaluated only once at $t = \Delta t$. We make use of the exponential identity

$$e^{A(k+1)\Delta t} = e^{A\Delta t}e^{Ak\Delta t} \tag{29}$$

to develop a recursive form of Eq. (23). Applying the identity in Eq. (29) to the definitions of the state transition matrix, Eq. (21), we have

$$\begin{bmatrix} \Phi_1[(k+1)\Delta t] & \Phi_{2i}[(k+1)\Delta t] \\ 0 & \Phi_3[(k+1)\Delta t] \end{bmatrix} = \begin{bmatrix} \Phi_1(\Delta t) & \Phi_{2i}(\Delta t) \\ 0 & \Phi_3(\Delta t) \end{bmatrix} \begin{bmatrix} \Phi_1(k\Delta t) & \Phi_{2i}(k\Delta t) \\ 0 & \Phi_3(k\Delta t) \end{bmatrix} \tag{30}$$

Carrying out the products indicated in the partitioned matrices yields a recursive equation for each partition:

$$\Phi_1[k+1)\Delta t] = \Phi_1(\Delta t)\Phi_1(k\Delta t) \tag{31a}$$

$$\Phi_{2i}[(k+1)\,\Delta t] = \Phi_1(\Delta t)\Phi_{2i}(k\,\Delta t) + \Phi_{2i}(\Delta t)\Phi_3(k\,\Delta t) \tag{31b}$$

$$\Phi_3[(k+1)\,\Delta t] = \Phi_3(\Delta t)\Phi_3(k\,\Delta t) \tag{31c}$$

where, by definition, we recognize that $\Phi_1(0) = I$, $\Phi_{2i}(0) = 0$, and $\Phi_3(0) = I$.

Similarly, evaluating Eq. (23) at $t = (k+1)\,\Delta t$ produces

$$\mathbf{X}_i[k+1)\,\Delta t] = \Phi_1[(k+1)\,\Delta t]\mathbf{X}_i(0) + \Phi_{2i}[(k+1)\,\Delta t]\mathbf{g}_0 \tag{32}$$

We can now simplify Eq. (32) by defining three vectors $\mathbf{v}_{ji}$, $j = 1,2,3$ such that

$$\begin{aligned} \mathbf{v}_{1i}[(k+1)\,\Delta t] &= \Phi_1[(k+1)\,\Delta t]\mathbf{X}_i(0) \\ \mathbf{v}_{2i}[(k+1)\,\Delta t] &= \Phi_{2i}[(k+1)\,\Delta t]\mathbf{g}_0 \\ \mathbf{v}_{3i}[(k+1)\,\Delta t] &= \Phi_3[(k+1)\,\Delta t]\mathbf{g}_0 \end{aligned} \tag{33}$$

Substituting Eq. (31) into Eq. (33) and substituting this result into Eq. (32) yields the recursive formula

$$\mathbf{X}_i[(k+1)\,\Delta t] = \mathbf{v}_{1i}[(k+1)\,\Delta t] + \mathbf{v}_{2i}[(k+1)\,\Delta t] \tag{34}$$

where

$$\begin{aligned} \mathbf{v}_{1i}[(k+1)\,\Delta t] &= \Phi_1(\Delta t)\mathbf{v}_{1i}(k\,\Delta t), \\ \mathbf{v}_{2i}[(k+1)\,\Delta t] &= \Phi_1(\Delta t)\mathbf{v}_{2i}(k\,\Delta t) + \Phi_{2i}(\Delta t)\mathbf{v}_{3i}(k\,\Delta t) \\ \mathbf{v}_{3i}[(k+1)\,\Delta t] &= \Phi_3(\Delta t)\mathbf{v}_{3i}(k\,\Delta t), \end{aligned}$$

and the initial conditions of the recursive vectors are defined to be

$$\mathbf{v}_{1i}(0) = \mathbf{X}_i(0) \qquad \mathbf{v}_{2i}(0) = \mathbf{0} \qquad \mathbf{v}_{3i}(0) = \mathbf{g}_0$$

By using Eq. (34) to generate the sampled data set for each order of the power series expansion, the matrix exponential must be calculated only twice for each $\mathbf{X}_i$: once at $t = t_f$ to determine the missing initial conditions and once at $t = \Delta t$ for the recursive formula. After completing the solutions of each $\mathbf{X}_i$ in the series, one can produce the optimal control profile and the state/costate trajectories by combining the corresponding data for each expansion variable in the series given by Eq. (11). We again stress the fact that the solution of the nonlinear optimal control problem has been produced by solving a series of strictly linear, constant coefficient subproblems without the need for iterative techniques. We shall illustrate the effectiveness of the perturbation method with numerical examples of low-order systems.

VII. ILLUSTRATIVE EXAMPLES

We illustrate the results that can be obtained through applying the asymptotic perturbation method by determining the solution of three simple, low-order optimal control problems. These problems serve only to indicate the utility of the perturbation method and therefore do not define any limitations on the types of problems suitable for solution by this algorithm. The perturbation method has been used successfully on a number of different problems [20] including systems with a large number of degrees of freedom. The first example is a scalar equation with quadratic and cubic nonlinearities. In the second and third examples, we examine a system of two equations coupled through a quadratic nonlinear term, in which the magnitude of the nonlinear terms is varied.

A. A SCALAR PROBLEM

We choose to begin the illustrative examples with a scalar problem because the size of the augmented state/costate system is minimized, and we can focus our attention on the methodology rather than on the "notational overhead" required for a system with many degrees of freedom.

To demonstrate the perturbation method, we solve a nonlinear, scalar optimal control problem with both quadratic and cubic nonlinear terms. The system, in configuration coordinates, is given by

$$\ddot{x} + c\dot{x} + kx = u + \varepsilon(\gamma ux - \alpha x^3) \tag{35}$$

where

$$c = 0.1 \qquad \gamma = 1.0 \quad \varepsilon = 0.1$$
$$k = 1.0 \qquad \alpha = 0.5$$
$$x(0) = 1.0 \qquad \dot{x}(0) = 0 \qquad t_f = 2$$

Our objective is to determine the optimal controls that will drive the variable x to zero (with a final velocity of zero) in a 2-sec time interval. To verify that the system is weakly nonlinear, the nondimensional form of Eq. (35) can be shown to be

$$\ddot{\eta} + \delta_1\dot{\eta} + \eta = \tilde{u} + \delta_2\tilde{u}\eta - \delta_3\eta^3 \tag{36}$$

with $\delta_1 = 0.1$, $\delta_2 = 0.1$, and $\delta_3 = 0.05$, and where η is the dimensionless position coordinate, and $\tilde{u}$ is the dimensionless control force. Clearly, from Eq. (36), the system is lightly damped with weak nonlinearities. We choose to penalize only the control accelerations and the final state in the performance measure, given in Eq. (3), so we let $R = 1$, $Q = 0$, and $S = 10^{20}[I]$. The effect of the numerically large weight matrix (S) is to rigidly enforce the final conditions in the optimal control problem. In the vernacular of optimal control theory, this example is a fixed-time, fixed-final-state optimal control problem when S is numerically large. We solve this problem in configuration space, and the matrix F is given by

$$F = \begin{bmatrix} 0 & 1 & 0 & 0 \\ -1 & -.1 & 1 & 0 \\ 0 & 0 & 0 & 1 \\ 0 & 0 & 0 & 0 \end{bmatrix}$$

Similarly, the vector of nonlinear terms in Eq. (9) can be shown to be

$$\mathbf{d} = \begin{Bmatrix} 0 \\ \gamma u x - \alpha x^3 \\ 0 \\ 0 \\ (3\alpha x^2 - \gamma u)\lambda_2 \\ 0 \\ -\gamma x \lambda_2 \\ 0 \end{Bmatrix}$$

where λ_2 is the second element of the costate vector λ. We evaluate the effectiveness of the optimal control approximations by integrating Eq. (35) numerically, using a 4-cycle Runge–Kutta routine and examining the errors in the final state of the system as determined by the numerically integrated solution.

A second-order expansion in the power series yields a final condition $x(t_f) = -0.000322$ from the integrated equation of motion. Although not exactly zero, the error is less than 0.04%. By comparison, the linearized optimal control, obtained by dropping the nonlinear terms (note that this is also the zeroth order expansion variable) produces $x(t_f) = -0.0402$ or an error of over 4%. The perturbation approach reduced the error by two orders of magnitude for a second-order expansion. The trajectories of the position and control are shown in Figs. 1a and b, respectively, in which each profile exhibits the smooth, continuous behavior expected of an optimal solution of this problem.

B. A WEAKLY NONLINEAR SYSTEM

For the second example, we apply the perturbation method to a two degree-of-freedom system that is coupled through a quadratic nonlinear term. Mathematically, the definition of the problem is to determine the optimal control that will drive the system state to zero in a 2-sec time interval, where the state trajectory is governed by the equations of motion:

$$\begin{aligned} \ddot{x}_1 + c_1\dot{x}_1 + k_1 x_1 &= u_1 + \varepsilon\alpha_1 x_1 x_2 \\ \ddot{x}_2 + c_2\dot{x}_2 + k_2 x_2 &= u_2 + \varepsilon\alpha_2 x_1 x_2 \end{aligned} \tag{37}$$

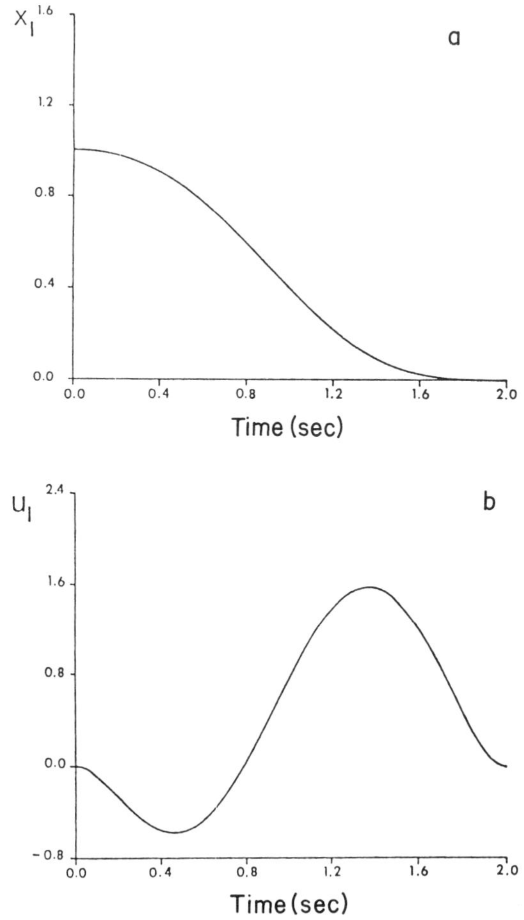

Fig. 1. (a) Position trajectory and (b) control trajectory for the scalar problem.

where

$$
\begin{array}{lll}
c_1 = 0.1 & k_1 = 1.0 & \alpha_1 = 1.0 \\
c_2 = 0.1 & k_2 = 0.5 & \alpha_2 = 0.5 \\
\dot{x}_1(0) = 1.0 & \dot{x}_1(0) = 0 & \varepsilon = 0.1 \\
x_2(0) = 2.0 & \dot{x}_2(0) = 0 &
\end{array}
$$

In nondimensional, matrix format, the equations of motion are

$$
\ddot{\eta} + \begin{bmatrix} 0.1 & 0 \\ 0 & 0.1 \end{bmatrix} \dot{\eta} + \begin{bmatrix} 1 & 0 \\ 0 & 0.5 \end{bmatrix} \eta = \tilde{\mathbf{u}} + \begin{Bmatrix} 0.1 & \eta_1 & \eta_2 \\ 0.05 & \eta_1 & \eta_2 \end{Bmatrix} \tag{38}
$$

We can see from Eq. (38), that the system is lightly damped and weakly nonlinear. We also choose to penalize the final states and the second derivatives of the controls in the performance index, by setting $R = I$, $Q = 0$, and $S = 10^{20}[I]$. The results of a second-order expansion, when compared with the linearized optimal control problem, can be shown to be

	$x_1(t_f)$	$x_2(t_f)$
Linearized optimal control approximation:	0.135	0.0868
Second-order control approximation:	0.0000166	0.00000945

The final position errors for the zeroth-order control approximation are 13.5% and 4.3%, respectively, for the state variables x_1 and x_2. The control determined from the second-order perturbation expansion reduces the errors by approximately four orders of magnitude. Such explosive convergence is not typical, but it does demonstrate how efficient the perturbation method can be for certain open-loop optimal control problems.

C. A STRONGLY NONLINEAR SYSTEM

As a final example, we test the perturbation method with a system containing larger nonlinearities. To accomplish this, we use the same system as in Section VII,B, with the following parameter changes:

$$\alpha_1 = 2 \qquad x_1(0) = 3 \qquad \varepsilon = 0.4 \qquad \alpha_2 = 3 \qquad x_2(0) = 2$$

In dimensionless form, the system is given by

$$\ddot{\eta} + \begin{bmatrix} 0.1 & 0 \\ 0 & 0.1 \end{bmatrix} \dot{\eta} + \begin{bmatrix} 1 & 0 \\ 0 & 0.5 \end{bmatrix} \eta = \tilde{\mathbf{u}} + \begin{Bmatrix} 2.4 & \eta_1 & \eta_2 \\ 3.6 & \eta_1 & \eta_2 \end{Bmatrix} \tag{39}$$

We notice immediately that this system is strongly nonlinear, and ordinarily we would not be optimistic that these equations would submit to a

TABLE I. FINAL STATE ERRORS

Approximation order	$x_1(t_f)$	$x_2(t_f)$
0	110.00	168.86
1	4.164	6.859
2	0.3654	0.6124
3	−0.01957	−0.03416
4	−0.01001	−0.01677
5	0.0006371	0.001106
6	0.0002444	0.0003835

perturbation solution. However, we proceed with the perturbation approach while recognizing that this is a significant test of the method. The final conditions are shown in Table I for controls computed from solutions of zero (linearized system) through sixth order.

The controls from the sixth-order expansion produce very accurate results with errors substantially less than 0.04% for both coordinates. The position and control profiles are shown in Figs. 2a and 2b, respectively; each trajectory is a smooth and continuous path to the origin. Thus, excellent convergence was achieved for a problem in which the nonlinear terms are of a significant magnitude.

VIII. CONCLUSIONS

A procedure for solving nonlinear, open-loop, optimal control problems has been presented. In this approach, an asymptotic perturbation method is applied, and we develop a solution algorithm without the traditional dependence on iterative numerical methods. The nonlinear system is "separated" into a set of nonhomogeneous, linear, optimal control problems that can be solved sequentially. On combining the solutions of the subproblems in a straightforward power series, an optimal control for the nonlinear system is generated. This novel process for solving nonlinear optimal control problems is a result of the marriage of a simple analytical technique (the perturbation method) and a powerful numerical algorithm (the matrix exponential).

Although the asymptotic perturbation method was conceived as a solution process for weakly nonlinear problems, the method has demonstrated extraordinary effectiveness when applied to many strongly nonlinear problems such as the system presented in Section VII,C. Certainly, the perturbation method does not converge for all nonlinear systems satisfactorily. However, the family of nonlinear problems for which the method is effective is considerably larger than we initially expected. We therefore anticipate that this asymptotic perturbation method will be found to be broadly applicable to a large family of general, nonlinear problems, including high degree-of-freedom systems.

ACKNOWLEDGMENTS

This work was supported by the Air Force Office of Scientific Research under contract No. F49620-83-K-0032-P00004. The technical liasion of Dr. A. K. Amos is gratefully acknowledged. We also appreciate the contributions of Dr. J. D. Turner, who brought Van Loan's work [18] to our attention, and whose paper [14] motivated the recursions of Eq. (34).

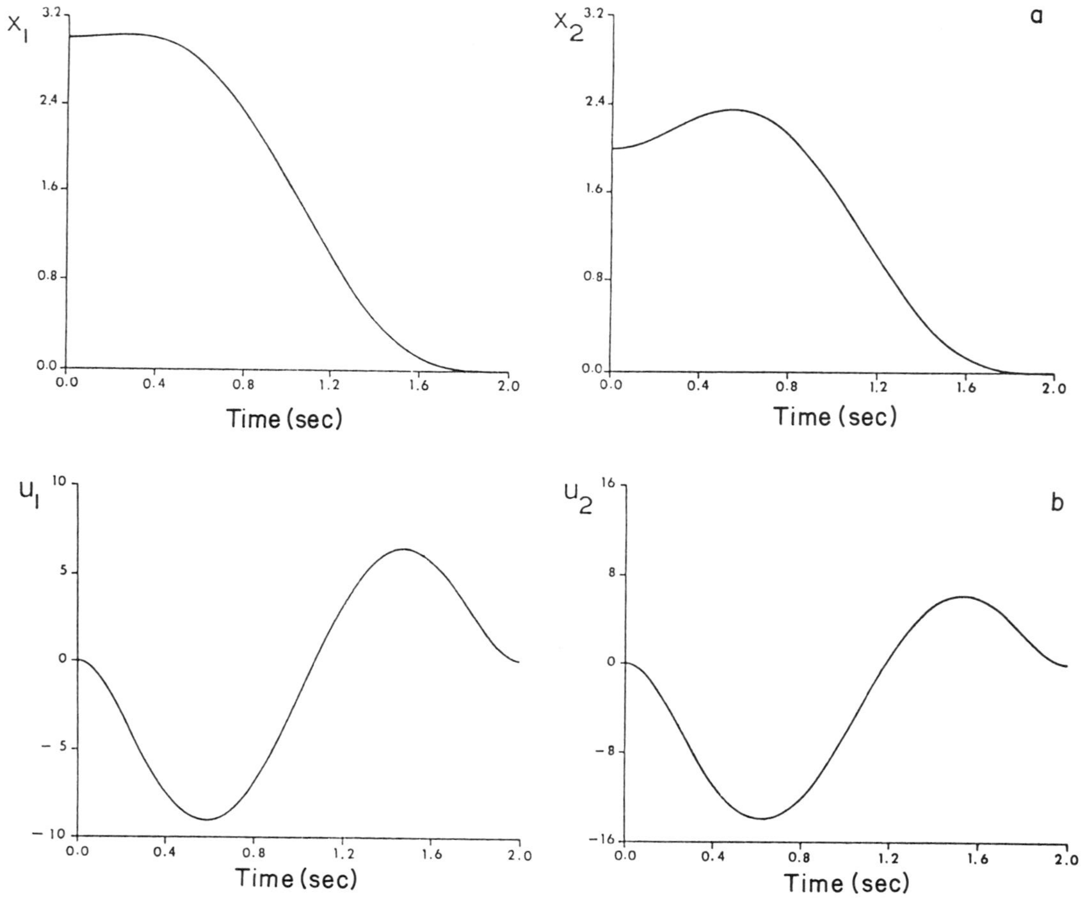

Fig. 2. (a) Position trajectories and (b) control trajectories for the strongly nonlinear system.

REFERENCES

1. J. F. HOLT, "Numerical Solution of Nonlinear Two-Point Boundary Value Problems by Finite Difference Methods," *Commun. Assoc. Comput. Mach.* **7**, 366–372 (1964).
2. S. M. ROBERTS and J. S. SHIPMAN, "Two-Point Boundary Value Problems: Shooting Methods," Am. Elsevier, New York, 1972.
3. M. KUBICEK and V. HLAVACEK, "Numerical Solution of Nonlinear Boundary Value Problems with Applications," Prentice-Hall, Englewood Cliffs, New Jersey, 1983.
4. R. E. BELLMAN and R. E. KALABA, "Quasilinearization and Nonlinear Boundary Value Problems," Am. Elsevier, New York, 1965.
5. R. J. SYLVESTER and F. MEYER, "Two-Point Boundary Value Problems by Quasilinearization," *J. SIAM* **13**, 586–602 (1985).
6. A. MIELE, "Method of Particular Solutions for Linear Two-Point Boundary-Value Problems," *J. Optim. Theory App.* **2**, 260–273 (1968).
7. A. MIELE and R. R. IYER, "General Technique for Solving Nonlinear, Two-Point Boundary-Value Problems Via the Method of Particular Solutions," *J. Optim. Theory App.* **5**, 382–399 (1970).
8. L. MEIROVITCH and G. RYLAND, "Response of Slightly Damped Gyroscopic Systems," *J. Sound Vib.* **67**, 1–19 (1979).
9. L. MEIROVITCH and G. RYLAND, "A Perturbation Technique for Gyroscopic Systems with Small Internal and External Damping," *J. Sound Vib.* **100**, 393–408 (1985).
10. H. M. CHUN and J. D. TURNER, "Frequency-Shaped Large-Angle Maneuvers," *AIAA Aerosp. Sci. Meet., 25th, Reno, Nev.* (1987).
11. S. M. ROBERTS, J. S. SHIPMAN, and W. J. ELLIS, "A Perturbation Technique for Nonlinear Two-Point Boundary Value," *SIAM J. Numer. Anal.* **6**, 347–358 (1969).
12. S. M., ROBERTS, "Variational Perturbation Methods and Power Series Approximation Method," *J. Optim. Theory Appl.* **32**, 441–450 (1980).
13. J. L. JUNKINS, "Comment on 'Optimal Feedback Slewing of Flexible Spacecraft'," *J. Guidance, Control, Dyn.* **5**, 318 (1982).
14. J. D. TURNER, H. M. CUN, and J.-N. JUANG, "Optimal Slewing Maneuvers for Flexible Spacecraft Using a Closed Form Solution for the Linear Tracking Problem," *AAS/AIAA Astrodyn. Conf., Lake Placid, N. Y.* (1983).
15. D. E. KIRK, "Optimal Control Theory: An Introduction," Prentice-Hall, Englewood Cliffs, New Jersey, 1970.
16. A. H. NAYFEH and D. T. MOOK, "Nonlinear Oscillations," Wiley, New York, 1979.
17. W. E. BOYCE and R. C. DIPRIMA, "Elementary Differential Equations and Boundary Value Problems," Wiley, New York, 1977.
18. C. F. VAN LOAN, "Computing Integrals Involving the Matrix Exponential," *IEEE Trans. Autom. Control* **AC-23**, 395–404 (1978).
19. R. C. WARD, "Numerical Computation of the Matrix Exponential with Accuracy Estimate," *SIAM J. Numer. Anal.* **14**, 600–610 (1977).
20. R. C. THOMPSON. "A Perturbation Approach to Control of Rotational/Translational Maneuvers of Flexible Space Vehicles," M. S. Thesis, Engineering Mechanics, Virginia Polytechnic Institute and State University, Blacksburg, VA, 1985.

RELIABILITY ISSUES IN STRUCTURAL CONTROL

HAIM BARUH
KANGYOUN CHOE

Department of Mechanical and Aerospace Engineering
Rutgers University
New Brunswick, New Jersey 08903

I. INTRODUCTION

Suppose a control system has been designed for a structure—for vibration suppression, maneuver, disturbance rejection, or a combination of these—and the performance of the control action is not satisfactory. What has gone wrong? Is the control design inadequate, are there errors in the mathematical model of the system, is a control system component faulty, or is there some other reason? It is very important that the source of error, malfunction, or poor design be pinpointed and corrected as quickly as possible. Problems such as these constitute the bulk of the reliability issues associated with structural control. The ultimate objective is to design a reliable and robust control law and to build additional reliability checks and redundancies around the control system. In this article, we examine the effects of having incorrect models and sensor and actuator malfunctions on the performance of structural control systems, summarize our research on control design and component failure detection, and make recommendations for future work.

When planning to build a reliability loop around a control system, one must primarily be concerned with the following main factors:

1. Determination of the accuracy of the system model
2. Monitoring the effectiveness of the control law
3. Detection of faulty control system components such as actuators, sensors and on-board computers that carry out the computations

Associated with these main issues are several additional problems in building a reliability loop around a control system:

1. Effects of failure of a sensor or actuator on the performance of the control system
2. Effects of modeling errors on the performance of the control system
3. Development of control laws relatively insensitive to component failures and model errors
4. Effects of sensor failure on the actuator failure detection
5. Effects of actuator failure on the sensor failure detection
6. Effects of modeling errors on the performance of failure detection
7. Effects of sensor, actuator, or other hardware failures on the parameter identification
8. Determination of the optimal number and location of the sensors and actuators and of their backups
9. Design of a sequential decision tree that enables one to pinpoint the source of the inaccuracy in the model or control system

Because of their paramount importance, and considering the vast number of systems to which controls are applied, the fields of parameter identification and component failure detection have received tremendous attention in the literature. We refer here only to publications that are pertinent to structures. Our existing research has so far considered component failure detection and parameter identification problems and has treated these issues separately, that is, failure detection methods have been developed that assume an accurate mathematical model, and parameter identification methods have been developed assuming fault-free sensors and actuators.

Failure detection research has been surveyed in [1,2], and associated individual problems have been analyzed in [3–27]. Initial work concentrated on low-order systems with very few components (see, e.g. [3–9]), with more recent work dealing with higher-order systems and a larger number of components. Although it was originally feared that having a large number of components complicates the failure detection, it has been observed and demonstrated in recent work that using a larger number of components increases the reliability of the failure detection [16–19]. This is so, because even though a larger number of components increases the probability of failure, more information is provided to the analyst to detect failure. Also, most work in failure detection assumes that the mathematical model is known, but some recent work has begun to look into the issues of having an imperfect model and errors associated with measurements. In most of the existing work, the failure detection methods are applicable if the component fails totally. It is much harder to detect failure if the components are only partially faulty. For example, a sensor may read half the actual output, or an actuator may impart twice the desired force.

Some of the first tests performed on structures (and still used today) for model determination consisted of exciting the structure with a variety of frequencies to detect the resonances [28]. Since then, numerous publications and experiments have outlined a variety of identification methods (see, e.g. [28–43]). Identification methods for structures can be broadly classified into two categories. In the first category, actual parameters in the structure equations are identified directly from the response (see, e.g. [32]). In the second category, an intermediate set of values are identified before identifying the actual parameters (see, e.g. [39,40]). The intermediate parameters are, for the most part, modal quantities. There are advantages and disadvantages to both approaches.

In recent years, the issue of optimally placing the control system components and their backups has begun to receive interest [13–17]. Our own results indicate that a relatively even spacing of both the operational and backup components does a good job, whereas an uneven distribution of control components excites the residual dynamics a lot and does not lead to satisfactory results [15,17].

As can be observed from the preceding review, the state of the art is still far from the design of a global reliability loop around a structural control system. Very few works in the literature analyze component failure detection in the presence of model errors, at least for structural control systems [19], and qualitative and quantitative control efficiency measures are still at the theoretical stage. We are currently unable to solve the "black box" problem, which is, given undesirable or unsatisfactory performance of a control system, to identify the source of inaccuracy or instability and to correct it on-line. However, the technical community is heading that way, as newer designs that are proposed are taking into consideration global reliability issues.

II. EQUATIONS OF MOTION

Consider the equation of motion for a linear, undamped, and non-gyroscopic system in the form

$$\mathscr{L}u(x,t) + m(x)\ddot{u}(x,t) = f(x,t), \qquad 0 < x < L \tag{1}$$

where $u(x,t)$ is the deformation at spatial coordinate x at time t, $m(x)$ is the mass distribution, $\mathscr{L}$ is a linear differential stiffness operator of order $2p$, and $f(x,t)$ is the excitation, including controls; 0 and L denote the boundaries of the domain, where the system is subject to $2p$ boundary conditions. Expanding the solution in the form $u(x,t) = U(x)e^{st}$ and solving the associated eigenvalue problem, we obtain a set of eigenvalues λ_r and associated eigenfunctions $\phi_r(x)$, which can be normalized to yield

$$(\phi_r(x), m(x)\phi_s(x)) = \delta_{rs}, \ (\phi_r(x), \mathscr{L}\phi_s(x)) = \lambda_r\,\delta_{rs} = \omega_r^2\,\delta_{rs}, \qquad (r, s = 1, 2, \ldots)$$

where $(a, b) = \int ab\,dx$ and ω_r are the natural frequencies. It then follows that one can obtain an infinite number of modal equations in the form

$$\ddot{u}_r(t) + \omega_r^2 u_r(t) = f_r(t), \qquad r = 1, 2, \ldots \tag{2}$$

in which $u_r(t)$ are modal coordinates and $f_r(t)$ are modal forces. The modal coordinates and modal forces are related to $u(x, t)$ and $f(x, t)$ as

$$u(x, t) = \sum_{r=1}^{\infty} \phi_r(x)u_r(t), \qquad u_r(t) = (u(x, t), m(x)\phi_r(x)) \tag{3a,b}$$

$$f(x, t) = \sum_{r=1}^{\infty} m(x)\phi_r(x)f_r(t), \qquad f_r(t) = (f(x, t), \phi_r(x)) \tag{3c,d}$$

We consider discrete actuators at locations x_{ai} $(i = 1, 2, \ldots, m)$, where m is the number of actuators, so that

$$f(x, t) = \sum_{i=1}^{m} F_{Ai}(t)\,\delta(x - x_{ai}) \tag{4}$$

and $F_{Ai}(t)$ are the actuator inputs. Substituting Eq. (4) into Eq. (3d), we obtain

$$f_r(t) = \sum_{i=1}^{m} \phi_r(x_{ai})F_{Ai}(t), \qquad r = 1, 2, \ldots \tag{5}$$

which can be introduced into the modal equations of motion to give

$$\ddot{\mathbf{u}}(t) + \Lambda\mathbf{u}(t) = \mathbf{f}(t) = B\mathbf{F}_A(t) \tag{6}$$

where $\mathbf{u}(t)$ and $\mathbf{f}(t)$ are infinite-dimensional vectors containing the modal coordinates and modal vectors, Λ is a diagonal matrix containing the eigenvalues, $\mathbf{F}_A(t)$ contains the actuator inputs and $B_{rs} = \phi_r(x_{as})$ $(r = 1, 2, \ldots;$ $s = 1, 2, \ldots, m)$.

Because of the infinite number of the modal coordinates, it is impossible to monitor and control them all at once, especially when one follows a modal control approach. Modal coordinates may also be needed for parameter identification and component failure detection. We then propose to monitor (and/or control) n of the modes and to ignore the remainder. When selecting the number of modes to monitor, a variety of criteria can be used. We assume here that the lowest n modes are monitored, because the lower modes contribute more to the system output than the higher modes. If a very high mode achieves large amplitudes, primarily as a result of receiving harmonic excitation close to its frequency, that mode can also be included among the monitored modes. Partitioning the modal coordinate vector as $\mathbf{u}(t) =$

$[\mathbf{u}_M^T(t) | \mathbf{u}_R^T(t)]^T$, we can write the modal equations in the form

$$\ddot{\mathbf{u}}_M(t) + \Lambda_M \mathbf{u}_M(t) = B_M \mathbf{F}_A(t) \qquad \ddot{\mathbf{u}}_R(t) + \Lambda_R \mathbf{u}_R(t) = B_R \mathbf{F}_A(t) \tag{7a,b}$$

with terms taking their obvious meaning.

Next, we consider and model sensor and actuator failures. We denote the actuator failure mode as

$$\mathbf{F}_A(t) = S_a(t)\mathbf{F}(t) + \mathbf{h}_a(t) \tag{8}$$

in which $\mathbf{F}(t)$ denotes the desired actuator input (actuator command), $S_a(t)$ is a time-varying matrix denoting the level of failure, and $\mathbf{h}_a(t)$ denotes actuator noise. If all components are operational $S_a = I$. For our work, we assume that $S_a(t)$ is a diagonal matrix, that is, malfunction of a certain actuator does not affect the performance of the other components.

To model sensor failures, we need to consider the system output at the sensors' locations, denoted by $\mathbf{y}(t)$, where $\mathbf{y}(t) = [y_1(t)\, y_2(t) \cdots y_k(t)]^T$ in which k is the number of sensors and $y_i(t) = u(x_{si}, t)\, (i = 1, 2, \ldots, k)$, with x_{si} denoting the sensors' locations. The sensors' measurements, denoted by the vector $\mathbf{y}_A(t) = [y_{A1}(t)\, y_{A2}(t) \cdots y_{Ak}(t)]^T$, are related to the system output by

$$\mathbf{y}_A(t) = S_s(t)\mathbf{y}(t) + \mathbf{h}_s(t) \tag{9}$$

in which $S_s(t)$ is a diagonal matrix denoting the level of sensor failure and $\mathbf{h}_s(t)$ the sensor noise. Note that for convenience we used displacement sensors in the preceding expressions. Similar expressions for velocity and acceleration sensors can easily be developed.

Naturally, the way a malfunctioning sensor or actuator affects the performance of a system depends on how these components are used. An important reliability issue in control design is the development of approaches that are relatively insensitive to sensor and actuator failures.

For control systems, one can broadly classify the approaches that have been developed as those that use the actual system output as feedback and those that use quantities synthesized from the system output, such as the modal coordinates, as feedback. In both cases, though, one can write the control gains in terms of gain operators acting on the modal coordinates in the form

$$\mathbf{F}(t) = K(t)[\mathbf{u}(t), \dot{\mathbf{u}}(t)] \tag{10}$$

in which $K(t)$ is the gain operator. Considering modal control, and confining ourselves to the linear proportional case, we have

$$\mathbf{F}(t) = K_1(t)\mathbf{u}_M(t) + K_2(t)\dot{\mathbf{u}}_M(t) \tag{11}$$

which result in the closed-loop equations

$$\ddot{\mathbf{u}}_M(t) + \Lambda_M \mathbf{u}_M(t) = B_M S_a(t)[K_1(t)\mathbf{u}_M(t) + K_2(t)\dot{\mathbf{u}}_M(t)] + B_M \mathbf{h}_a(t) \tag{12}$$

Naturally, the gain matrices K_1 and K_2 are designed such that Eq. (12) has stable eigenvalues when $S_a = I$. Failure of an actuator either reduces the stability margin or it induces instabilities. Under most circumstances, the residual dynamics is not affected by the actuator malfunctions.

When the control law is based on the actual output, the forcing can be expressed as

$$\mathbf{F}(t) = K'[\mathbf{y}'(t), \dot{\mathbf{y}}'(t)] \tag{13}$$

in which K' is the control gain operator, and $\mathbf{y}'(t)$ denotes the system output at the actuators locations as $\mathbf{y}'(t) = [u(x_{a1}, t), u(x_{a2}, t), \ldots, u(x_{am}, t)]^T$. In general the control law has the form

$$\mathbf{F}(t) = K'_1\mathbf{y}'(t) + K'_2\dot{\mathbf{y}}'(t) \tag{14}$$

in which K'_1 and K'_2 are diagonal gain matrices. Considering that the actuator locations can be expressed in the modal form as $\mathbf{y}'(t) = B^T\mathbf{u}(t)$, one arrives at the closed-loop equations

$$\ddot{\mathbf{u}}(t) + \Lambda\mathbf{u}(t) = BS_a(t)K'_1B^T\mathbf{u}(t) + BS_a(t)K'_2B^T\dot{\mathbf{u}}(t) + B\mathbf{h}_a(t) \tag{15}$$

Note that in such a control action all the modes are affected by the controls and by the actuator malfunctions.

To analyze the effects of sensor failures, one has first to decide how to process the sensors' output. One approach is to use these measurements directly, such as in the control law of Eq. (14). In this case, the vectors $\mathbf{y}(t)$ and $\mathbf{y}'(t)$ coincide. Considering that the control input in such cases is based on $\mathbf{y}_A(t)$ and not $\mathbf{y}(t)$, we introduce Eq. (9) into Eqs. (14 and 15) and obtain the closed-loop relations

$$\begin{aligned}\ddot{\mathbf{u}}(t) + \Lambda\mathbf{u}(t) = {} & BS_a(t)K'_1S_s(t)B^T\mathbf{u}(t) + BS_a(t)K'_2\dot{S}_s(t)B^T\dot{\mathbf{u}}(t)\\ & + B[S_a(t)(K'_1\mathbf{h}_s(t) + K'_2\dot{\mathbf{h}}_s(t)) + \mathbf{h}_a(t)]\end{aligned} \tag{16}$$

Note that if different sensors are used to measure displacements and velocities, then $S_s(t) \neq \dot{S}_s(t)$ and $\mathbf{h}_s(t) \neq \dot{h}_s(t)$.

Another approach to feedback control is to extract certain measures from the system output and to use these extracted measures to synthesize the feedback gains. The most common example is extraction of modal coordinates. The subject of extraction of modal coordinates has received a lot of attention in the literature. Basic approaches such as modal filtering and observer design are summarized in the appendix. Here, we use the general formulation of

$$\mathbf{w}(t) = G(t)\mathbf{y}_A(t), \qquad \mathbf{y}_A(t) = S_s(t)H\mathbf{u}(t) + \mathbf{h}_s(t) \tag{17a,b}$$

in which $\mathbf{w}(t)$ is a vector denoting the extracted modal coordinates, $G(t)$ depend on the type of modal coordinate extraction, and $H_{ij} = \phi_j(x_{si})$. The matrix H

can be partitioned into parts corresponding to the monitored (H_M) and residual (H_R) modes, so that in the absence of any sensor malfunctions one can relate the extracted modal coordinates to the actual ones by

$$\mathbf{w}(t) = G(t)H_M\mathbf{u}_M(t) + G(t)H_R\mathbf{u}_R(t) + G(t)\mathbf{h}_s(t) \tag{18}$$

The extraction mechanism design is based on making the $G(t)H_M$ matrix approach an identity matrix. Some approaches, such as modal filtering, make $G(t)H_R$ approach a null matrix as well. In the event of sensor failure, the matrix $G(t)$ may become dependent on the failure mode, and, considering Eq. (9), the above relation becomes

$$\mathbf{w}(t) = G(S_s(t), t)S_s(t)H_M\mathbf{u}_M(t) + G(S_s(t), t)S_s(t)H_R\mathbf{u}_R(t) + G(S_s(t), t)\mathbf{h}_s(t) \tag{19}$$

so that substituting Eq. (19) into the modal control law, Eq. (11), we obtain the closed-loop equations

$$\begin{aligned}\ddot{\mathbf{u}}_M(t) + \Lambda_M\mathbf{u}_M(t) &= B_M S_a K_1 G S_s[H_M\mathbf{u}_M(t) + H_R\mathbf{u}_R(t)] \\ &\quad + B_M S_a K_2 G \dot{S}_s[H_M\dot{\mathbf{u}}_M(t) + H_R\dot{\mathbf{u}}_R(t)]\end{aligned} \tag{20}$$

It is clear from both Eqs. (16) and (20) that failure of a component affects the closed-loop performance. The amount of degradation depends on the level of failure, the number of components in use, and on the way in which the control components are used.

It was observed from system simulations and evaluation of closed-loop eigenvalues that sensor failure has a less degrading effect than actuator failure, especially as the number of sensors are increased.

Another important reliability issue in modeling a structure is that of parameter uncertainties and the need to use a discretized model to describe the system behavior. More often than not, the parameters used in the equations are not known very accurately. Even if these parameters are known, because spatial discretization is necessary to obtain the system eigensolution, the eigenfunctions, eigenvalues, and consequently the extracted modal coordinates differ from their actual values. These two factors also have a degrading effect on the system model and on the control system.

Consider a series type spatial discretization of the form

$$u(x, t) = \sum_{i=1}^{N} \Psi_i(x)a_i(t) = \boldsymbol{\Psi}^T(x)\mathbf{a}(t) \tag{21}$$

where $\boldsymbol{\Psi}(x) = [\Psi_1(x)\,\Psi_2(x)\cdots\Psi_N(x)]^T$ is an N-dimensional vector of admissible functions (global or local), $\mathbf{a}(t) = [a_1(t)\,a_2(t)\cdots a_N(t)]^T$ are time-dependent amplitudes, and N is the order of discretization. Minimization of the Rayleigh's quotient leads to the discretized eigenvalue problem

$$\mathbf{K}\mathbf{v} = \Lambda\mathbf{M}\mathbf{v} \tag{22}$$

where the entries of the stiffness and mass matrices $\mathbf{K}$ and $\mathbf{M}$ are

$$\mathbf{K}_{ij} = [\Psi_i(x), \Psi_j(x)], \qquad \mathbf{M}_{ij} = (\Psi_i(x), m(x)\Psi_j(x)), \qquad i, j = 1, 2, \ldots, N \quad (23)$$

in which the square brackets denote the appropriate energy inner product associated with the stiffness operator $\mathscr{L}$ [44]. Solution of the eigenvalue problem yields a set of eigenvalues $\Lambda_1, \Lambda_2, \ldots, \Lambda_N$ and associated eigenvectors $\mathbf{v}_r$. The eigenvectors can be used to approximate the eigenfunctions $\phi_r(x)$ by

$$\theta_r(x) = \mathbf{v}_r^{\mathrm{T}}\boldsymbol{\Psi}(x) \qquad \text{or} \qquad \boldsymbol{\theta}(x) = V^{\mathrm{T}}\boldsymbol{\Psi}(x) \quad (24)$$

where $\theta_r(x)$ are the approximate eigenfunctions, and V is the modal matrix in the form $V = [\mathbf{v}_1 \;\; \mathbf{v}_2 \;\; \cdots \;\; \mathbf{v}_N]$. The approximate eigenfunctions are orthogonal with respect to the mass distribution and the energy inner product. The expansion theorem for the approximate eigenfunctions has the form

$$u(x,t) = \sum_{r=1}^{N} \theta_r(x)q_r(t), \qquad q_r(t) = (u(x,t), m(x)\theta_r(x)) \quad (25)$$

where $q_r(t)$ are modal coordinates associated with the approximate eigenfunctions.

When modeling parameter uncertainties, we assume that the form of the equations of motion are known but that the values of the parameters contained in these equations are not known. That is, in Eq. (1) we postulate the mass distribution as $m'(x)$. If the actual stiffness operator is $\partial^2[EI(x)\,\partial^2 u(x,t)/\partial x^2]/\partial x^2$, with $EI(x)$ being the stiffness distribution, we postulate the stiffness distribution as $E'I'(x)$. Use of the values of $m'(x)$ and the postulated stiffness leads to the eigenvalue problem

$$\mathbf{K}'\mathbf{v}' = \Lambda'\mathbf{M}'\mathbf{v}' \quad (26)$$

where the entries of the postulated stiffness and mass matrices $\mathbf{K}'$ and $\mathbf{M}'$ are

$$\mathbf{K}'_{ij} = [\Psi_i(x), \Psi_j(x)]', \qquad \mathbf{M}'_{ij} = (\Psi_i(x), m'(x)\Psi_j(x)), \qquad i, j = 1, 2, \ldots, N \quad (27)$$

It follows that one obtains another set of eigenvalues Λ'_r and associated eigenvectors $\mathbf{v}'_r$ $(r = 1, 2, \ldots, N)$. The eigenvectors can be used to generate the approximate eigenfunctions associated with the postulated system as

$$\theta'_r(x) = \mathbf{v}_r'^{\mathrm{T}}\boldsymbol{\Psi}(x) \qquad \text{or} \qquad \boldsymbol{\theta}'(x) = V'^{\mathrm{T}}\boldsymbol{\Psi}(x) \quad (28)$$

with the expansion theorem having the form

$$u(x,t) = \sum_{r=1}^{N} \theta'_r(x)q'_r(t), \qquad q'_r(t) = (u(x,t), m'(x)\theta'_r(x)) \quad (29)$$

The modal equations of motion associated with the postulated discretized system have the form

$$\ddot{q}'_r(t) + \Lambda'_r q'_r(t) = \mathbf{b}_r'^{\mathrm{T}}\mathbf{F}_{\mathrm{A}}(t), \qquad r = 1, 2, \ldots, N \quad (30)$$

in which $\mathbf{b}_r'^{\mathrm{T}} = [\theta'_r(x_{\mathrm{a}1})\theta'_r(x_{\mathrm{a}2})\cdots\theta'_r(x_{\mathrm{a}m})]$.

It is of interest to examine the relations among the actual, discretized, and postulated systems. To this end, we first consider the actual and discretized systems. The approximate eigenfunctions $\theta_r(x)$ can be expanded in terms of the actual eigenfunctions by

$$\theta_r(x) = \sum_{i=1}^{\infty} d_{ri}\phi_i(x) \tag{31}$$

where the coefficients d_{ri} can be found by exploiting the orthogonality properties of the eigenfunctions. Multiplication of Eq. (31) by $\phi_j(x)$, integration along the domain, and use of the orthogonality relations yield $d_{ri} = (\theta_r(x), m(x)\phi_i(x))$. In vector form,

$$\boldsymbol{\theta}(x) = D\boldsymbol{\phi}(x) \tag{32}$$

in which $\boldsymbol{\phi}(x)$ is an infinite dimensional vector containing the actual eigenfunctions, and it can be shown that $DD^{\mathrm{T}} = I$ [45]. It follows that the modal coordinates associated with the actual and discretized systems can be related by

$$\mathbf{q}(t) = D\mathbf{u}(t) \tag{33}$$

where $\mathbf{q}(t) = [q_1(t)\, q_2(t) \cdots q_N(t)]^{\mathrm{T}}$.

Next, consider the relation between the discretized and postulated systems. Using the orthogonality properties of the eigenvectors and defining a matrix C as [39],

$$C = V'^{\mathrm{T}}\mathbf{M}V \tag{34}$$

one can easily show that the approximate and postulated modal coordinates and eigenfunctions can be related by [45],

$$\mathbf{q}'(t) = C^{-\mathrm{T}}\mathbf{q}(t), \qquad \boldsymbol{\theta}'(x) = C\boldsymbol{\theta}(x) \tag{35}$$

which, when combined with Eqs. (32 and 33) yields the relation between the actual and postulated modal coordinates

$$\mathbf{q}'(t) = C^{-\mathrm{T}}D\mathbf{u}(t), \qquad \boldsymbol{\theta}'(x) = CD\boldsymbol{\phi}(x) \tag{36}$$

If one introduces the preceding equations into the modal coordinate extraction equations and then to the closed-loop control laws, the level of degradation is seen even further.

III. ROBUST CONTROL DESIGN

In this section, we summarize earlier work on robust control design. We consider two approaches, direct feedback [46] and natural control [47–49]. Direct feedback is usually referred to as colocation, in which the sensors and actuators are located at the same points, even though we can have direct feedback without colocated components. To demonstrate stability, we use the Kelvin–Tait–Chetayev stability theorem, which gives a sufficient condition for stability by stating that if the gain matrices of the closed-loop system exhibit symmetry and sign semidefiniteness stability can be ascertained [50].

First, we consider direct feedback, the equations of which (assuming colocation) are given by Eqs. (13–16) and in which the system output is a function of the actuator's location only. Most approaches in this category have been linear proportional control laws in which K'_1 and K'_2 are diagonal gain matrices, with K'_2 being negative definite. One of the most important issues in direct feedback has been the determination of the control gains.

In the event of no failure, we observe from Eq. (15) that both gain matrices are symmetric and negative definite, so the closed-loop system is guaranteed to be stable. In the event of failure, Eq. (16) describes the closed-loop system. The stability of the gain matrices $BS_a(t)K'_1S_s(t)B^T$ and $BS_a(t)K'_2\dot{S}_s(t)B^T$ depends on the failure modes. If, as assumed ealier, S_a, S_s, and $\dot{S}_s$ are diagonal matrices and their entries are nonnegative (that is, if there is no phase failure), then the gain matrices retain their negative semidefinite properties. This indicates that direct feedback has some desirable stability properties in the presence of sensor and actuator failures.

In the presence of parameter uncertainties, the way one designs the gains K'_1 and K'_2 is based on the postulated erroneous model, but these matrices are still designed so that they are diagonal and negative definite. The conclusion is that when the system parameters are not known, the desired stability margin cannot be achieved, but no instabilities occur.

Let us next consider natural control. The objective here is first to design a control law assuming that there are no hardware limitations, that is, spatially continuously distributed sensing and actuation mechanisms are available. After the control law is designed, it is then approximated considering the available hardware and implemented by discrete components. There are several approaches for the approximation, each having its own advantages and disadvantages.

In its most general form, the closed-loop system can be expressed as

$$m(x)\ddot{u}(x,t) + \mathscr{L}u(x,t) = f(x,t) = K_1(x)u(x,t) + K_2(x)\dot{u}(x,t) \tag{37}$$

in which $K_1(x)$ and $K_2(x)$ are spatial gain operators. Use of the expansion theorem and orthogonality relations leads to the modal equations

$$\ddot{u}_r(t) + \omega_r^2 u_r(t) = \sum_{s=1}^{\infty} [K_{1rs}u_s(t) + K_{2rs}\dot{u}_s(t)], \qquad r = 1, 2, \ldots \tag{38}$$

where

$$K_{1rs} = (\phi_r(x), K_1(x)\phi_s(x)), \qquad K_{2rs} = (\phi_r(x), K_2(x)\phi_s(x)), \qquad r,s = 1, 2, \ldots \tag{39}$$

are modal gains.

It has been shown in [49] that the globally optimal solution is reached when $K_{1rs} = K_{1rr}\delta_{rs}$ and $K_{2rs} = K_{2rr}\delta_{rs}$, that is, if the control gains for one mode are independent of the control gains for another mode. This property also makes the control design very simple. One first calculates the control gains for each mode individually and then determines the gain operators $K_1(x)$ and $K_2(x)$. If Eqs. (39) and the orthogonality conditions are compared, the resemblance between $K_1(x)$ and $K_2(x)$ and the mass and stiffness operators $m(x)$ and $\mathscr{L}$ is striking. In essence, natural control tells us that the optimal control gain operators should be linear combinations of the mass and stiffness operators and that the eigenfunctions of the open-loop and closed-loop systems coincide.

We next consider implementation of the control law designed by using natural control by discrete components. To this end, one approach is to consider a subset of the modes and to make sure that the closed-loop eigenvalues of those modes do not change when the control law is approximated by discrete components. This approach has come to be known as independent modal space control (IMSC). Assuming that the set of modes that are controlled are the n monitored modes, we can write the modal equations associated with them as, from Eq. (7a),

$$\ddot{\mathbf{u}}_{\mathrm{M}}(t) + \Lambda_{\mathrm{M}}\mathbf{u}_{\mathrm{M}}(t) = \mathbf{f}_{\mathrm{M}}(t) = B_{\mathrm{M}}\mathbf{F}_{\mathrm{A}}(t) \tag{40}$$

The control design is based first on designing the modal control inputs $f_r(t)$ $(r = 1, 2, \ldots, n)$ independent of each other and then on synthesizing the actuator command $\mathbf{F}(t)$. It follows that the modal control law has the form

$$\mathbf{f}_{\mathrm{M}}(t) = K_1^*\mathbf{u}_{\mathrm{M}}(t) + K_2^*\dot{\mathbf{u}}_{\mathrm{M}}(t) \tag{41}$$

in which K_1^* and K_2^* are diagonal gain matrices. If the number of actuators and the number of monitored modes are selected as the same, one can synthesize the actuator commands by

$$\mathbf{F}(t) = B_{\mathrm{M}}^{-1}\mathbf{f}_{\mathrm{M}}(t) \tag{42}$$

This approximation to natural control does not consider the residual dynamics at all. The net result of using discrete components is that the modes that are not controlled receive an unnecessary excitation, a phenomenon known as control spillover [48]. This excitation does not lead to any instabilities [48], but it is the price paid for using discrete actuators. In the occurrence of sensor and actuator failures, substituting Eqs. (8) and (19) for the values of $\mathbf{F}(t)$ and $\mathbf{u}_{\mathrm{M}}(t)$, we obtain

$$\begin{aligned}\ddot{\mathbf{u}}_{\mathrm{M}}(t) + \Lambda_{\mathrm{M}}\mathbf{u}_{\mathrm{M}}(t) &= B_{\mathrm{M}}S_{\mathrm{a}}B_{\mathrm{M}}^{-1}K_1^*GS_{\mathrm{s}}[H_{\mathrm{M}}\mathbf{u}_{\mathrm{M}}(t) + H_{\mathrm{R}}\mathbf{u}_{\mathrm{R}}(t)] \\ &\quad + B_{\mathrm{M}}S_{\mathrm{a}}B_{\mathrm{M}}^{-1}K_2^*G\dot{S}_{\mathrm{s}}[H_{\mathrm{M}}\dot{\mathbf{u}}_{\mathrm{M}}(t) + H_{\mathrm{R}}\dot{\mathbf{u}}_{\mathrm{R}}(t)] + \mathbf{n}(t)\end{aligned} \tag{43}$$

in which $\mathbf{n}(t)$ denotes the combined effect of noise. As can be seen, no guarantee of stability can be inferred from this equation in the event of actuator and sensor failures. Also, the residual dynamics are affected by failure as well, so an eigenvalue analysis now has to include the residual modes. Our analyses and evaluation of the closed-loop poles have indicated that this control law is more sensitive to actuator failures than to sensor failures. When there are parameter uncertainties in the system model, it is shown in [50] that IMSC yields stable closed-loop poles when all components are operational and that the monitored modes are extracted with very good accuracy. However, considering (43), we cannot make any general remarks about stability of the closed-loop system in the presence of both component failures and model errors.

Another approach to approximating the natural control law by discrete sensors was first outlined in [49]. A variant of that approach is presented here. The distributed domain is divided into m subdomains D_j so that there is an actuator in each subdomain. Then, the control input in the ith domain $F_i(t)$ is calculated as

$$F_i(t) = \alpha_i \int_{D_i} m(x)\,dx\; y_i(t) + \beta_i \int_{D_i} m(x)\,dx\; \dot{y}_i(t), \qquad i = 1, 2, \ldots, m \tag{44}$$

Note the similarity between the preceding equation and natural control being proportional to the mass and stiffness, Eq. (39). It is proposed in [51] to select the gains α_i and β_i so that they are all the same, which leads to a uniform decay rate. One advantage of using Eq. (44) as opposed to IMSC is that all the modes get controlled. The disadvantage is that the closed-loop poles of all the modes are affected by the discretization of the control law. One has to decide, depending on the system at hand, which approach to use.

We observe that Eq. (44) are basically the same as direct feedback, Eq. (14), with the difference being in the way the control gains are synthesized. The advantage of the preceding approach is twofold. First, one benefits from all the stability and robustness properties associated with direct feedback described earlier. Second, there is a simple, straightforward, and meaningful way of determining the feedback gains. It seems from the discussion that overall it is more advantageous to approximate a natural control law using Eq. (44).

It should be noted here that there are other approaches that approximate a distributed natural control law by discrete components, such as the integral formulation of the control problem [52]. Also, there exist several other control designs on which robustness analyses have been conducted, thus the approaches we have described are not the only ones considered.

IV. COMPONENT FAILURE DETECTION

In this section, we summarize our previous and ongoing research in the area of component failure detection. We outline two methods, one to detect actuator failures and another to detect sensor failures. The actuator failure detection is based on estimating the system input at the actuators' locations and comparing it with the commands given to the actuators. The sensor failure detection is based on estimating the displacement (or velocity or acceleration) at a sensor's location using the outputs of other sensors and comparing the estimated value with the sensor's measurement.

Assume for the time being that the system parameters are known accurately and that, at least for the monitored modes, the discretization method used to obtain the eigensolution yields very good results. Considering that a sampling period T is used such that the control input is constant during the sampling period, the response of a certain mode can be expressed as

$$u_r(jT + T) = u_r(jT)\cos\omega_r T + \dot{u}_r(jT)\sin\omega_r T/\omega_r + f_r(jT)(1 - \cos\omega_r T)/\omega_r^2,$$
$$j = 0, 1, 2, \ldots; \quad r = 1, 2, \ldots \tag{45a}$$

$$\dot{u}_r(jT + T) = -\omega_r u_r(jT)\sin\omega_r T + \dot{u}_r(jT)\cos\omega_r T + f_r(jT)\sin\omega_r T/\omega_r \tag{45b}$$

The approach is first to identify from the modal coordinates the modal input and then to synthesize from the modal inputs the actuator inputs. Given the preceding two relations, one can easily calculate the value of the modal control input $f_r(t)$. However, such an approach is very unstable, and it does not yield accurate results. Take, for example, Eq. (45a), from which one can obtain the value of $f_r(t)$ as

$$f_r(jT) = \omega_r^2[u_r(jT + T) - u_r(jT)\cos\omega_r T - \dot{u}_r(jT)\sin\omega_r T/\omega_r]/(1 - \cos\omega_r T) \tag{46}$$

and consider the coefficient of $u_r(jT + T)$, which is $\omega_r^2/(1 - \cos\omega_r T)$. Since the sampling period T is selected such that $\omega_r T$ is small ($r = 1, 2, \ldots, m$), $\cos\omega_r T$ can be approximated as $1 - (\omega_r T)^2/2$, which makes the coefficient of $u_r(jT + T)$ come very close to $2/T^2$. This is a very large number. Considering that when it comes to actual system measurements, one has to use a modal coordinate extraction routine and that there is noise in the system measurements, any error in modal coordinate extraction and measurement noise, as reflected by the difference between $w_r(jT)$ and $u_r(jT)$, is multiplied by the factor $2/T^2$ and thus is amplified greatly.

To alleviate the amplification problem, we seek combinations of the system response equations, including the acceleration, such that the modal forces are related to the displacement, velocity, or acceleration measurements with coefficients in the terms that are not very large. One relation that was developed in [16] is

$$\hat{f}_r(jT) = \hat{f}_r(jT - T) + \dot{w}_r(jT)\omega_r \sin \omega_r T/\cos \omega_r T$$
$$- \ddot{w}_r(jT) + \ddot{w}_r(jT + T)/\cos \omega_r T \qquad (47)$$

where the hats denote estimated quantities, and we have replaced $u_r(t)$ by $w_r(t)$, which is the value of the modal coordinate extracted from the sensors' output. We note that in Eq. (47) the coefficients of the velocity and acceleration terms are much lower. Also, there are no modal displacements. This can be explained by considering that modal forces are proportional to modal accelerations; thus, terms with accelerations describing the forces tend to have lower amplitudes. To begin the identification process, an initial estimate of $f_r(0)$ is required. It is shown in [16] that any error in the initial estimate does not propagate with time. On the other hand, Eq. (47) is sensitive to parameter uncertainties. Other relations have also been considered in [16].

Having identified the modal inputs, we consider idenfication of the actual inputs. The relation between the modal forces and actual forces is given by Eqs. (5) and (7a) for the monitored modes. If the number of monitored modes and actuators is selected as the same, then one can invert Eq. (5) for the monitored modes only and obtain

$$\hat{\mathbf{F}}(t) = B_{\mathrm{M}}^{-1}\hat{\mathbf{f}}_{\mathrm{M}}(t) \qquad (48)$$

where $\hat{\mathbf{f}}_{\mathrm{M}}(t)$ contains the estimated modal forces. Note the similarity between Eq. (48) and the control synthesis for independent modal space control, described in the previous section.

The results of [16] indicate that the actuator failure detection works well if the system model is known and if the modal coordinates can be extracted from the system output accurately. Thus, the approach requires use of a large number of sensors.

The sensor failure detection scheme outlined in [20] is based on a similar idea. The modal coordinates are estimated first, and the output at the sensors' locations are then synthesized and compared with the output of the sensors. Here we summarize the results for the case of velocity sensors only. The relation that is arrived at for estimating the modal velocities in [20] is

$$\dot{u}_r(jT + 2T) = 2\dot{u}_r(jT + T)\cos \omega_r T - \dot{u}_r(jT)$$
$$+ [f_r(jT + T) - f_r(jT)] \sin \omega_r T/\omega_r \qquad (49)$$

If the sampling period T is selected so that the force input remains constant during two sampling periods (or if the controls are sampled at twice the rate of measurements), the last term of Eq. (49) vanishes. This is attractive because the modal coordinate estimation is now independent of the control input. The sensor failure detection can then be carried out for cases in which the control input is not known. Also, the sensor failure detection becomes insensitive to actuator failures. This is a desirable feature, as it provides a certain amount of robustness to the sensor failure detection scheme.

To estimate the system velocity at the sensors' locations, we use Eq. (49) with the expansion theorem, which yields

$$\hat{\dot{y}}_i(jT + 2T) = 2 \sum_{r=1}^{m} \phi_r(x_{si})\dot{w}_r(jT + T)\cos \omega_r T - \hat{\dot{y}}_i(jT),$$
$$i = 1, 2, \ldots, k; \quad j = 0, 1, 2, \ldots \tag{50}$$

where the hats denote estimated quantities, and instead of $u_r(t)$ we have used $w_r(t)$. The modal velocities used are synthesized from all the sensors' measurements. This implies that failure of a sensor affects all the modal velocities. However, to detect failure, we want to estimate the output at the ith sensor's location without using the output of the ith sensor. This implies that the modal coordinate extraction routines have to be altered for the estimate of each sensor. A procedure to accomplish this with a minimal amount of computational effort is outlined in [20], and it involves use of modal filters and Rayleigh–Ritz type interpolation (see Appendix).

It was observed that using this general concept, displacement sensor failure is the easiest to detect and acceleration sensor failure the most difficult. This is because the participation to the acceleration from the higher modes is much more. Using a limited number of modes to express the system acceleration may not be sufficient. Fortunately, because of the limited failure modes of accelerometers, their failures are easier to detect, especially when one bases the failure detection criteria on the system hardware as well.

We are currently developing another approach to detect sensor failures that takes advantage of the property that when a large number of sensors are used, failure does not affect the closed-loop system adversely. The approach is based on using observers at the modal level [53], and it has given very promising results.

References [16] and [20] have illustrative examples that demonstrate the sensor and actuator failure detection algorithms. It should be noted that the two examples have been developed independently of each other. Because of the relative robustness of the sensor failure detection scheme, though, they can be used together. That is, if we are looking for possible sensor or actuator malfunctions, first we check for sensor failure. If there is a malfunctioning sensor, it is identified, and a backup is brought on line. Then, actuator failure detection is performed. This procedure can be considered as an initial step of a sequential decision-making scheme to detect failure and identify faulty components.

V. OPTIMAL ALLOCATION OF SENSORS, ACTUATORS, AND THEIR BACKUPS

The previous section summarized our research on detecting and isolating faulty components. Here, we concentrate on the issue of placement of sensors and actuators to minimize the effects of failure and to make it possible to identify the faulty components with greater ease. These two objectives, though, are at odds with each other. If we design the system so that the effects of having a faulty component are minimized, then detection of the faulty component becomes more difficult.

Our earlier analyses indicate that placement of the actuators does not affect the actuator failure detection process too much as long as the actuator locations are relatively evenly distributed. It is proposed in [16] that one possible placement criterion for actuators is to locate them to facilitate the failure detection. If, for example, the ith actuator is placed on one of the nodes of the jth mode, then failure of the ith actuator will not affect the jth mode. This can be used as an additional criterion to detect failure.

Placement of the sensors is more critical. When locating the sensors, one has to consider the following issues. First, the sensors should be placed so that the modal coordinates are extracted from the system output as accurately as possible, with the effects from the unmodeled modes minimized. This is important for both control and failure detection. Also, the sensors should be placed so that the effects of failure are minimized. To investigate this issue, a performance index is defined in [15] that is a measure of the quality of the model coordinate extraction for the case in which modal filters are used. The quality of the modal coordinate extraction is also an indirect measure of observability. When all components are operational, the difference between the actual and the extracted modal coordinates (for the monitored modes) can be expressed as

$$\mathbf{u}_{\mathrm{M}}(t) - \mathbf{w}(t) = [I - GH_{\mathrm{M}}]\mathbf{u}_{\mathrm{M}}(t) - GH_{\mathrm{R}}\mathbf{u}_{\mathrm{R}}(t) - G\mathbf{h}_{\mathrm{s}}(t) \tag{51}$$

We also note that the lower modes contribute more to the system output, so they need to be extracted with higher accuracy than the higher modes. Another way of stating this is that because the higher modes have lower amplitudes, they can tolerate more errors in their extraction. The performance functional that has to be minimized was defined in [15] as $J = J(x_1, x_2, \ldots, x_k)$, where

$$J = \sum_{i=1}^{m} \left[\sum_{j=1}^{m} (GH_{\mathrm{M}} - I)_{ij}^2/\omega_i\omega_j + \sum_{j=1}^{n-m} (GH_{\mathrm{R}})_{ij}^2/\omega_i\omega_{m+j} \right] \tag{52}$$

s.t. $0 < x_i \leq L, \qquad i = 1, 2, \ldots, k, \qquad x_{i-1} < x_i < x_{i+1}, \qquad i = 2, 3, \ldots, k-1$

in which the elements of GH_{M} and GH_{R} are weighted according to the natural frequencies of the modes they affect.

The results obtained in [15] indicate than an even distribution of the sensors, which is proportional to the mass distribution, yields good results. On the other hand, an uneven distribution does not give satisfactory results. This latter result implies that when backups are to be placed on the system, they should be placed so that replacement of a faulty sensor by a backup does not result in an uneven distribution of sensors. Based on this, guidelines are proposed in [15] that determine the number and location of the backup components.

We should note that if in Eq. (52) the weighting factors $(\omega_i \omega_j)$ are varied, the results of the optimization can vary as to which interpolation approach is more suitable to use and as to the optimal locations of the sensors and of their backups. The variation is mainly due to the decay rates of the residual dynamics and to the damping characteristics of the monitored modes. These modal contribution characteristics should be studied more thoroughly along with experimental investigation.

The actuator placement methods proposed in [17] are based on a concept similar to those for the sensor placement. Consider IMSC. It was stated earlier that in this approach, as in other modal control approaches developed for reduced-order models, the design is aimed at regulating a set of controlled modes, with the remaining modes uncontrolled. The effect of using a set of discrete inputs is that they impart unnecessary excitation to the uncontrolled modes, a price one has to pay for not having spatially continuously distributed actuators. Combining Eqs. (41), (42), and (7b), obtains

$$\ddot{\mathbf{u}}_R(t) + \Lambda_R \mathbf{u}_R(t) = B_R B_M^{-1} [K_1^* \mathbf{u}_M(t) + K_2^* \dot{\mathbf{u}}_M(t)] \tag{53}$$

The actuator placement criteria then considers minimization of the excitation received by the uncontrolled modes, and minimization of the work done to accomplish the control action. The reasoning behind this is that if the actuators excite the residual dynamics less, they waste less energy. Because, of all the residual modes, the $(n + 1)$ mode is the easiest to excite and has the highest amplitudes, it was proposed in [17] to locate the actuators so that the $(n + 1)$ mode receives no excitation. That is, the actuators were to be placed on the nodes (or nodal lines) of the $(n + 1)$ mode. Note that such a distribution corresponds to a very even distribution of the actuators. System simulations indicate that a relatively even distribution of the actuators yields satisfactory results, a conclusion almost identical to that obtained for the placement of the sensors. A relatively even distribution of the actuators also uses less fuel [17].

From these results, we conclude that both the sensors and the actuators should be spread evenly along the structure and proportional to the mass distribution. The number and location of the backups should be selected so that if a component is found to be faulty and is replaced by a backup, the resulting sensor or actuator distribution should also be relatively even. To make the actuator failure detection itself more reliable, one should place each actuator on one of the nodes of the monitored modes while preserving a relatively even distribution.

VI. FUTURE DIRECTIONS

We have discussed some of the reliability issues associated with structural control and have summarized our existing research. We have presented the equations of motion in the presence of uncertainties in the system model and faulty components and have proposed ways to detect failure and take corrective action. The proposed approaches make use of the system software alone.

The existing research (including ours) on the overall reliability of structural control systems is far from complete. Our failure detection methods assume that the model is accurate, and our parameter identification research [39, 40, 43, 45], not outlined here, assumes operational components and certain ideal conditions. In addition, the problems discussed here are only a small portion of the reliability problems for structures, especially with respect to spacecraft control. For example, for modeling purposes one should also consider statistical approaches. Reliable and accurate hardware implementation must be considered. After the faulty components are detected and isolated, strategies must be developed for reconfiguration of the system. Also, more than one approach has to be developed to detect failures, and the system hardware and software should be used together in a sequential decision-making scheme.

So far, the work reported in reliability analysis for structural control systems has been theoretical. In most cases, the actuator and sensor dynamics are not modeled. Anyone involved with experimental work knows that in the event of failure the actuator and sensor dynamics is altered as well. These effects have to be considered in future work. Also, we have not yet considered other types of hardware failures, such as malfunction of computers. With the current trend being toward parallel computers, the issue of failure of a processor and the reconfiguration of the on-board computational system is critical, especially in space applications.

In most analyses—for control, for failure detection, or for parameter identification—one selects a set of monitored (or controlled) modes and leaves the balance as residual. There have been very few criteria to suggest how to select the number of monitored modes. Modal contribution characteristics of structures and development of modal truncation criteria need more looking into, at both the theoretical and the experimental levels. In addition, most models that have been considered have been linear. Nonlinear models not only may be required for more accurate representation of structures, but one must use them when large-angle rigid-body motions are considered.

Finally, we would like to see that a hierarchical decision-making sequence—to detect and isolate failure, to model errors and poor designs, and then to take corrective action—is developed and implemented. The elusive "black box" problem, in which one has to determine the source of inaccuracies, inefficiencies, and malfunctions by just looking at the system output, cannot be solved unless methods are generated to pinpoint these problems and then are integrated into one large decision-making sequence. To this end, concepts from artificial intelligence must be utilized. We currently have some pieces of the puzzle. What is needed is to develop the remaining pieces and then to put the whole thing together.

APPENDIX. METHODS FOR EXTRACTING MODAL COORDINATES FROM THE SYSTEM OUTPUT

To extract the modal coordinates from the system output, we consider two approaches: modal filtering [54] and a full or reduced-order observer. In the modal coordinates from the system output. This requires distributed measurements, which, of course, are not in the state of the art. To implement modal filters in the presence of discrete measurements we generate an approximation of the distributed profile by interpolating or extrapolating the sensors measurements as

$$w(x, t) = \sum_{j=1}^{k} u(x_j, t) G(x, x_j) \tag{A1}$$

where $w(x, t)$ is the approximated profile, x_j denotes the location of the sensors ($j = 1, 2, \ldots k$); and the $G(x, x_j)$ are interpolation or extrapolation functions in which the time and space dependency are separate. Note that such an approach can easily be extended to cases for which the measurements are piecewise-continuous.

Introducing Eq. (A1) into the expansion theorem, we obtain expressions for the extracted modal coordinates, defined by

$$w_r(t) = (w(x, t), m(x)\phi_r(x)) = \sum_{j=1}^{k} g_{rj} u(x_j, t), \qquad r = 1, 2, \ldots \tag{A2}$$

where $g_{rj} = (G(x, x_j), m(x)\phi_r(x))$ ($j = 1, 2, \ldots, k$; $r = 1, 2, \ldots$).

The accuracy of modal filtering depends on the number and location of the sensors, as well as on the type of interpolation or extrapolation functions used.

In the existing literature, finite-element, Rayleigh–Ritz type and splines have been used as interpolation functions to implement modal filters [15]. Here, we summarize these approaches.

Using the expansion theorem to express the sensors measurements, we can relate the extracted modal coordinates to the actual measurements by Eq. (17):

$$\mathbf{w}(t) = G\mathbf{y}_{\mathrm{A}}(t) \tag{A3}$$

where the entries of G are g_{rj} $(r = 1, 2, \ldots, m;\ j = 1, 2, \ldots, k)$. It follows that the extracted modes are related to the actual modal coordinates by

$$\mathbf{w}(t) = GS_{\mathrm{s}}H_{\mathrm{M}}\mathbf{u}_{\mathrm{M}}(t) + GS_{\mathrm{s}}H_{\mathrm{R}}\mathbf{u}_{\mathrm{R}}(t) + G\mathbf{h}_{\mathrm{s}}(t) \tag{A4}$$

Equation (A4) is identical to Eq. (18) in the absence of faulty components. The objective in modal filter design is to select the number and location of the sensors, the interpolation functions, and the number of monitored modes such that GH_{M} approaches an identity matrix and GH_{R} approaches a null matrix. It is shown in [15] that to implement modal filters with accuracy, the number of sensors must be at least as large as the number of monitored modes. We also note from Eqs. (A1–A4) that the design of modal filters is independent of the actuators; thus, failure of an actuator does not affect the performance of the modal filters.

Next, we investigate implementation by specific interpolation functions. When finite-element type interpolation functions are used, the distributed domain is divided into p intervals D_j, and the displacement in each interval is approximated by

$$w_j(x, t) = \mathbf{L}^{\mathrm{T}}(x)\mathbf{s}_j(t), \qquad j = 1, 2, \ldots, p \tag{A5}$$

in which $\mathbf{L}(x)$ denotes a set of local interpolation functions from the finite-element method, and $\mathbf{s}_j(t)$ denotes the set of measurements in the jth domain. Introducing Eq. (A5) into Eq. (A2) and performing the algebra, we obtain the extracted modal coordinates in the form

$$w_r(t) = \sum_{j=1}^{p} \mathbf{h}_{jr}^{\mathrm{T}}\mathbf{s}_j(t) \tag{A6}$$

where

$$\mathbf{h}_{jr} = \int_{D_j} m(x)\phi_r(x)\mathbf{L}(x)\,dx \tag{A7}$$

Through assembly of $\mathbf{h}_{jr}$ for each sensor, the modal filter gain matrix G can be computed. If only one set of measurements (such as only displacements) is available, one can use quadratic, cubic, or even hierarchical finite elements. If, in addition to displacements, slope measurements are also available, one can use hermite cubics, which permit slope continuity as well, thus resulting in a more accurate representation [15].

When Rayleigh–Ritz type modal filters are used, the interpolation functions (unlike in the case of finite-element type) are global functions, where the interpolated profile has the form

$$w(x,t) = \sum_{r=1}^{k} \Psi_r(x)\eta_r(t) \tag{A8}$$

where $\Psi_r(x)$ are admissible functions. To determine the amplitudes $\eta_r(t)$, we express the system output as

$$\mathbf{y}(t) = E\boldsymbol{\eta}(t) \tag{A9}$$

where $E_{ij} = \Psi_j(x_i)$ $(j = 1, 2, \ldots; i = 1, 2, \ldots, k)$ and $\boldsymbol{\eta}(t) = [\eta_1, \eta_2, \ldots]^{\mathrm{T}}$. If the number of extracted modes is selected to be the same as the number of sensors, $k = n$, these coordinates can be computed by inverting the matrix constructed by the first k columns of E (denoted by E_{M}) to yield

$$\boldsymbol{\eta}_{\mathrm{M}}(t) = E_{\mathrm{M}}^{-1}\mathbf{y}(t) \tag{A10}$$

in which $\boldsymbol{\eta}_{\mathrm{M}}(t)$ denotes the first n entries of $\boldsymbol{\eta}(t)$. The term E_{M}^{-1} is the counterpart of G in Eq. (A3). Substituting Eq. (A10) into Eq. (A8) yields the approximate deformation profile in the form

$$w(x,t) = \sum_{s=1}^{k} \Psi_s(x) \sum_{j=1}^{k} [E_{\mathrm{M}}^{-1}]_{sj} y_j(t) \tag{A11}$$

and the entries of the modal filter gain matrix become

$$G_{rj} = \sum_{s=1}^{k} [E_{\mathrm{M}}^{-1}]_{sj} \int m(x)\phi_r(x)\Psi_s(x)\,dx \tag{A12}$$

A special situation is encountered when the admissible functions are selected as the eigenfunctions of the system. In this case, E_{M} becomes the same as H_{M}, and $\boldsymbol{\eta}_{\mathrm{M}}(t) = \mathbf{w}(t)$; so

$$\mathbf{w}(t) = H_{\mathrm{M}}^{-1}\mathbf{y}(t) \tag{A13}$$

where it is observed that Eq. (A13) can be obtained without considering interpolation of the system output at all.

We next consider use of splines as interpolation functions. Here, one must decide to determine which order spline functions to use. The answer is dependent on the number of boundary conditions one can specify.

For illustrative purposes, let us consider beam vibrations and use cubic splines as interpolation functions. As is well known, cubic splines yield functions with continuous first and second derivatives. We divide the beam length, taken as L, into k elements, each of length d_i $(i = 1, 2, \ldots, k)$ and denote the locations of the nodal points by x_i, such that $x_1 = 0$, $x_2 = d_1$, $x_3 = d_2 + d_3, \ldots, x_{k+1} = L$. The number of sensors is related to k by the types of boundary conditions used. The approximate profile at the ith interval can be expressed as [54, 55]

$$w_i(x,t) = A_i(x)M_i(t) + B_i(x)M_{i+1}(t) + C_i(x)y_i(t) + D_i(x)y_{i+1}(t) \tag{A14}$$

in which

$$A_i(x) = \frac{1}{6d_i}(x_{i+1} - x)^3 - \frac{d_i}{6}(x_{i+1} - x), \qquad B_i(x) = \frac{1}{6d_i}(x - x_i)^3 - \frac{d_i}{6}(x - x_i)$$
$$C_i(x) = \frac{1}{d_i}(x_{i+1} - x), \qquad D_i(x) = \frac{1}{d_i}(x - x_i) \tag{A15}$$

and $M_i(t)$ and $M_{i+1}(t)$ are the values of the second derivatives of the approximated profile at the nodal points, that is, $M_i(t) = w''(x_i, t)$ $(i = 1, 2, \ldots, k + 1)$. In standard spline interpolations, one knows y_i and finds M_i using the continuity relation for the first derivative. We use the same approach and set $w_i'(x_{i+1}) = w_{i+1}'(x_{i+1})$, which yields for the intermediate nodes [55,56],

$$\frac{d_i}{6}M_i(t) + \frac{d_i + d_{i+1}}{3}M_{i+1}(t) + \frac{d_{i+1}}{6}M_{i+2}(t)$$
$$= \frac{y_i}{d_i} - y_{i+1}\left(\frac{1}{d_i} + \frac{1}{d_{i+1}}\right) + \frac{y_{i+2}}{d_{i+1}}, \qquad i = 1, 2, \ldots, k - 1 \tag{A16}$$

The next step is to determine relations for the second derivatives at the end points. To accomplish this, we consider the boundary conditions. Without loss of generality, at $x = 0$, if there is a pinned or free end, we can write

$$M_1(t) = 0 \tag{A17}$$

For a fixed end or if the slope $q'(0, t)$ is prespecified, $w_1'(x, t)$ is evaluated at $x = 0$, which yields

$$w_1'(0, t) = -\frac{d_1}{3}M_1(t) - \frac{d_1}{6}M_2(t) - \frac{y_1(t)}{d_1} + \frac{y_2(t)}{d_1} \tag{A18}$$

In a similar fashion, one can find the appropriate relation for the end $x = L$. The $k - 1$ relations of Eq. (A16) and the two boundary terms are then assembled in matrix form as

$$P\mathbf{M}(t) = Q\mathbf{y}(t) + \mathbf{F}(t) \tag{A19}$$

where

$$\mathbf{M}(t) = [M_1(t) \quad M_2(t) \quad \cdots \quad M_{k+1}(t)]^{\mathrm{T}}, \mathbf{y}(t) = [y_1(t) \quad y_2(t) \quad \cdots \quad y_{k+1}(t)]^{\mathrm{T}}$$

and P and Q are tridiagonal matrices. They are symmetric for at least the second through $k-1$ rows and columns, depending on the boundary conditions. $\mathbf{F}(t)$ is a vector containing expressions related to the slopes at the boundaries. One can then relate the values of $\mathbf{M}(t)$ to the values of $\mathbf{y}(t)$ by inverting Eq. (A19), which yields

$$\mathbf{M}(t) = P^{-1}Q\mathbf{y}(t) \tag{A20}$$

where it is observed that the matrices P and Q are not time-dependent; so the inversion has to be performed once, before the modal filter extraction begins.

Next, we introduce the interpolated profile into the modal filter equations and carry out the algebra, which yields

$$w_r(t) = \sum_{i=1}^{k} \int_{D_i} m(x)\phi_r(x)w_i(x,t)\,dx = \mathbf{A}_r^{\mathrm{T}}\mathbf{M}(t) + \mathbf{B}_r^{\mathrm{T}}\mathbf{y}(t) \tag{A21}$$

where

$$\begin{aligned}\mathbf{A}_r &= [a_{r1} \quad b_{r1}+a_{r2} \quad b_{r2}+a_{r3} \quad \cdots \quad b_{r,k-1}+a_{r,k} \quad b_{r,k}]^{\mathrm{T}}\\ \mathbf{B}_r &= [c_{r1} \quad d_{r1}+c_{r2} \quad d_{r2}+c_{r3} \quad \cdots \quad d_{r,k-1}+c_{r,k} \quad d_{r,k}]^{\mathrm{T}}\end{aligned} \tag{A22}$$

in which

$$\begin{aligned} a_{ri} &= \int_{D_i} m(x)\phi_r(x)A_i(x)\,dx, \qquad b_{ri} = \int_{D_i} m(x)\phi_r(x)B_i(x)\,dx\\ c_{ri} &= \int_{D_i} m(x)\phi_r(x)C_i(x)\,dx, \qquad d_{ri} = \int_{D_i} m(x)\phi_r(x)D_i(x)\,dx\end{aligned} \tag{A23}$$

Equations (A21) can be expressed in the matrix form

$$\mathbf{w}(t) = A\mathbf{M}(t) + B\mathbf{y}(t) \tag{A24}$$

where $A = [\mathbf{A}_1 \quad \mathbf{A}_2 \quad \cdots \quad \mathbf{A}_{\mathrm{m}}]^{\mathrm{T}}$ and $B = [\mathbf{B}_1 \quad \mathbf{B}_2 \quad \cdots \quad \mathbf{B}_{\mathrm{m}}]^{\mathrm{T}}$. When Eq. (A24) is combined with Eq. (A20), we obtain the relation between the extracted modal coordinates and system measurements as

$$\mathbf{w}(t) = G_{\mathrm{M}}\mathbf{y}(t) = [AP^{-1}Q + B]\mathbf{y}(t) \tag{A25}$$

For axial or torsional vibration problems, because there is only one boundary condition at each end, one cannot use cubic splines for interpolation. The spline functions suitable for such problems are quadratic splines [55], which provide continuous profiles with continuous slopes. Their implementation is almost identical to the implementation of cubic splines, and their description is not included here.

Next, we investigate the performance of modal filters in the presence of parameter uncertainties and spatial discretization. Consider model uncertainties in the form $m'(x)$ and $\mathscr{L}'$, where the primes denote that the mass and stiffness operators are erroneous and based on some postulated model. Denoting the associated computed eigenfunctions by $\theta'_r(x)$ $(r = 1, 2, \ldots, N)$, the expansion theorem can be written as (Eq. (29))

$$u(x,t) = \sum_{r=1}^{N} q'_r(t)\theta'_r(x), \qquad q'_r(t) = (u(x,t), m'(x)\theta'_r(x)) \tag{A26}$$

where $q'_r(t)$ are modal coordinates of the postulated system, and N is the order of spatial discretization. When discrete sensors are used, the distributed profile can be approximated by Eq. (4), which, when substituted into the preceding equation, yields for the extracted postulated coordinates denoted by $\boldsymbol{\zeta}(t)$ (in the event of no failure)

$$\boldsymbol{\zeta}(t) = G'H_{\mathrm{M}}\mathbf{u}_{\mathrm{M}}(t) + G'H_{\mathrm{R}}\mathbf{u}_{\mathrm{R}}(t) + G'\mathbf{n}(t) \tag{A27}$$

or

$$\boldsymbol{\zeta}(t) = G'J_{\mathrm{M}}\mathbf{q}'_{\mathrm{M}}(t) + G'J_{\mathrm{R}}\mathbf{q}'_{\mathrm{R}}(t) + G'\mathbf{n}(t) \tag{A28}$$

where

$$G'_{rj} = (G(x, x_j), m(x)\theta'_r(x)), \qquad r = 1, 2, \ldots, m; \quad j = 1, 2, \ldots, k$$

$$J_{\mathrm{M}}(i,j) = \theta'_j(x_i), \qquad i = 1, 2, \ldots, k; \quad j = 1, 2, \ldots, m$$

$$J_{\mathrm{R}}(i,j) = \theta'_{m+j}(x_i), \qquad i = 1, 2, \ldots, k; \quad j = 1, 2, \ldots, N - m$$

One would select the number and location of the sensors so that $G'J_{\mathrm{M}}$ approaches an identity matrix. Of course, the coordinates extracted are not the actual modal coordinates.

The second approach to modal parameter extraction to be described here is by means of an observer. We consider here full-order observers and express the equations of motion for the reduced-order model (m modes) in state form as

$$\dot{\mathbf{x}}(t) = A\mathbf{x}(t) + B\mathbf{F}_{\mathrm{A}}(t), \; \mathbf{y}_{\mathrm{A}}(t) = S_{\mathrm{s}}C\mathbf{x}(t) + \mathbf{h}_{\mathrm{s}}(t) \tag{A29}$$

where $\mathbf{x}(t)$ is the $2n$-dimensional state vector, in the form $\mathbf{x}(t) = \mathbf{u}_{\mathrm{M}}(t)^{\mathrm{T}} \,|\, \dot{\mathbf{u}}_{\mathrm{M}}(t)^{\mathrm{T}}]^{\mathrm{T}}$, and A and B are state and control influence matrices of orders $2n*2n$ and $2n*m$, respectively. C is the $k*2n$ observation matrix. The observer is defined as

$$\dot{\mathbf{z}}(t) = A\mathbf{z}(t) + B\mathbf{F}(t) + P[\mathbf{y}_{\mathrm{A}}(t) - \mathbf{y}'(t)], \qquad \mathbf{y}'(t) = C\mathbf{z}(t) \tag{A30}$$

where $\mathbf{z}(t)$ denotes estimated quantities and P is the observer gain matrix. Defining an error vector $\mathbf{e}(t) = \mathbf{x}(t) - \mathbf{z}(t)$ and a control law in the form $\mathbf{F}(t) = K\mathbf{z}(t)$, and using Eqs. (A29) and (A30), one can arrive at the well-known observer equations, which, in the absence of actuator and sensor failures and noise, have the form

$$\begin{bmatrix} \dot{\mathbf{x}}(t) \\ \dot{\mathbf{e}}(t) \end{bmatrix} = \begin{bmatrix} A + BK & -BK \\ 0 & A - PC \end{bmatrix} \begin{bmatrix} \mathbf{x}(t) \\ \mathbf{e}(t) \end{bmatrix} \tag{A31}$$

in which P is chosen so that the observer poles are stable. From Eq. (A31) one can determine the $G(t)$ matrix that satisfies Eq. (17a). Note the deterministic separation principle.

One implementation problem, of course, is the design of P, especially for high-order systems. Added to this are problems encountered because the state vector used is a finite-dimensional reduced-order vector, and the residual dynamics contaminates the results, a phenomenon that has come to be known as observation spillover [57].

When we consider sensor and actuator malfunctions, the observer equations can be shown to become

$$\begin{bmatrix} \dot{\mathbf{x}}(t) \\ \dot{\mathbf{e}}(t) \end{bmatrix} = \begin{bmatrix} A + BS_{\mathrm{a}}K & -BS_{\mathrm{a}}K \\ B(S_{\mathrm{a}} - I)K - P(S_{\mathrm{s}} - I)C & A - PC - B(S_{\mathrm{a}} - I)K \end{bmatrix} \begin{bmatrix} \dot{\mathbf{x}}(t) \\ \dot{\mathbf{e}}(t) \end{bmatrix} + \begin{bmatrix} B\mathbf{h}_{\mathrm{a}}(t) \\ B\mathbf{h}_{\mathrm{a}}(t) - P\mathbf{h}_{\mathrm{s}}(t) \end{bmatrix} \tag{A32}$$

where we note that the deterministic separation principle is no longer valid and that actuator and sensor failures both affect the observer poles.

In the presence of parameter uncertainties and component failures, the state equations are postulated as

$$\dot{\mathbf{z}}(t) = A'\mathbf{z}(t) + B'\mathbf{u}(t) + K[\mathbf{y}_{\mathrm{A}}(t) - \mathbf{y}'(t)], \qquad \mathbf{y}'(t) = C\mathbf{z}(t) \tag{A33}$$

where A' and B' are postulated state and input coefficient matrices. Use of Eq. (A33) as the model leads to the closed-loop observer equations in the form

$$\begin{bmatrix} \dot{\mathbf{x}}(t) \\ \dot{\mathbf{e}}(t) \end{bmatrix} = \begin{bmatrix} A + BS_{\mathrm{a}}K & -BS_{\mathrm{a}}K \\ A - A' + (BS_{\mathrm{a}} - B')K - P(S_{\mathrm{s}}C - C') & A' - PC' - (BS_{\mathrm{a}} - B')K \end{bmatrix} \times \begin{bmatrix} \mathbf{x}(t) \\ \mathbf{e}(t) \end{bmatrix} + \begin{bmatrix} B\mathbf{h}_{\mathrm{a}}(t) \\ B\mathbf{h}_{\mathrm{a}}(t) - P\mathbf{h}_{\mathrm{s}}(t) \end{bmatrix} \tag{A34}$$

where the effect of further contamination is clear.

A full-scale comparison of observers and modal filters has not yet been conducted. The two approaches have been compared qualitatively in [16,20,54] for certain implementation aspects and robustness. Each procedure has its advantages and disadvantages. In our research, we have preferred to use modal filters because of their ease of design and their insensitivity to actuator failures.

ACKNOWLEDGMENT

This work was supported by NSF Grant MSM 85-01877.

REFERENCES

1. A. S. WILLSKY, "A Survey of Design Methods for Failure Detection in Dynamic Systems," *Automatica* **12**, 601–611 (1976).
2. R. ISERMAN, "Process Fault Detection Based on Modeling and Estimation Methods—A Survey," *Automatica* **20**, 387–404 (1984).
3. J. J. DEYST, J. V. HARRISON, Jr., E. GAI, and K. E. DALY, "Fault Detection, Identification and Reconfiguration for Spacecraft Systems," *J. Astronaut. Sci.* **29**, 113–126 (1981).
4. J. L. TYLEE, "Providing Nuclear Reactor Control Information in the Presence of Instrument Failures," *Proc. Am. Control Conf., Seattle*, 170–175 (1986).
5. R. N. CLARK and B. CAMPBELL, "Instrument Fault Detection in a Pressurized Water Reactor Pressurizer," *Nucl. Technol.* **56**, 23–32 (1982).
6. A. EMAMI-NAEINI, M. M. AKHTER, and S. M. ROCK, "Robust Detection, Isolation, and Accommodation for Sensor Failures," *NASA* [*Contract. Rep.*] *CR* **NASA-CR-174825** (1986).
7. G. G. LEININGER and K. BEHBEHANI, "Sensor/Actuator Failure Detection and Isolation for Airbreathing Propulsion Systems," *1980 Joint Autom. Control Conf., San Francisco* (1980).
8. G. G. LEININGER, "Model Degradation Effects on Sensor Failure Detection," *1981 Joint Autom. Control Conf., Charlottesville, Va.* (1981).
9. W. MERRILL and J. DEL, "A Real-Time Simulation Evaluation of an Advanced Detection, Isolation, and Accommodation Algorithm for Sensor Failures in Turbine Engines," *Proc. Am. Control Conf., Seattle*, 162–169 (1986).
10. F. E. ERDLE, I. A. FIGENBAUM, annd J. W. TALCOTT, Jr., "Reliability Programs for Commercial Communication Satellites," *IEEE Trans. Reliab.* **R-32**, 236–239 (1983).
11. T. NAKAGOWA, "Optimal Number of Failures Before Replacement Time," *IEEE Trans. Reliab.* **R-32**, 115–116 (1983).
12. W. E. VANDERVELDE, "Component Failure Detection in Flexible Spacecraft Control Systems," *Proc. VPI AIAA Symp. Dyn. Control Large Flexible Struct., Blacksburg, Va.*, 481–497 (1983).
13. R. C. MONTGOMERY and W. E. VANDERVELDE, "Reliability Considerations in the Placement of Control System Components," *J. Guidance, Control, Dyn.* **8**, 411–413 (1985).
14. W. E. VANDERVELDE and C. R. CARIGNAN, "Number and Placement of Control System Components Considering Possible Failures," *J. Guidance, Control, Dyn.* **7**, 703–709 (1984).
15. H. BARUH and K. CHOE, "Sensor Placement in Structural Control," *Proc. AIAA Guidance, Navigation Control Conf., Minneapolis, Minn.*, 41–50 (1988); also *J. Guidance, Control Dyn.* (to appear).
16. H. BARUH, "Actuator Failure Detection in the Control of Distributed Systems," *J. Guidance, Control Dyn.* **9**, 181–189 (1986).
17. H. BARUH and L. MEIROVITCH, "On the Placement of Actuators in the Control of Distributed-Parameter Systems," *Proc. AIAA Dyn. Spec. Conf., Atlanta, Ga.*, Pap. No. 81-0638 (1981).
18. H. BARUH, "Sensor Failure Detection in Distributed Systems," *Proc. 24th IEEE Conf. Decision Control, Ft. Lauderdale, Fla.*, pp. 753–754 (1985).
19. A. M. SAN MARTIN and W. E. VANDERVELDE, "Design of Robust Failure Detection Filters," *Proc. Am. Control Conf., Seattle*, 1052–1059 (1986).

20. H. BARUH and K. CHOE, "Sensor Failure Detection Method for Flexible Structures," *J. Guidance, Control Dyn.* **10**, 474–482 (1987).
21. S. M. JOSHI, "Failure Accommodating Control of Large Flexible Spacecraft," *Proc. Am. Control Conf., Seattle*, 156–161 (1986).
22. M. N. WAGDI, "An Adaptive Control Approach to Sensor Failure Detection and Isolation," *AIAA Pap.* 82-0182 (1982).
23. M. DESAI and A. RAY, "A Fault Detection and Isolation Methodology—Theory and Application," *Proc. Am. Control Conf., San Diego*, 262–270 (1984).
24. E. Y. CHOW and A. S. WILLSKY, "Issues in the Development of a General Design Algorithm for Reliable Failure Detection," *Proc. Conf. Decision Control, New York*, 1006–1012 (1980).
25. F. J. ALEXANDRO and J. TJOV, "Instrument Failure Detection and Isolation in a System with Variable Plant Parameters," *Proc. AIAA Guidance Control Conf.*, 176–181 (1984).
26. R. J. PATTON, S. W. WILLCOX, and J. S. WINTER, "Parameter Insensitive Technique for Aircraft Sensor Fault Analysis," *J. Guidance, Control Dyn.* **19**, 359–367 (1987).
27. R. L. KOST and R. E. WALKER, "Robust Fault Detection: The Effect of Model Error," *Proc. Am. Control Conf., San Diego*, 1094–1096 (1984).
28. A. BERMAN, "Parameter Identification Techniques for Vibrating Structures," *Shock Vib. Dig.* **11**, No. 1, 13–15 (1979).
29. V. STREJC, "Trends in Identification," *Automatica* **17**, 7–21 (1981).
30. C. S. KUBRUSLY, "Distributed Parameter Idenfication, A Survey," *Int. J. Control* **26**, 509–535 (1977).
31. L. LJUNG and K. GLOVER, "Frequency Domain versus Time Domain Methods in System Identification," *Automatica* **17**, 71–86 (1981).
32. H. T. BANKS and J. M. CROWLEY, "Parameter Identification in Continuum Models," *J. Astronaut. Sci.* **33**, 85–94 (1985).
33. L. A. BERGMAN, A. L. HALE, and J. C. GOODING, "Identification of Linear Systems by Poisson Moment Functionals in the Presence of Noise," *AIAA* **23**, 1234–1235 (1985).
34. D. C. SAHA and G. PRASADA RAO, "Identification of Distributed Systems via Multidimensional Distributions," *IEE Proc. Part D: Control Theory Appl.* **127**, 45–50 (1980).
35. S. R. IBRAHIM, "Computation of Normal Modes from Identified Complex Modes," *AIAA J.* **21**, 446–451 (1983).
36. S. R. IBRAHIM and E. C. MIKULCIK, "The Experimental Determination of Vibration Parameters from Time Responses," *Shock Vib. Bull.* **47**, 183–198 (1977).
37. D. J. EWINS and P. T. GLEESON, "A Method for Modal Identification in Lightly Damped Structures," *J. Sound Vib.* **84**, 57–79 (1982).
38. J.-N. JUANG and R. S. PAPPA, "An Eigensystem Realization Algorithm for Modal Parameter Identification," *J. Guidance, Control Dyn.* **9**, 620–627 (1985).
39. H. BARUH and H. P. KHATRI, "Identification of Modal Parameters in Flexible Structures," *J. Sound Vib.* **125**, 413–427 (1988).
40. H. BARUH and L. MEIROVITCH, "Parameter Identification in Distributed Systems," *J. Sound Vib.* **101**, 551–564 (1985).
41. M. BARUCH, "Correction of Stiffness Matrix Using Vibration Tests," *AIAA J.* **20**, 441–442 (1982).
42. A. BERMAN, "Mass Matrix Correction Using an Incomplete Set of Measured Modes," *AIAA J.* **17**, 1147–1148 (1979).
43. H. BARUH and L. SILVERBERG, "Identification of External Excitations in Self-Adjoint Systems Using Modal Filters," *J. Sound Vib.* **108**, 247–260 (1986).
44. L. MEIROVITCH, "Computational Methods in Structural Dynamics," Sijthoff & Noordhoff, Leiden, 1980.

45. H. BARUH and J. B. BOKA, "Implementation Problems in Modal Identification of Vibrating Structures," *Proc. AIAA Struct., Struct. Dyn. Mater. Conf., Williamsburg, Va.*, 1542–1556 (1988).
46. J. N. AUBRUN, "Theory of Structures with Low Authority Controllers," *J. Guidance, Control Dyn.* **3**, 444–451 (1980).
47. L. MEIROVITCH, H. BARUH, and H. OZ, "A Comparison of Control Techniques for Large Flexible Systems," *J. Guidance, Control Dyn.* **6**, 302–310 (1983).
48. L. MEIROVITCH and H. BARUH, "Control of Self-Adjoint Distributed-Parameter Systems," *J. Guidance, Control Dyn.* **5**, No. 1, 60–66 (1982).
49. L. MEIROVITCH and L. M. SILVERBERG, "Globally Optimal Control of Self-Adjoint Distributed Systems," *Optimal Control Appl. Methods* **4**, 365–386 (1983).
50. H. BARUH and L. M. SILVERBERG, "On the Natural Robust Control of Distributed Systems," *J. Guidance, Control Dyn.* **8**, 717–724 (1985).
51. L. M. SILVERBERG, "Uniform Damping Control of Spacecraft," *J. Guidance, Control Dyn.* **9**, 221–227 (1986).
52. H. OZ, "Another View of Optimality for Control of Flexible Systems; Natural and Unnatural Controls," *Proc. 4th VPI SU/AIAA Symp. Dyn. Control Flexible Spacecr., Blacksburg, Va.* (1983).
53. K. CHOE and H. BARUH, "Sensor Failure Detection in Flexible Structures Using Modal Observers," *Proc. 7th VPI SU Symp. Dyn. Control Large Struct., Blacksburg, Va.* (1989).
53. L. MEIROVITCH and H. BARUH, "Implementation of Modal Filters for Flexible Structures," *J. Guidance, Control Dyn.* **8**, 707–716 (1986).
54. K. ATKINSON, "Elementary Numerical Analysis," Wiley, New York, 1985.
56. R. L. BURDEN and J. D. FAIRES, "Numerical Analysis," Prindle, Weber & Schmidt, Boston, 1985.
57. L. MEIROVITCH and H. BARUH, "Effect of Damping on Observation Spillover Instability," *J. Optim. Theory Appl.* **35**, 31–46 (1981).

CONTROL LAW SYNTHESIS AND STABILITY ROBUSTNESS IMPROVEMENT USING CONSTRAINED OPTIMIZATION TECHNIQUES

VIVEKANANDA MUKHOPADHYAY

NASA Langley Research Center
Hampton, Virginia 23665-5225

I. INTRODUCTION

A modern flexible aircraft or a large space structure with active control is typically modeled by a high-order state-space system of equations in order to accurately represent the rigid and flexible body modes, unsteady aerodynamic forces, actuator dynamics, antialiasing filters, and gust spectrum. The control law of this multiinput–multioutput (MIMO) system is expected to satisfy a set of conflicting design requirements on the dynamic loads, responses, actuator deflection, and rate limitations. It should also be robust to maintain certain stability margins over the flight envelop, yet be simple enough for implementation in a digital flight computer. In this article, a practical robust control law synthesis and optimization procedure for such a system is described.

The stability robustness of a multiloop feedback control system of an aerospace vehicle is an important aspect of the control law synthesis. For single input–single output systems (SISO), the classical concepts of gain and phase margins are employed as a quantitative measure of stability robustness. In multiloop systems, these classical single-loop measures may not always provide a good measure of system robustness since the gain or phase is perturbed in one loop at a time. In recent years, several authors have used matrix singular value properties of complex matrices and proposed the minimum singular value of a MIMO system return difference matrix as a measure of system robustness [1,2]. To draw a parallel with SISO systems, the minimum singular value was also related quantitatively to a new definition of guaranteed MIMO gain and phase margins, in which the gain and phase are perturbed simultaneously in all the loops [3,4].

Singular value shaping is a suitable method for MIMO system stability robustness improvement. Safonov and Chen [5] discussed a procedure for maximizing singular values for stability margin optimization. Doyle and Stein [2] developed the frequency domain interpretation of the linear quadratic Gaussian (LQG) design techniques, in terms of singular values. They showed how the LQG methodology can be used to design robust feedback control laws that satisfy design requirements expressed as singular value bounds. This procedure is popularly known as LQG/LTR (loop transfer recovery) in which the full state optimal feedback system stability robustness properties can be asymptotically recovered at the plant input or output. However, a robust LQG controller is of same high-order as the plant and is often difficult to implement in a flight computer. Hence, the high-order LQG controller must be reduced to a lower order without sacrificing the performance and stability robustness properties substantially. The balanced truncation or residualization techniques can be used for control law order reduction. This usually results in loss of performance and stability robustness properties, but the control system can be reoptimized to recover most of the loss [6–9].

A direct method for improving the stability robustness by shaping the singular value spectrum was developed by Mukhopadhyay and Newsom [6]. There, selected parameters of an existing controller were used as design variables to minimize feedback gains while satisfying a minimum singular value constraint at the plant input. In this article, a procedure for synthesis and optimization of a low-order controller for high-order systems [7] is combined with the method of [6] to arrive at a realistic compromise. The synthesis procedure minimizes a standard LQG cost function while attempting to satisfy the constraints on the minimum singular value at the plant input or output, or both. The design requirements—such as control surface deflection and rate limits, maximum allowable root-mean-square (RMS) response, and dynamic loads on the structure—are imposed as constraints instead of lumping them into the cost function. This is necessary because in general, a stability margin improvement at the plant input is accompanied by a stability margin degradation at the plant output [8] and an increase in response and control activity. Expressions for the gradients of the cost function and the constraints with respect to the control law design variables are derived analytically to facilitate rapid convergence of the numerical optimization process. The designer can choose the structure of the control law, the design variables, and a set of inequality constraints. This enables optimization of a classical control law and a Kalman estimator-based full- or reduced-order control law [7] to meet specific design demands. A parallel procedure for synthesis and optimization of a low-order robust digital controller for high-order systems is also described. Direct digital controller design is important because most of the controllers are implemented using a digital microprocessor, and the effects of digitization, computational delay, and the antialiasing filter can be taken into account at the design stage [9]. The system hardware may enjoy a cost benefit if a high-performance robust controller with a lower sampling rate and less complexity can be designed. The various aspects of a multiloop digital control law synthesis problem are outlined in Fig. 1.

Other techniques for synthesis of reduced-order robust controllers are also available. Safonov and Chiang [10] presented a numerically robust algorithm for balanced order reduction. Lenz *et al.* [11] addressed the problem of maintaining closed-loop stability and performance simultaneously using the Hankel norm model reduction technique to obtain suboptimal controllers. Bernstein and Haddad [12] developed optimal projection formulation for synthesis of fixed-order robust compensators.

The presentation is organized as follows. In Section II, a procedure for developing the state-space equations of Section III for a flexible aircraft from modal equations and unsteady aerodynamics data is described. The singular value based stability robustness analysis is reviewed in Section IV. The optimization scheme is presented in Section V. The analytical gradients of the LQG-type cost function and RMS response constraints are derived in Section VI. In Section VII, the analytical gradients of the singular value are developed. The formulation for a discrete system is presented in Section VIII. Design variable selection procedure is described in Section IX. Examples

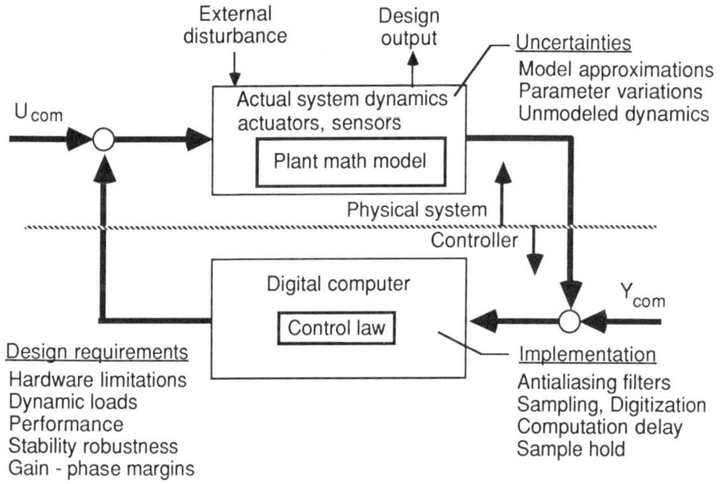

Fig. 1. Multiloop digital control law synthesis considerations.

using a lateral attitude stabilization system and a gust load alleviation system are presented in Section X.

II. EQUATIONS OF MOTION

The linear equations of motion for a flexible aircraft in the Laplace domain can be written using the generalized mass, damping, and stiffness matrices $[M_s]$, $[D_s]$, and $[K_s]$ and the unsteady aerodynamic force coefficient matrices $[Q_s \quad Q_c \quad Q_g]$, as

$$[[M_s]s^2 + [D_s]s + [K_s]]\{x_s\} + [M_{sc}]s^2\{x_c\} + q[Q_s \quad Q_c \quad Q_g]\begin{Bmatrix} x_s \\ \xi_c \\ \xi_g/V \end{Bmatrix} = 0 \tag{1}$$

where s is the Laplace variable, q is the dynamic pressure $0.5\,\rho V^2$, V is the free stream velocity, and ξ_s, ξ_c, and ξ_g are the generalized displacements of the structural modes, control surface, and gust, respectively [7]. The control surface inertia coupling is denoted by $[M_{sc}]$. The functions in the last term in Eq. (1), which represent the unsteady aerodynamic forces, are not rational functions and cannot be expressed in state-space form. The $[Q_s \quad Q_c \quad Q_g]$ matrices are usually available in the frequency domain and are computed in tabular form as a complex function of $(\omega b/V)$ for each structural mode due to the sinusoidal modal oscillation, control surface deflection, and a sinusoidal gust, using suitable linear aerodynamic theory or a computational fluid dynamics code. A procedure for developing the approximate state-space equations from Eq. (1) using the complex unsteady aerodynamic data is described here. An s-plane rational function approximation $[Q_s(s) \quad Q_c(s) \quad Q_g(s)]$ of the unsteady aerodynamic forces coefficient matrix $[Q_s(j\omega) \quad Q_c(j\omega) \quad Q_g(j\omega)]$ due to a sinusoidal input at frequency ω can be expressed as

$$\begin{aligned}[Q_s \quad Q_c \quad Q_g] = {} & [A_{os} \quad A_{oc} \quad A_{og}] + [A_{1s} \quad A_{1c} \quad A_{1g}]\bar{s} + [A_{2s} \quad A_{2c} \quad 0]\bar{s}^2 \\ & + [D_a](I\bar{s} - [R_a])^{-1}[E_s \quad E_c \quad E_g]\bar{s}\end{aligned} \tag{2}$$

where $\bar{s} = sb/V$ and b is the reference chord length used to define the nondimensional reduced frequency $\omega b/V$. The real coefficient matrices, such as $[A_{os}]$, are determined by a suitable curve fitting of the tabular data by the real and imaginary part of Eq. (2) with s replaced by $j\omega$ over a reduced frequency range of interest. Thus, Eq. (2) regenerates the oscillatory aerodynamic force data in the limited frequency domain and approximates them in the Laplace or time domain. This procedure of rational approximation is necessary since the unsteady aerodynamic forces are not available as ordinary differential equations and cannot be expressed in the state-space form directly.

Using Eqs. (1) and (2), we can write the state-space equations of motion as

$$\frac{d}{dt}\begin{Bmatrix}\xi_s\\ \dot{\xi}_s\\ \xi_a\end{Bmatrix} = \begin{bmatrix}0 & I & 0\\ -\bar{M}_s^{-1}\bar{K}_s & -\bar{M}_s^{-1}\bar{D}_s & -\bar{M}_s^{-1}D_a q\\ 0 & E_s & R_a(V/b)\end{bmatrix}\begin{Bmatrix}\xi_s\\ \dot{\xi}_s\\ \xi_a\end{Bmatrix}$$
$$+\begin{bmatrix}0 & 0 & 0\\ -\bar{M}_s^{-1}A_{oc}q & -\bar{M}_s^{-1}A_{1c}q(b/V) & -\bar{M}_s^{-1}\bar{M}_c\\ 0 & E_c & 0\end{bmatrix}\begin{Bmatrix}\xi_c\\ \dot{\xi}_c\\ \ddot{\xi}_c\end{Bmatrix}$$
$$+\begin{bmatrix}0 & 0\\ -\bar{M}_s^{-1}A_{oc}q & -\bar{M}_s^{-1}A_{1g}q(b/V)\\ 0 & E_g\end{bmatrix}\begin{Bmatrix}\xi_g/V\\ \dot{\xi}_g/V\end{Bmatrix} \tag{3}$$

or

$$dx^*/dt = F^*x^* + G_1^*u_1^* + G_2^*u_2^*$$

where

$$\bar{M}_s = M_s + A_{2s}q(b/V)^2, \qquad \bar{K}_s = K_s + A_{os}q, \qquad \bar{D}_s = D_s + A_{1s}q(b/V)$$

$$\bar{M}_c = M_{sc} + A_{2c}q(b/V)^2, \qquad \xi_a = (I\bar{s} - [R_a])^{-1}[E_s \quad E_c \quad E_g]\begin{Bmatrix}\xi_s\\ \xi_c\\ \xi_g/V\end{Bmatrix}$$

Let us assume that the actuator dynamics transfer functions and the gust spectrum can be expressed in state-space form as

$$\begin{aligned}\dot{x}_{ac}^* &= A_{ac}x_{ac}^* + B_{ac}u & \dot{x}_g^* &= A_g x_g^* + B_g w\\ u_1^* &= C_{ac}x_{ac}^* & u_2^* &= C_g x_g^*\end{aligned} \tag{4}$$

where u is the control input command and w is a white noise process. Augmenting Eq. (3) with (4), we write the final state-space equations as

$$\frac{d}{dt}\begin{Bmatrix}x^*\\ x_{ac}^*\\ x_g^*\end{Bmatrix} = \begin{bmatrix}F^* & G_1^*C_{ac} & G_2^*C_g\\ 0 & A_{ac} & 0\\ 0 & 0 & A_g\end{bmatrix}\begin{Bmatrix}x^*\\ x_{ac}^*\\ x_g^*\end{Bmatrix} + \begin{bmatrix}0\\ B_{ac}\\ 0\end{bmatrix}u + \begin{bmatrix}0\\ 0\\ B_g\end{bmatrix}w \tag{5}$$

or

$$\frac{dx_s}{dt} = Fx_s + G_u u + G_w w$$

The accelerometer sensor output equations also need to be expressed as a function of the state vector x_s from the product of the modal matrix $[\Phi]_y$ at the sensor location and the modal acceleration given by the second row of matrices in Eq. (3). Let the matrices H_s, H_c, and H_g represent the second row of matrices in Eq. (3); then, substituting Eq. (4), we write the acceleration output equation as

$$y_{\text{accl}} = [\Phi]_y [H_s \quad H_c C_{\text{ac}} \quad H_g C_g] \begin{Bmatrix} x^* \\ x^*_{\text{ac}} \\ x^*_g \end{Bmatrix} \equiv H_{\text{accl}} x_s$$

The other sensor and design output equations can also be formulated as linear functions of the plant system state vector x_s.

III. SYSTEM DESCRIPTION

Let us consider the linear multiloop feedback control system shown in Fig. 2. The system can be described in the time domain by a set of constant coefficient state-space equations, shown in Eqs. (6) to (11):

Plant:

$$dx_s/dt = Fx_s + G_u u + G_w w \tag{6}$$

$$y' = Hx_s \tag{7}$$

Controller:

$$x_c = Ax_c + By \tag{8}$$

$$u' = Cx_c + Dy \tag{9}$$

Interconnection:

$$u = u' + u_{\text{com}} \tag{10}$$

$$y = y' + y_{\text{com}} \tag{11}$$

The plant Eq. (6) represents a N_sth-order linear equation of motion, due to a small perturbation from a steady-state equilibrium condition of a flexible aircraft or a large space structure, as shown in Section II. The active control system has N_0 output measurements y' modeled by Eq. (7), N_c control inputs u, and N_w disturbance input w. Equations (8) and (9) represent an Mth-order feedback controller driven by the output feedback y. The plant and controller are interconnected by Eqs. (10) and (11), which include external inputs u_{com} and y_{com}. Fictitious white noise processes η and υ can be inserted at the plant input and output, respectively, to improve the stability robustness of an LQG controller at these two points [2,3].

The plant and the controller transfer matrices in the Laplace domain $G(s)$ and $K(s)$ are defined (assuming $w = 0$, for simplicity) as

$$Y'(s) = H(Is - F)^{-1}G_u U(s) = G(s)U(s) \tag{12}$$

$$U'(s) = [C(Is - A)^{-1}B + D]Y(s) = -K(s)Y(s) \tag{13}$$

The argument s of the Laplace domain transfer matrices will be dropped in the subsequent sections, for convenience. For the closed-loop system, one can write the input-to-output transfer matrices as follows:

$$\begin{Bmatrix} Y' \\ Y \\ U' \\ U \end{Bmatrix} = \begin{bmatrix} (I + GK)^{-1}G & -(I + GK)^{-1}GK \\ (I + GK)^{-1}G & (I + GK)^{-1} \\ -(I + KG)^{-1}KG & -(I + KG)^{-1}K \\ (I + KG)^{-1} & -(I + KG)^{-1}K \end{bmatrix} \begin{Bmatrix} U_{com} \\ Y_{com} \end{Bmatrix} \tag{14}$$

In these transfer matrix relations, the return difference matrices $(I + KG)$ and $(I + GK)$ are used for stability robustness analysis at the plant input and output. These physical points in the loop are denoted by 1 and 2, respectively, in Fig. 2. A brief review of the stability margins and their relation to the matrix singular values is presented in Section IV.

IV. STABILITY ROBUSTNESS REVIEW

The stability robustness of a multiloop system and its relation to the singular value of the return-difference matrix were discussed in detail in [3,4]. The singular values of a complex matrix G are defined as the positive square roots of the nonzero eigenvalues of the Hermitian matrix G^*G, where G^* is

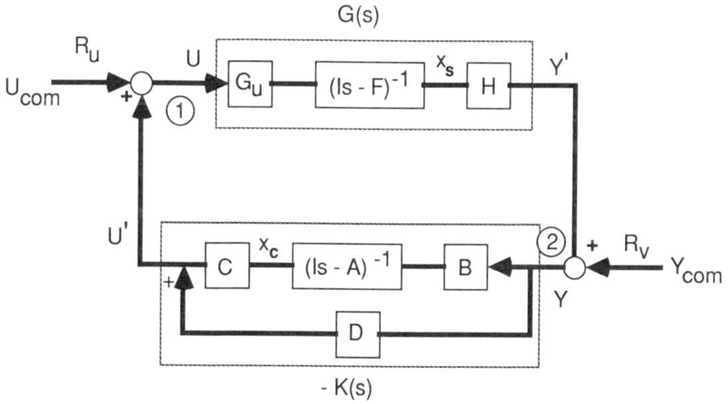

Fig. 2. Multiloop feedback control system block diagram.

the complex conjugate transpose of G. The minimum singular value of the return-difference matrix at the plant input $\boldsymbol{\sigma}(I + KG)$ and the inverse return-difference matrix $\boldsymbol{\sigma}(I + (KG)^{-1})$ are measures of guaranteed simultaneous stability margins at the plant input in the following sense. Let a multiplicative perturbation matrix L, whose nominal value is unity, be introduced at the plant input, denoted by 1 in Fig. 2. It was shown in [3] that, if the nominal system $(I + KG)$ is stable, then under certain conditions the stability of the gain perturbed system is guaranteed if

$$\sigma_{\max}(L^{-1} - I) < \boldsymbol{\sigma}(I + KG) \tag{15}$$

or

$$\sigma_{\max}(L - 1) < \boldsymbol{\sigma}(I + (KG)^{-1}) \tag{16}$$

over all frequencies ($s = j\omega$). The proof follows from the fact that the perturbed system $(I + KGL)$ can be expressed as

$$[(L^{-1} - I)(I + KG)^{-1} + I](I + KG)L = (I + KG)[I + (I + (KG)^{-1})^{-1}(L - I)],$$

and will remain nonsingular **if** $(I + KG)$ is nonsingular and the magnitude of $(L^{-1} - I)(I + KG)^{-1}$ or $(I + (KG)^{-1})^{-1}(L - I)$ is less than unity. Using the matrix singular value properties,

1. $\sigma_{\max}(G)\sigma_{\max}(L) \geq \sigma_{\max}(GL)$,
2. if G^{-1} exists, then $\sigma_{\max}(G) = 1/\sigma_{\min}(G^{-1})$, and
3. if G is nonsingular, then a sufficient condition for $(G + L)$ to remain nonsingular is $\sigma_{\max}(L) < \sigma_{\min}(G)$,

one can derive Eqs. (15) and (16). The proof is left to the reader. The stability robustness of a MIMO system can now be expressed quantitatively in terms of gain and phase margins, as follows. Consider a specific L matrix that represents simultaneous gain and phase perturbations k_n and ϕ_n in every loop:

$$L = \text{diag}[k_n \exp(j\phi_n)], \qquad m = 1, 2, \ldots, N_c, \qquad k_n > 0. \tag{17}$$

At the nominal condition, $k_n = 1$ and $\phi_n = 0$ for all n (i.e., $L = I$). The stability conditions in Eqs. (15) and (16) can be expressed graphically, as shown in Fig. 3, by the solid lines and the broken lines, respectively. The solid line is the parametric plot of

$$\sigma_{\max}(L^{-1} - 1) = \max[(1 - 1/k_n)^2 + 2(1 - \cos\phi_n)/k_n]^{0.5},$$
$$n = 1, 2, \ldots, N_c \tag{18}$$

versus k_n for various ϕ_n. The plot of $\sigma_{\max}(L - 1)$, shown in broken line, is a mirror image of this plot about the vertical zero-decibel gain line, since

$$\sigma_{\max}(L - 1) = \max[(1 - k_n)^2 + 2k_n(1 - \cos\phi_n)]^{0.5}$$
$$n = 1, 2, \ldots, N_c. \tag{19}$$

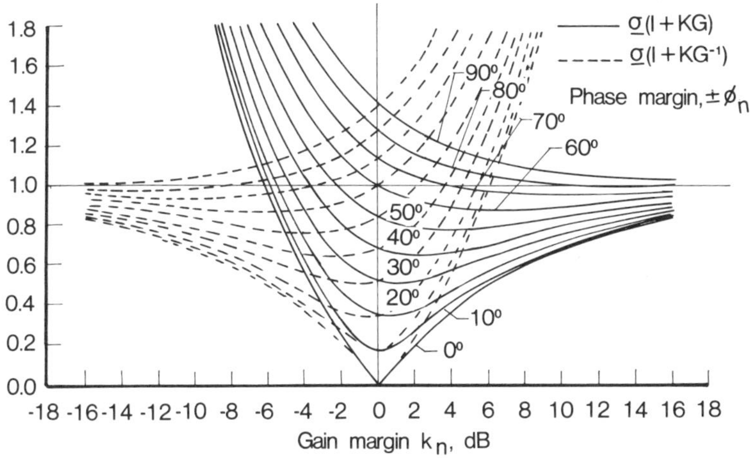

Fig. 3. Universal diagram for gain and phase margin evaluation.

From the appropriate minimum singular values, one can obtain the minimum range of variation of the gain k_n and the phase ϕ_n at the plant input within which the system is guaranteed to be stable. Since the inequalities of Eqs. (15) and (16) are sufficient but not necessary conditions, one can choose the larger of the range. For example, if the minimum $\underline{\sigma}(I + KG) \geq 0.6$ for a system over all frequencies and ± 30-deg phase margins are required in all loops, then guaranteed simultaneous gain margins are -1.5 dB and $+5.3$ dB (*i.e.*, both the phase and gain can be changed in all loops within these limits at the plant input without destabilizing the closed-loop system). When either gain or phase is changed in all the loops at the plant input, the MIMO system simultaneous gain margins are -4.2 dB and $+8$ dB ($\phi_n = 0$), or the phase margins are ± 35 deg ($k_n = 1$). For the same system, if $\underline{\sigma}(I + (KG)^{-1}) \geq 0.5$, then the simultaneous gain margins are -6.0 dB and $+3.5$ dB ($\phi_n = 0$). Taking the larger of the range, the MIMO gain margins would be -6.0 dB and $+8$ dB ($\phi_n = 0$) at the plant input. The MIMO phase margins would be ± 35 deg ($k_n = 1$). The actual gain and phase margins can be higher than those obtained from Fig. 3. This conservative estimation of stability margins can be beneficial in real design since the actual system is always different from the design model. Note that in Eqs. (15) and (16) it is also possible to use the minimum eigenvalue magnitude of $(I + KG)$, and so on, instead of the singular value, for the special case in which the perturbations in all loops are equal. The minimum eigenvalue plot contains important qualitative information on the conservativeness of the stability margin results based on the minimum singular value [4].

Equation (18) can also be plotted with the left-hand side as the constant parameter, as shown in Fig. 4. For a given minimum singular value of

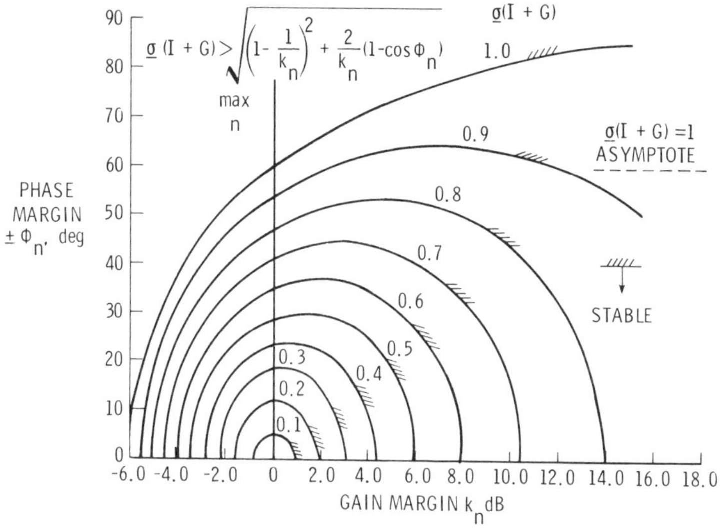

Fig. 4. Minimum singular value based regions of guaranteed stability.

$\underline{\sigma}(I + KG)$, the regions of guaranteed stability are the elliptic regions. For example, if $\underline{\sigma}(I + KG) \geq 0.7$ for all frequencies and ± 30-deg phase margins are required in all loops, then guaranteed simultaneous gain margins are -2.6 dB and $+8.5$ dB (i.e., both the phase and gain can be changed in all loops within these limits at the plant input without destabilizing the closed-loop system).

If the perturbation is introduced at the plant output, denoted by point 2 in Fig. 2, the guaranteed stability conditions are similar to the inequalities of Eqs. (15) and (16), if all the KG terms are replaced by GK in the equations and in Fig. 3. For a SISO system, the terms KG and GK are scalar functions of frequency ω; hence $KG = GK$ for all frequencies. Consequently, the stability margins are the same at all points in the loop. However, a MIMO system with a good stability margin at the plant input may have a poor stability margin at the plant output. It is desirable to have good stability margins at both these locations, and small perturbations at either input or output should not destabilize the system. In [1–3], fictitious input noise or frequency-shaped weighting matrices were used to improve stability margins at the plant input or output. This technique is useful in designing full-order robust LQG control laws for a MIMO feedback control system. However, when the control law is reduced for practical implementation, the robustness properties deteriorate. The stability robustness and the performance of this controller or other existing classical control laws can be improved by the constrained optimization procedure described in Section V. A detailed description of this scheme without any constraint was presented in [7], where full- and reduced-order robust controller design for a wing flutter suppression problem was described.

V. OPTIMIZATION SCHEME

The basic objective of the control law optimization scheme is to find the values of the matrices A, B, C, and D in Eqs. (8) and (9), which represent a control law or a dynamic compensator for a closed-loop stable system, such that a cost function is minimized and a set of inequality constraints are satisfied. A general purpose optimization software [13], which employs the method of usable-feasible directions, is used to search for the selected controller design variables that minimize the cost function subject to the inequality constraints. The algorithm uses the cost function and constraint gradient information to determine a parameter movement direction and a scalar multiplier in the usable-feasible direction to satisfy the constraints. All the gradient expressions are derived analytically. This results in rapid convergence of the optimization process. A block diagram of the overall scheme for synthesis of reduced-order analog and digital control laws is shown in Fig. 5. The numerical optimization scheme is shown in the dashed rectangle in the figure. The cost function and the constraints are described next. The derivation of gradients are presented in Section VI.

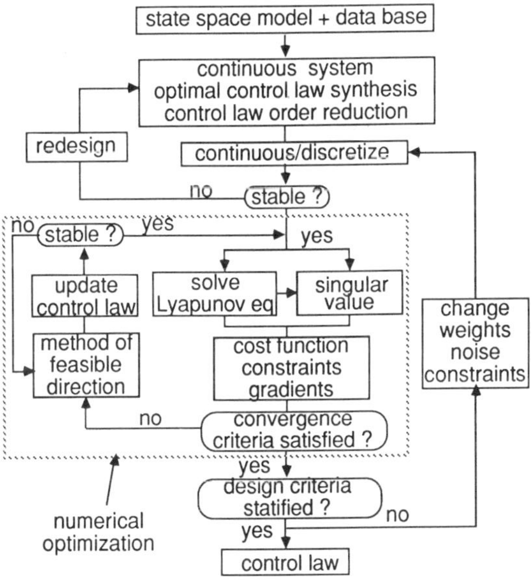

Fig. 5. Control law synthesis scheme block diagram.

A. COST FUNCTION

The LQG-type cost function, defined in Eq. (20), is a weighted sum of the steady-state mean-square values of the closed-loop plant and controller output, defined in Eqs. (7) and (9).

$$J = E[y'^{\mathrm{T}} Q_1 y' + u'^{\mathrm{T}} Q_2 u'] \tag{20}$$

The external inputs u_{com} and y_{com} in Eqs. (10) and (11) are replaced by the uncorrelated stochastic zero-mean white noise processes η and v, with intensity matrices R_{u} and R_{v}, respectively. The cost function J can be computed by solving a steady-state Lyapunov equation of order $(N_{\mathrm{s}} + M)$. The gradients of the cost function can be computed by solving an adjoint Lyapunov equation of the same order, as described in the next section. To visualize the role of each noise intensity matrix and weighting matrix in shaping the singular values of different transfer matrices shown in Eq. (14), the cost function in Eq. (20) can be expressed (assuming $w = 0$ for simplicity) as

$$J = \frac{1}{\pi}\int_0^{\infty} \sum_i \sigma_i[Q_1(I + GK)^{-1}GR_{\mathrm{u}}] + \sum_i \sigma_i[Q_1(I + GK)^{-1}GKR_{\mathrm{v}}] + \sum_i \sigma_i[Q_2(I + KG)^{-1}KGR_{\mathrm{u}}] + \sum_i \sigma_i[Q_2(I + KG)^{-1}KR_{\mathrm{v}}]\, d\omega \tag{21}$$

In Eq. (21), by increasing R_{u} relative to R_{v}, one imposes more weight on the first and third term, and minimizing J can be interpreted as reducing the general magnitude of $(I + GK)^{-1}G$ and $(I + KG)^{-1}KG$. Since $(I + GK)^{-1}G = G(I + KG)^{-1}$ and $(I + KG)^{-1}KG = (I + (KG)^{-1})^{-1}$, the minimum magnitude of $(I + (KG)^{-1})$ and $(I + KG)$ are increased as a consequence. This increases stability margins at the plant input. Similarly, increasing R_{v}, relative to R_{u} imposes more weight on $(I + GK)^{-1}GK$ and $(I + KG)^{-1}K$. By the same argument, minimizing J would increase stability margins at the plant output. Increasing R_{v} also has the effect of rapid attenuation or reduced bandwidth because of the term $(I + KG)^{-1}K$. The weighting matrices Q_1 and Q_2 also play similar roles, as explained in [1–3]. Other types of cost function, such as the square sum of the controller gains trace$[C^{\mathrm{T}}C]$ can also be chosen for constrained optimization [6].

B. CONSTRAINTS

In the constrained optimization approach, the cost function J is minimized by changing selected design variables p subject to a set of N_{g} inequality constraints defined as

$$g_n(p) \leq 0, \qquad n = 1, 2, \ldots, N_{\mathrm{g}} \tag{22}$$

$$g_1(p) = \frac{1}{N}\sum_{n=1}^{N}\left[\max\left\{0, \sigma_D(\omega_n) - \sigma[I+KG(j\omega_n, p)]\right\}\right]^2$$

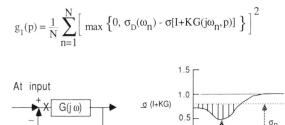

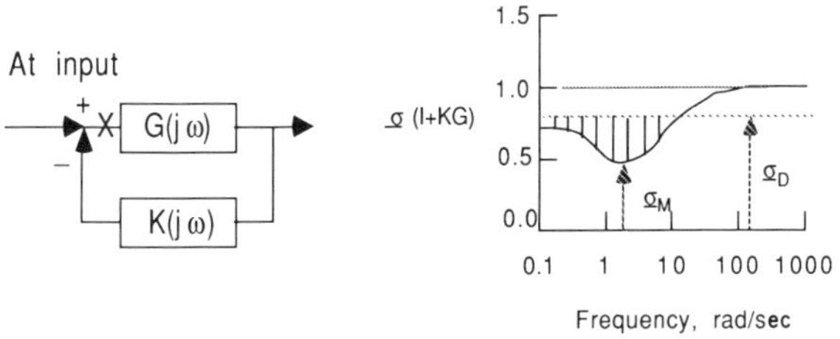

Fig. 6. Cumulative constraint on minimum singular value at plant input.

Here $g_n(p)$ may represent a constraint on the minimum singular value $\boldsymbol{\sigma}(I + KG)$ or $\boldsymbol{\sigma}(I + GK)$, or on selected mean-square (MS) responses, dynamic loads, control surface deflection and rate, and so forth.

1. Constraints on Singular Value

Let us assume that the minimum singular value $\boldsymbol{\sigma}(I + KG)$ of a stable system is $\boldsymbol{\sigma}_M$, as shown in Fig. 6. We want to increase the minimum singular value to a higher level denoted by the line $\boldsymbol{\sigma}_D$. It is also possible to impose a frequency-dependent lower bound $\boldsymbol{\sigma}_D(\omega)$, where the singular values are required to attenuate rapidly after a specified break frequency. The selection of an achievable $\boldsymbol{\sigma}_D(\omega)$ is based on experience and engineering judgment, depending on the control power and response limitations since control power may be wasted in designing a compensator to satisfy a tight bound with high $\boldsymbol{\sigma}_D(\omega)$. Moreover, because of the conservative nature of the singular value measures, the inability to obtain such a compensator does not necessarily imply a robustness problem.

The constraint function $g_1(p)$ or $g_2(p)$ is basically a cumulative measure of the vertical distance between $\boldsymbol{\sigma}_D(\omega)$ and $\boldsymbol{\sigma}(I + KG)$ or $\boldsymbol{\sigma}(I + GK)$, as shown in Fig. 6; it is defined as

$$g_1(p) = \frac{1}{N}\sum_{n=1}^{N}[\max\{0, \sigma_D(\omega_n) - \sigma[I + KG(j\omega_n, p)]\}]^2 \tag{23}$$

and

$$g_2(p) = \frac{1}{N}\sum_{n=1}^{N}[\max\{0, \sigma_D(\omega_n) - \sigma[I + GK(j\omega_n, p)]\}]^2 \tag{24}$$

The summation is taken over a range of frequency points ω_n, and the spacing of the frequency points in the frequency range can be chosen by the designer, depending on the specific problem. The objective is to reduce (preferably to zero) the shaded area below the $\boldsymbol{\sigma}_{\mathrm{D}}(\omega)$ line by minimizing $g_1(p)$ and $g_2(p)$. The expressions for the singular values and their gradients with respect to the design variables are derived analytically and will be described in Section VII. The constraints based on Eq. (16) can be defined in a similar manner. These constraints are complementary to Eq. (15) and may impose an unnecessary computational burden without tangible improvement in results.

2. Constraints on Design Responses

In the constrained optimization approach, the designer can choose the individual design RMS response requirements as a set of inequality constraints, instead of lumping them in the cost function J. The design response constraint is defined as

$$g_n(p) = E[y_{\mathrm{d}_n}^2]/E[y_{\mathrm{dmax}_n}^2] - 1 \leq 0, \qquad n = 3, 4, \ldots, N_{\mathrm{g}} \tag{25}$$

The $E[y_{\mathrm{d}_n}^2]$ is the steady-state mean-square response of the nth design output y_{d_n}, and $E[y_{\mathrm{dmax}_n}^2]$ is the corresponding maximum allowable value; y_{d} is the design output vector. $E[y_{\mathrm{d}_n}^2]$ is computed from selected diagonal elements of the covariance matrix:

$$E[y_{\mathrm{d}}y_{\mathrm{d}}^{\mathrm{T}}] = [H_{\mathrm{d}}E_{\mathrm{d}}]E\left[\begin{Bmatrix} x \\ u \end{Bmatrix}\begin{Bmatrix} x \\ u \end{Bmatrix}^{\mathrm{T}}\right][H_{\mathrm{d}}E_{\mathrm{d}}]^{\mathrm{T}} \tag{26}$$

where

$$y_{\mathrm{d}} = H_{\mathrm{d}}x_{\mathrm{s}} + E_{\mathrm{d}}u$$

The response constraints and their gradients with respect to the design variables are derived analytically and computed by solving a set of Lyapunov equations. The details are presented in Section VI.

VI. ANALYTICAL GRADIENTS

The general analytical expressions for the gradients of the cost function and the constraints on the singular value and design MS responses are derived in this section. A general LQG-type cost function, which also includes the controller states and their derivatives, is considered. The direct feedthrough term D in Eq. (9) and E_{d} in Eq. (26) are retained, with the assumption that for the LQG design in the continuous-time domain, some associated terms are set to zero to avoid an infinite RMS response due to the white noise in the system. From Eqs. (6)–(11), the closed-loop system equation can be written as

$$\begin{Bmatrix} \dot{x}_s \\ \dot{x}_c \end{Bmatrix} = \begin{bmatrix} F + G_u DH & G_u C \\ BH & A \end{bmatrix} \begin{Bmatrix} x_s \\ x_c \end{Bmatrix} + \begin{bmatrix} G_u & G_w & G_u D \\ 0 & 0 & B \end{bmatrix} \begin{Bmatrix} \eta \\ w \\ v \end{Bmatrix} \tag{27}$$

or

$$\dot{x}_a = F_a x_a + G_a \eta_a$$

The steady-state RMS responses are computed by solving for the steady-state condition of the Lyapunov Eq. (28), which is satisfied by Eq. (27), since the augmented state vector x_a and noise vector η_a are assumed to be uncorrelated, and the expected value of their cross products is zero [14,15]:

$$F_a X_a + X_a F_a^T + G_a R_a G_a^T = 0 \tag{28}$$

Here, $X_a = E[x_a x_a^T]$ and R_a is the noise covariance matrix of η_a. A steady-state solution exists if the closed-loop system is stable (i.e., if all the eigenvalues of F_a have a negative real part). Once the steady-state value of the X_a matrix is known, the cost function and other mean-square responses can be computed.

To separate the design variables or the A, B, C, and D matrices in Eq. (27) into a single matrix, and to simplify the derivation of the gradients, the system Eqs. (6)–(11) are expressed in a special augmented form that is similar to a simple output feedback system, as follows:

$$\begin{Bmatrix} \dot{x}_s \\ \dot{x}_c \end{Bmatrix} = \begin{bmatrix} F & 0 \\ 0 & 0 \end{bmatrix} \begin{Bmatrix} x_s \\ x_c \end{Bmatrix} + \begin{bmatrix} G_u & 0 \\ 0 & I \end{bmatrix} \begin{Bmatrix} u \\ \dot{x}_c \end{Bmatrix} + \begin{bmatrix} G_u & G_w & 0 \\ 0 & 0 & 0 \end{bmatrix} \begin{Bmatrix} \eta \\ w \\ v \end{Bmatrix} \tag{29}$$

or

$$\dot{x}_a = \hat{F} x_a + \hat{G} u_a + \hat{G}_w \eta_a$$

$$\begin{Bmatrix} y \\ x_c \end{Bmatrix} = \begin{bmatrix} H & 0 \\ 0 & I \end{bmatrix} \begin{Bmatrix} x_s \\ x_c \end{Bmatrix} + \begin{bmatrix} 0 & 0 & I \\ 0 & 0 & 0 \end{bmatrix} \begin{Bmatrix} \eta \\ w \\ v \end{Bmatrix} \tag{30}$$

or

$$y_a = \hat{H} x_a + \hat{I} \eta_a$$

$$\begin{Bmatrix} u \\ \dot{x}_c \end{Bmatrix} = \begin{bmatrix} D & C \\ B & A \end{bmatrix} \begin{Bmatrix} y \\ x_c \end{Bmatrix} \tag{31}$$

or

$$u_a = \hat{C} y_a$$

Note that the closed-loop system Eq. (27) can also be derived by substituting Eqs. (30) and (31) into (29) and using the identities

$$F_a \equiv \hat{F} + \hat{G}\hat{C}\hat{H} \qquad \text{and} \qquad G_a \equiv \hat{G}_w + \hat{G}\hat{C}\hat{I} \tag{32}$$

A. GRADIENTS OF THE COST FUNCTION

The general cost function is defined as

$$J = E\left[\begin{Bmatrix} x_a \\ u_a \end{Bmatrix}^{\mathrm{T}} \begin{bmatrix} \hat{Q}_1 & \hat{M} \\ \hat{M}^{\mathrm{T}} & \hat{Q}_2 \end{bmatrix} \begin{Bmatrix} x_a \\ u_a \end{Bmatrix}\right] \tag{33}$$

Equation (33) can be reduced to the standard LQG cost function $J = E[y_d^{\mathrm{T}} Q_d y_d + u'^{\mathrm{T}} Q_2 u']$, if one sets

$$\hat{Q}_1 = \begin{bmatrix} Q_x & 0 \\ 0 & 0 \end{bmatrix} \qquad \hat{Q}_2 = \begin{bmatrix} Q_u & 0 \\ 0 & 0 \end{bmatrix} \qquad \hat{M} = \begin{bmatrix} M_d & 0 \\ 0 & 0 \end{bmatrix} \tag{34}$$

where

$$Q_x = (H_d^{\mathrm{T}} Q_d H_d), \qquad Q_u = (Q_2 + E_d^{\mathrm{T}} Q_d E_d), \qquad \text{and} \qquad M_d = (H_d^{\mathrm{T}} Q_d E_d).$$

Equation (33) can also be reduced to the cost function $J = E[y'^{\mathrm{T}} Q_1 y' + u'^{\mathrm{T}} Q_2 u']$ of Eq. (20), if one sets $Q_x = H^{\mathrm{T}} Q_1 H$, $Q_u = Q_2$, and $M_d = 0$ (i.e., $H_d = H$, $E_d = 0$) in Eq. (34). After some elementary matrix algebra, and using Eqs. (29)–(31), the cost function can be expressed as a function of the covariance matrix X_a and the weighting matrices.

$$J = \mathrm{trace}[\{\hat{Q}_1 + (\hat{C}\hat{H})^{\mathrm{T}} \hat{Q}_2 (\hat{C}\hat{H}) + (\hat{M}\hat{C}\hat{H}) + (\hat{M}\hat{C}\hat{H})^{\mathrm{T}}\} X_a] \equiv \mathrm{tr}[Q_a X_a] \tag{35}$$

In deriving Eq. (35), we assume that the term $E[\hat{Q}_2(\hat{C}\hat{I})\eta_a \eta_a^{\mathrm{T}}(\hat{C}\hat{I})^{\mathrm{T}}]$ or DR_v is zero to avoid an unbounded result. Since X_a also satisfies the Lyapunov Eq. (28), a symmetric Lagrange multiplier matrix Λ is used to augment Eq. (35) as

$$J = \mathrm{tr}[Q_a X_a + \Lambda^{\mathrm{T}}(F_a X_a + X_a F_a^{\mathrm{T}} + G_a R_a G_a^{\mathrm{T}})] \tag{36}$$

The necessary optimality conditions for J are Eq. (28) (from $\delta J/\delta \Lambda = 0$) along with

$$\delta J/\delta X_a = F_a^{\mathrm{T}} \Lambda + \Lambda F_a + Q_a^{\mathrm{T}} = 0 \tag{37}$$

and

$$\begin{aligned} \delta J/\delta p = \mathrm{tr}[(\delta Q_a/\delta p) X_a + \Lambda^{\mathrm{T}}[(\delta F_a/\delta p) X_a + X_a (\delta F_a/\delta p)^{\mathrm{T}} \\ + \delta(G_a R_a G_a^{\mathrm{T}})/\delta p]] = 0 \end{aligned} \tag{38}$$

where p is any design variable. In the control law optimization problem in which the plant parameters are fixed, selected elements of the matrix $\hat{C}$ are chosen as the design variable. Using Eq. (32) and the matrix trace properties, we can express the gradients of the cost function J with respect to $\hat{C}$ in a matrix form, as shown in Eq. (39). The steps involved in the partial differentiation of matrix expressions are presented in Appendix A. Partial derivatives of matrix expressions occur frequently in optimization and parameter sensitivity study. The software programming is greatly simplified by reducing them to a compact matrix form.

$$\frac{\delta J}{\delta \hat{C}} = 2[(\hat{Q}_2 \hat{C} \hat{H} + \hat{G}^{\mathrm{T}} \Lambda + \hat{M}^{\mathrm{T}}) X_{\mathrm{a}} \hat{H}^{\mathrm{T}} + \hat{G}^{\mathrm{T}} (\Lambda G_{\mathrm{a}} R_{\mathrm{a}} \hat{I}^{\mathrm{T}})] \tag{39}$$

Note that Eq. (39) is a matrix of dimension $(N_{\mathrm{c}} + M) \times (N_{\mathrm{s}} + M)$, whereas Eq. (38) is a scalar. From equations similar to Eqs. (28), (37), and (38), explicit optimality conditions for a fixed-order dynamic compensator were derived by Hyland and Bernstein [16]. However, since all the elements of $\hat{C}$ are not independent or free variables, one cannot set Eq. (39) to zero to solve for $\hat{C}$. Instead, Eq. (39) is used to compute the gradients in the present numerical optimization approach.

B. GRADIENTS OF DESIGN RESPONSES

The gradient of mean-square design response constraints defined in Eq. (25) are obtained from the derivative of selected diagonal terms of the matrix $E[y_{\mathrm{d}} y_{\mathrm{d}}^{\mathrm{T}}]$. This procedure is similar to that for the cost function gradient. For example, one can write the covariance matrix

$$E[y_{\mathrm{d}} y_{\mathrm{d}}^{\mathrm{T}}] = H_{\mathrm{c}} X_{\mathrm{a}} H_{\mathrm{c}}^{\mathrm{T}} + E[(E_{\mathrm{d}} D) v v^{\mathrm{T}} (E_{\mathrm{d}} D)^{\mathrm{T}}] \tag{40}$$

where

$$H_{\mathrm{c}} = [H_{\mathrm{d}} + E_{\mathrm{d}} D H \colon E_{\mathrm{d}} C] \tag{41}$$

The second term in Eq. (40) is set to zero, since $DR_{\mathrm{v}} = 0$, to avoid an infinite response. Assuming y_{d} to be a scalar $y_{\mathrm{d}n}$, chosen as the nth design response, and $H_{\mathrm{d}n}$ and E_{dn} to be the row vectors consisting of the nth row of the matrices H_{d} and E_{d}, respectively, one can write the scalar equation

$$E[y_{\mathrm{d}n}^2] = \mathrm{tr}[H_{\mathrm{c}n}^{\mathrm{T}} H_{\mathrm{c}n} X_{\mathrm{a}}] \tag{42}$$

for each of the n design responses. Equation (42) is similar to the cost function of Eq. (36), in which Q_{a} is replaced by $[H_{\mathrm{c}n}^{\mathrm{T}} H_{\mathrm{c}n}]$. This is equivalent to setting $Q_{\mathrm{x}} = (H_{\mathrm{d}n}^{\mathrm{T}} H_{\mathrm{d}n})$, $Q_{\mathrm{u}} = (E_{\mathrm{d}n}^{\mathrm{T}} E_{\mathrm{d}n})$, and $M_{\mathrm{d}} = (H_{\mathrm{d}n}^{\mathrm{T}} E_{\mathrm{d}n})$ in Eq. (34). Using the Lagrange multiplier Λ_n for each element of the $y_{\mathrm{d}n}$ vector and proceeding in same manner as in the cost function gradient derivation, we find that the necessary conditions for minimization of Eq. (42) are Eq. (28) (from $\delta E[y_{dn}^2]/\delta\Lambda_n = 0$) along with

$$\delta E[y_{dn}^2]/\delta X_a = F_a^T\Lambda_n + \Lambda_n F_a + H_{cn}^T H_{cn} = 0 \tag{43}$$

and

$$\delta E[y_{dn}^2]/\delta p = \mathrm{tr}[[\delta(H_{cn}^T H_{cn})/\delta p]X_a + \Lambda_n^T[(\delta F_a/\delta p)X_a + X_a(\delta F_a/\delta p)^T + \delta(G_a R_a G_a^T)/\delta p]] = 0 \tag{44}$$

where p is any design variable. If the design variables are some selected elements of controller quadruple matrix $\hat{C}$, the gradient of the nth constraint with respect to $\hat{C}$ can be expressed in a matrix form, as shown in Eq. (45).

$$\frac{\delta E[y_{dn}^2]}{\delta\hat{C}} = 2[(\tilde{Q}_2\hat{C}\hat{H} + \hat{G}^T\Lambda_n + \tilde{M}^T)X_a\hat{H}^T + \hat{G}^T(\Lambda_n G_a R_a \hat{I}^T)] \tag{45}$$

where

$$\tilde{Q}_2 = \begin{bmatrix} E_{dn}^T E_{dn} & 0 \\ 0 & 0 \end{bmatrix} \qquad \tilde{M} = \begin{bmatrix} H_{dn}^T E_{dn} & 0 \\ 0 & 0 \end{bmatrix}$$

Here X_a satisfies the Lyapunov Eq. (28), and the Lagrange multiplier matrix Λ_n satisfies the adjoint Lyapunov Eq. (43). Note that Eq. (45) is a matrix of dimension $(N_c + M) \times (N_s + M)$ whereas Eq. (44) is a scalar.

VII. GRADIENTS OF SINGULAR VALUES

To perform the constrained optimization it is necessary to determine the gradients of the singular value $\sigma(I + KG)$ with respect to the elements of the controller quadruple matrices or any general design parameter p. For a distinct singular value σ_n of a general complex matrix G, the gradient with respect to a real parameter p is given by

$$\frac{\delta\sigma_n}{\delta p} = Re\left[u_n^*\frac{\delta G}{\delta p}v_n\right] \tag{46}$$

where u_n and v_n are, respectively, the right and left normalized singular vectors of G. See Appendix B for proof. For repeated singular values, see [17] for the corresponding Gateaux differential expressions. The gradients of $\sigma_n(I + KG)$ and $\sigma_n(I + GK)$ with respect to the controller quadruple matrix $\hat{C}$ can be derived in a compact matrix form as follows. The technique is to write KG or

GK in an augmented form to separate the $\hat{C}$ matrix and then carry out matrix differentiation.

A. SINGULAR VALUE GRADIENTS AT PLANT INPUT

From Eqs. (12) and (13), it can be shown that

$$(I + KG) = I + \mathbf{C\Phi B} \tag{47}$$

where

$$\mathbf{B} = \begin{bmatrix} G_u \\ 0 \end{bmatrix}_{(N_s+M)\times N_c} \qquad \mathbf{C} = -[DH \quad C]_{N_c\times(N_s+M)} = \hat{I}_1\hat{C}\hat{H},$$

$$\Phi = (Is - \mathbf{A})^{-1}$$

$$\mathbf{A} = \begin{bmatrix} F & 0 \\ BH & A \end{bmatrix} \equiv \hat{F} + \hat{I}_2\hat{C}\hat{H} \qquad \hat{I}_1 = [-I \quad 0]_{N_c\times(N_c+M)}$$

$$\hat{I}_2 = \begin{bmatrix} 0 & 0 \\ 0 & I \end{bmatrix}_{(N_s+M)\times(N_c+M)}$$

and

$$\begin{aligned} \frac{\delta\sigma_n(I + KG)}{\delta p} &= \operatorname{Re}\operatorname{Tr}\left[\frac{\delta(I + \mathbf{C\Phi B})}{\delta p} v_n u_n^*\right] \\ &= \operatorname{Re}\operatorname{Tr}\left[\left\{\frac{\delta\mathbf{C}}{\delta p}\mathbf{\Phi B} + \mathbf{C\Phi}\frac{\delta\mathbf{B}}{\delta p} + \mathbf{C\Phi}\frac{\delta\mathbf{A}}{\delta p}\mathbf{\Phi B}\right\} v_n u_n^*\right] \end{aligned} \tag{48}$$

Let us assume that p is an element of $\hat{C}$. Noting that $\delta\mathbf{B}/\delta p = 0$, we can now write Eq. (48) as

$$\frac{\delta\sigma_n(I + KG)}{\delta p} = \operatorname{Re}\operatorname{Tr}\left[\left\{\frac{\delta(\hat{I}_1\hat{C})}{\delta p} + \mathbf{C\Phi}\frac{\delta(\hat{I}_2\hat{C})}{\delta p}\right\}\hat{H}\mathbf{\Phi B}v_n u_n^*\right] \tag{49}$$

Using the matrix trace properties $\operatorname{Re}\operatorname{Tr}(G) = \operatorname{Re}\operatorname{Tr}(G^*)$, we can express a matrix relation for the gradients with respect to all the elements of matrix $\hat{C}$ as

$$\frac{\delta\sigma_n(I + KG)}{\delta\hat{C}} = \operatorname{Re}[\{\hat{I}_1^{\mathrm{T}} + (\mathbf{C\Phi}\hat{I}_2)^*\}\{\hat{H}\mathbf{\Phi B}v_n u_n^*\}^*]_{(N_c+M)\times(N_O+M)} \tag{50}$$

Taking the complex conjugate transpose and simplifying, one finally obtains

$$\frac{\delta\sigma_n(I + KG)}{\delta\hat{C}} = \operatorname{Re}[\{\hat{H}\mathbf{\Phi B}v_n u_n^*\}[-I_{N_c} \quad \mathbf{C\Phi I}]]_{(N_O+M)\times(N_c+M)} \tag{51}$$

where

$$\mathbf{I} = \begin{bmatrix} 0 \\ I \end{bmatrix}_{(N_s + M) \times M}$$

The gradient expression for $\sigma_n[(I + KG)^{-1}KG]$ is similarly given by

$$\frac{\delta\sigma_n[(I + KG)^{-1}KG]}{\delta\hat{C}} = \mathrm{Re}[\{\hat{H}\Phi_a\mathbf{B}v_n u_n^*\}[-(I + KG)^{-1} \quad \mathbf{C}\Phi_a\mathbf{I}]] \tag{52}$$

where

$$\Phi_a = (Is - \mathbf{A} + \mathbf{BC})^{-1} = (Is - F_a)^{-1}$$

Note that $(I + KG)^{-1}KG = \mathbf{C}\Phi_a\mathbf{B}$. In Eq. (52), v_n and u_n are right and left singular vectors of $[(I + KG)^{-1}KG]$. The gradient expressions for $(I + KG)^{-1}$ is similar to Eq. (52) but with a negative sign since $(I + KG)^{-1} + (I + KG)^{-1}KG = I$. The singular values and gradients of $(I + (KG)^{-1})$ can be obtained from Eq. (52) and the singular value property $\sigma_{\max}(G) = 1/\sigma_{\min}(G^{-1})$.

B. SINGULAR VALUE GRADIENTS AT PLANT OUTPUT

The gradients of $\sigma_n(I + GK)$ and $\sigma_n[(I + GK)^{-1}GK]$ with respect to $\hat{C}$ are also derived in same manner. One can show that

$$I + GK = (I + \tilde{C}\tilde{\Phi}\tilde{B}), \qquad (I + GK)^{-1}GK = \tilde{C}\Phi_a\tilde{B} \tag{53}$$

where

$$\tilde{C} = -[H \quad 0_M], \qquad \tilde{\Phi} = (Is - \tilde{A})^{-1}, \qquad \tilde{B} = \begin{bmatrix} G_u D \\ B \end{bmatrix} = \hat{G}\hat{C}\tilde{I}_1,$$

$$\tilde{I}_1 = \begin{bmatrix} I_{N_O} \\ 0_{M \times N_O} \end{bmatrix}$$

$$\tilde{A} = \begin{bmatrix} F & G_u C \\ A & 0 \end{bmatrix} = \hat{F} + \hat{G}\hat{C}\tilde{I}_2, \qquad \tilde{I}_2 = \begin{bmatrix} 0 & 0 \\ 0 & I \end{bmatrix}_{(N_O + M) \times (N_s + M)},$$

$$\tilde{I} = [0 \quad I]_{M \times (N_s + M)}$$

Proceeding as before and simplifying, we can express the gradient expressions as follows. The derivation is left to the reader.

$$\frac{\delta\sigma_n(I + GK)}{\delta\hat{C}^{\mathrm{T}}} = \mathrm{Re}\left[\begin{Bmatrix} I_{N_O} \\ \tilde{I}\tilde{\Phi}\tilde{B} \end{Bmatrix} v_n u_n^* \tilde{C}\tilde{\Phi}\hat{G}\right] \tag{54}$$

$$\frac{\delta\sigma_n[(I + GK)^{-1}GK]}{\delta\hat{C}^{\mathrm{T}}} = \mathrm{Re}\left[\begin{Bmatrix} I_{N_O} - \tilde{C}\Phi_a\tilde{B} \\ \tilde{I}\Phi_a\tilde{B} \end{Bmatrix} v_n u_n^* \tilde{C}\Phi_a\hat{G}\right] \tag{55}$$

Note that the gradient expressions for $\sigma(I + GK)^{-1}$ is similar to Eq. (55) with a negative sign, since $(I + GK)^{-1} + (I + GK)^{-1}GK = I$.

Since the computation of singular values requires inversion of a $(N_s + M)$th-order complex matrix of the type $(j\omega I - \mathbf{A})$ at a large number of frequency points, an efficient computational method is used [18,19]. The basic procedure is to transform F_a into an upper Hessenberg matrix so that, for all ω, $(j\omega I - \mathbf{A})$ remains in upper Hessenberg form, and the inversion problem can be solved quickly by the simple forward and backward substitution. Thus, the repeated upper and lower triangular transformation at each ω_n is avoided. Two additional steps are involved in computing the singular value gradients at each frequency point. The first step is the solution of a set of $(N_s + M)$ simultaneous equations and is relatively inexpensive since the matrix $\mathbf{A}$ is already available in upper Hessenberg form. The second step is the computation of the singular vectors and usually involves a low-order complex matrix for systems with a few feedback loops.

VIII. DISCRETE SYSTEM

The constrained optimization formulation for a discrete system is similar to that of the continuous system and is presented in this section for a single sampling rate system. Since most of the implementation is done using an onboard digital microprocessor, control law synthesis and stability robustness improvement and simulation in the discrete domain is a practical necessity. Also, many of the design considerations unique to digital systems (such as the effects of discretization, sampling time, computational delay, and antialiasing filters) can be taken into account and compensated for during the design stage. For the discrete system, the complete state-space equations including the computational delay and antialiasing filters can be expressed as

$$\text{Plant:} \quad x_{k+1} = Fx_k + G_u u_k + G_w w_k \tag{56}$$

$$\text{Output:} \quad y'_k = Hx_k \tag{57}$$

$$\text{Design output:} \quad y_{dk} = H_d x_k + E_d u_k \tag{58}$$

$$\text{Control law:} \quad z_{k+1} = Az_k + By_k$$

$$u'_k = Cz_k + Dy_k \tag{59}$$

$$\text{Interconnection:} \quad y_k = y'_k + y_{k\text{com}}$$

$$u_k = u'_k + u_{k\text{com}}, \qquad k = 0, 1, 2, \ldots, N_{k-1} \tag{60}$$

These constant coefficient finite difference linear equations can represent discrete-time equations of motion due to a small perturbation from a steady-state equilibrium condition for a flexible aircraft or large space structure. They can be derived from the corresponding continuous equations using the Z transform [20]. The subscript k represents the data at the kth sampling stage. For a stochastic system, the plant disturbance w_k, the output measurement noise v_k (at $y_{k\text{com}}$), and the plant input noise η_k (at $u_{k\text{com}}$) are zero mean discrete white-noise processes with covariance R_w, R_v, and R_u, respectively.

$$\begin{aligned} &E[w_k] = E[v_k] = E[\eta_k] = [0] \\ &E[w_k w_1^T] = R_w \delta_{k1}, \qquad E[v_k v_1^T] = R_v \delta_{k1} \\ &E[\eta_k \eta_1^T] = R_u \delta_{k1} \end{aligned} \tag{61}$$

where δ_{k1} is the Kroneker delta, which is 1 when $k = 1$ and 0 when $k \neq 1$. The plant and the controller transfer matrices in the Z domain are (for plant noise $w_k = 0$)

$$Y'_k(Z) = H(IZ - F)^{-1} G_u U_k(Z) = G(Z) U_k(Z) \tag{62}$$

$$U'_k(Z) = [C(IZ - A)^{-1} B + D] Y_k(Z) = -K(Z) Y_k(Z) \tag{63}$$

The stability robustness conditions for the discrete system are similar to those of the continuous system. Here the Z is replaced by $\exp(j\omega T)$, where T is the sampling time period and ω is a set of frequency points below the Nyquist frequency π/T radians, or $1/2T$ Hz. The augmented system equations can be written as

$$\hat{x}_{k+1} = \hat{F}\hat{x}_k + \hat{G}\hat{u}_k + \hat{G}_w \hat{\eta}_k \tag{64}$$

$$\hat{y}_k = \hat{H}_k \hat{x}_k + \hat{I}\hat{\eta}_k \tag{65}$$

$$\hat{u}_k = \hat{C}_k \hat{y}_k \tag{66}$$

where

$$\hat{x}_k = \begin{Bmatrix} x_k \\ z_k \end{Bmatrix}, \qquad \hat{u}_k = \begin{Bmatrix} u_k \\ z_{k+1} \end{Bmatrix}, \qquad \hat{y}_k = \begin{Bmatrix} y_k \\ z_k \end{Bmatrix}, \qquad \hat{\eta}_k = \begin{Bmatrix} \eta_k \\ w_k \\ v_k \end{Bmatrix}$$

The matrices $\hat{F}$, and so forth, are as defined in Eqs. (29)–(31). Other forms of control laws, which include control input rates as additional states (i.e., $z_{k+1} = Az_k + By_k + B_u u_k$ and $u_{k+1} = Cz_k + Dy_k + D_u u_k$) [21] or averaged delayed sampling (i.e., $y_k = Hx_{k-1} + Eu_{k-1} + v_{k-1}$) [22] can also be cast into the form of Eqs. (64)–(66).

A. OPTIMIZATION PROBLEM FORMULATION

For a given closed-loop stable system described by Eqs. (64)–(66), the optimization algorithm updates the selected free parameters of the controller quadruple matrix $\hat{C}$ to minimize the steady-state expected value of the cost function J, defined by Eq. (67):

$$J = E\left[\begin{Bmatrix}\hat{x}_k\\\hat{u}_k\end{Bmatrix}^{\mathrm{T}}\begin{bmatrix}\hat{Q}_1 & \hat{M}\\\hat{M}^{\mathrm{T}} & \hat{Q}_2\end{bmatrix}\begin{Bmatrix}\hat{x}_k\\\hat{u}_k\end{Bmatrix}\right] \tag{67}$$

The minimization is subject to a set of inequality constraints on the steady-state mean-square values of selected design responses, defined by Eq. (25). In Eq. (67), the subscript k has been dropped to indicate a stochastic steady-state condition and for clarity. Although the cost function J is defined in general terms, most of the design requirements can be imposed as inequality constraints in Eq. (25) instead of lumping them all in the cost function. This feature can be used to modify an existing control law, to meet individual maximum RMS response limitations, actuator deflection, and rate limits, and for other special design requirements. The constraints are also imposed on the minimum singular value of the return-difference matrix at the plant input and output, as defined in Eqs. (23) and (24). The analytical expressions for the gradients of the cost function and the constraints, with respect to the elements of the control law quadruple matrix $\hat{C}$, are presented next. With these analytical gradients, a numerical constrained optimization technique, called *the method of feasible directions* [13], is used to update the selected free parameters of the control law while attempting to satisfy the inequality constraints. The designer can choose the structure of the control law as well as the design variables. This enables optimization of classical control laws as well as an estimator-based full- or reduced-order digital control laws.

B. GRADIENTS OF COST FUNCTION

Substituting Eq. (66) into (64), we can write the closed-loop system equations with discrete white noise input as

$$\hat{x}_{k+1} = F_a\hat{x}_k + G_a\hat{\eta}_k \tag{68}$$

where

$$F_a = \hat{F} + \hat{G}\hat{C}\hat{H} \qquad \text{and} \qquad G_a = \hat{G}_w + \hat{G}\hat{C}\hat{I}$$

The steady-state mean-square responses can now be computed by solving for the steady-state condition of the discrete Lyapunov Eq. (69):

$$X_{k+1} = F_a X_k F_a^{\mathrm{T}} + G_a R_a G_a^{\mathrm{T}} \tag{69}$$

where

$$X_k = E[\hat{x}_k\hat{x}_k^{\mathrm{T}}] \qquad \text{and} \qquad G_a = E[\hat{\eta}_k\hat{\eta}_k^{\mathrm{T}}]$$

A steady-state solution exists if the closed-loop system is stable (i.e., all eigenvalues of F_a have magnitude less than 1). After the steady-state value of X_k is known, the cost function and the other mean-square responses can also be computed from Eqs. (64–66). After some matrix manipulation, the cost function in Eq. (67) can be expressed as

$$J = \mathrm{tr}[Q_a X_k] + \mathrm{tr}[(\hat{C}\hat{I})^T \hat{Q}_2 (\hat{C}\hat{I}) R_a] \tag{70}$$

where

$$Q_a = [\hat{Q}_1 + (\hat{C}\hat{H})^T \hat{Q}_2 (\hat{C}\hat{H}) + (\hat{M}\hat{C}\hat{H}) + (\hat{M}\hat{C}\hat{H})^T]$$

Using a Lagrange multiplier matrix Λ_k and matrix trace properties, we can express the gradients of the cost function J with respect to the elements of the control law quadruple matrix $\hat{C}$ in a compact matrix form, as shown in Eq. (71). The derivation is similar to that presented for the continuous case in Section VI.

$$\frac{\delta J}{\delta \hat{C}} = 2[(\hat{Q}_2 + \hat{G}^T \Lambda_\kappa \hat{G})\hat{C}(\hat{H} X_k \hat{H}^T + \hat{I} R_a \hat{I}^T) + (\hat{G}^T \Lambda_k \hat{F} + \hat{M}^T) X_k \hat{H}^T] \tag{71}$$

Here, X_k and Λ_k satisfy the steady-state conditions of the Lyapunov Eqs. (69) and (72).

$$\Lambda_k = F_a^T \Lambda_{k+1} F_a + Q_a \tag{72}$$

Equation (71) has exactly the same form as in the direct output feedback case [21,23], and one can write explicit expressions for $\hat{C}$ by setting the gradient to zero. From equations similar to Eqs. (69)–(72), explicit optimality conditions were derived by Bernstein *et al.* [22] for fixed-order, sampled-data, dynamic compensation. In the present approach, the gradient expressions were used for numerical parameter search.

C. GRADIENTS OF DESIGN RESPONSES

The gradients of the constraints g_n, defined in Eq. (25) are computed from the analytical gradient expressions of selected diagonal terms of the design mean-square response or covariance matrix $E[y_d y_d^T]$. The derivation is similar to that for the continuous system. For the discrete system, the last term of Eq. (40) is finite, and one can write the covariance matrix

$$E[y_d y_d^T] = H_c X_k H_c^T + (E_d D) R_v (E_d D)^T \tag{73}$$

where

$$H_c = [H_d + E_d D H \colon E_d C]$$

As before, assuming y_d to be a scalar y_{dn}, chosen as the nth design response, and H_{dn} and E_{dn} to be the row vectors consisting of the nth row of the matrices

H_d and E_d, respectively, one can write the scalar equation

$$E[y_{dn}^2] = \mathrm{tr}[H_{cn}^T H_{cn} X_k] + \mathrm{tr}[(E_d D)^T (E_d D) R_v] \tag{74}$$

for each of the constraints, and the corresponding analytical gradient expression in matrix form is

$$\frac{\delta E[y_{dn}^2]}{\delta \hat{C}} = 2[\tilde{Q}_2 + \hat{G}^T \Lambda_k \hat{G})\hat{C}(\hat{H} X_k \hat{H}^T + \hat{I} R_a \hat{I}^T) + (\hat{G}^T \Lambda_k \hat{F} + \tilde{M}^T) X_k \hat{H}^T] \tag{75}$$

where $\tilde{Q}_2$ and $\tilde{M}$ are defined in Eq. (45). Here X_k satisfies the discrete Lyapunov Eq. (69), and the Lagrange multiplier matrix Λ_k satisfies the steady-state condition of the adjoint discrete Lyapunov Eq. (76) for the nth constraint.

$$\Lambda_k = F_a^T \Lambda_{k+1} F_a + [H_{cn}^T H_{cn}] \tag{76}$$

Simplifying Eq. (75), we can write the individual gradient expressions as

$$\delta E[y_{dn}^2]/\delta A = 2[\Lambda_c^*] \tag{77}$$

$$\delta E[y_{dn}^2]/\delta B = 2[\Lambda_{sc}^T G_u D + \Lambda_c B) R_v + (\Lambda_{sc}^* H)^T] \tag{78}$$

$$\delta E[y_{dn}^2]/\delta C = 2[E_d^T E_d (D H X_{sc} + C X_c) + E_d^T H_d X_{sc} + G_u^T \Lambda_{sc}^*] \tag{79}$$

$$\delta E[y_{dn}^2]/\delta D = 2[E_d^T E_d ((D H X_s + C X_{sc}^T) H^T + D R_v) + E_d^T H_d X_s H^T + G_u^T ((\Lambda_s G_u D + \Lambda_{sc} B) R_v + \Lambda_s^* H^T)] \tag{80}$$

where

$$\Lambda^* \equiv \Lambda_k F_a X_k \equiv \begin{bmatrix} \Lambda_s^* & \Lambda_{sc}^* \\ \Lambda_{sc}^{*T} & \Lambda_c^* \end{bmatrix}_{(N_s+M)\times(N_s+M)}$$

and

$$X_k \equiv \begin{bmatrix} X_s & X_{sc} \\ X_{sc}^T & X_c \end{bmatrix}_{(N_s+M)\times(N_s+M)}$$

The gradients of the singular value constraints defined in Eqs. (23) and (24) are derived as in the continuous-time case, with the Laplace variable s replaced by Z, and $j\omega_n$ replaced by $\exp(j\omega_n T)$.

IX. DESIGN VARIABLES

Since all the elements of the control law quadruple matrices A, B, C, and D in Eqs. (8) and (9) are not independent, it is necessary to choose a set of design variables from the $M(N_0 + N_c) + N_0 N_c$ free variables. There are several possible ways of doing this. For a transfer function type control law, the variable elements can be identified. If the control law state-space equations are expressed in block diagonal form, the nonzero elements of the matrix A can be identified as the real and imaginary parts of the compensator eigenvalues. The elements of the matrix C can be treated as feedback gains and can be used as design variables. In the interactive control law synthesis software, the designer can initially select all the elements of the controller quadruple matrices. The elements that do not change substantially over the iterations can be excluded from the design variable set in the subsequent iteration. For a Kalman state-estimator based full-order ($M = N_s$) LQG controller, B is the estimator gain, and C is the optimal state-feedback gain and can be chosen as the independent design variables since the matrix A is a function of B and C, namely,

$$A = A_0 = (F - B_0 H + G_u C_0) \tag{81}$$

$$B = B_0 = PH^T R_v^{-1} \tag{82}$$

$$C = C_0 = -Q_2^{-1} G_u^T S \tag{83}$$

$$D = 0 \tag{84}$$

In Eqs. (81) and (82), the symmetric, positive definite matrices P and S satisfy the steady-state matrix Riccati equations [14,15].

$$FP + PF^T - PH^T R_v^{-1} HP + G_u R_u G_u^T + G_w R_w G_w^T = 0 \tag{85}$$

$$F^T S + SF - SG_u Q_2^{-1} G_u^T S + H^T Q_1 H + H_d^T Q_d H_d = 0 \tag{86}$$

If a reduced-order LQG-type controller structure [7] is selected, then the designer can select a subset of Eqs. (81)–(83) using $M \times N_s$ order-reduction matrices L and R of rank M, which may signify simple truncation or can be obtained from optimal projection technique [16,22].

$$A = LA_0 R^T, \qquad B = LB_0, \qquad C = C_0 R^T \tag{87}$$

If this controller is stable, then the B and C matrices can be chosen as the design variables. Since the matrix A is now a linear function of B and C, the cost function and design response gradients with respect to B and C must be modified.

$$\frac{d(J, g_n)}{dB} = \frac{\delta(J, g_n)}{\delta B} - \frac{\delta(J, g_n)}{\delta A} RH^T \tag{88}$$

$$\frac{d(J, g_n)}{dC} = \frac{\delta(J, g_n)}{\delta C} + [LG_u]^T \frac{\delta(J, g_n)}{\delta A} \tag{89}$$

The partial derivatives are obtained by partitioning Eq. (39) and (45). Note that for a full-order controller (i.e., $L = R = I$), Eqs. (88) and (89) are identically zero. For the discrete system, the design variables can be selected in a similar manner [9,23], but the structure of the Kalman estimator based controller depends on the choice of 'current' or 'predictive' type filter [23]. Starting with a stable control law and using the optimization scheme shown in Fig. 5, we can modify the design variables of the continuous or discrete controller to minimize the cost function and satisfy the design constraints.

X. EXAMPLES

Numerical examples are presented for lateral stability control of a rigid aircraft for robustness study and for gust load alleviation of a flexible drone aircraft for low-order robust digital controller design. For an example of low-order, robust, active control law synthesis for flutter suppression of a flexible wing-model in a wind-tunnel, see [24].

A. LATERAL ATTITUDE CONTROL

Let us consider a two-input two-output system that represents a rigid drone aircraft with a lateral attitude control system. A block diagram of the system is shown in Fig. 7. The 6th-order plant state vector is defined as

$$x_s = [\beta \quad d\phi/dt \quad d\Psi/dt \quad \phi \quad \delta_1/20 \quad \delta_2/20]^T \tag{90}$$

where β, ϕ, Ψ, δ_1, and δ_2 are sideslip, roll, yaw angles, elevon and rudder deflections, respectively. The plant matrices F, G_u, and H for rigid drone

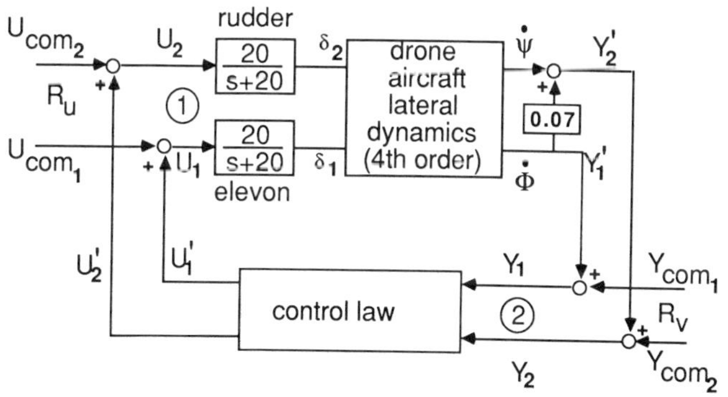

Fig. 7. Lateral stability control block diagram of a rigid drone aircraft.

aircraft are given by

$$F = \begin{bmatrix} -0.08527 & -0.0001423 & -0.9994 & 0.04124 & 0.0 & 0.1826 \\ -46.86 & -2.757 & 0.3896 & 0.0 & -124.3 & 128.6 \\ -0.4248 & -0.06224 & -0.06714 & 0.0 & -8.792 & -20.46 \\ 0.0 & 1.0 & 0.0 & 0.0 & 0.0 & 0.0 \\ 0.0 & 0.0 & 0.0 & 0.0 & -20.0 & 0.0 \\ 0.0 & 0.0 & 0.0 & 0.0 & 0.0 & -20.0 \end{bmatrix}$$

$$G_{\mathrm{u}} = \begin{bmatrix} 0.0 & 0.0 \\ 0.0 & 0.0 \\ 0.0 & 0.0 \\ 0.0 & 0.0 \\ 1.0 & 0.0 \\ 0.0 & 1.0 \end{bmatrix} \qquad H = \begin{bmatrix} 0.0 & 1.0 & 0.0 & 0.0 & 0.0 & 0.0 \\ 0.0 & 0.07 & 0.0 & 0.0 & 0.0 & 0.0 \end{bmatrix}$$

The eigenvalues of the nominal open-loop system are given in Table I. The unstable complex eigenvalue represents the dutch-roll mode. The plant input position 1 is defined at the entry point to the elevon and rudder actuators, denoted by u_1 and u_2 in degrees. The plant output position 2 is defined at the roll-rate and yaw-rate sensor outputs denoted by y_1 and y_2 in degrees per second. A detailed stability margin improvement study of this system with a classical rate feedback control law was presented in [4,6].

$$A = \begin{bmatrix} 0 & 0 \\ 0 & -2 \end{bmatrix} \quad B = \begin{bmatrix} 1 & 0 \\ 0 & 1 \end{bmatrix} \quad C = \begin{bmatrix} 0.1491 & 0 \\ 0 & a_{22}^* d_{22} \end{bmatrix} \quad D = \begin{bmatrix} 0 & 0 \\ 0 & 2.058 \end{bmatrix}$$

Design of full-order robust LQG controller for roll stabilization is presented here. The objective is to demonstrate the ability to shape the minimum singular value by adjusting the noise intensity matrices and by the constrained optimization technique. The results are presented in Figs. 8a,b. The noise intensity matrices used in the six designs are shown beside each plot. In all the

TABLE I. PLANT EIGENVALUES FOR OPEN- AND CLOSED-LOOP SYSTEMS

Mode	Open-loop	Closed-loop (Design 6)
Spiral	-0.03701	-0.04662
Dutch roll	$0.1889 \pm j1.058$	$-1.1887 \pm j1.752$
Roll	-3.25	-3.56
Actuator	-20.0	-19.98
Actuator	-20.0	-20.474

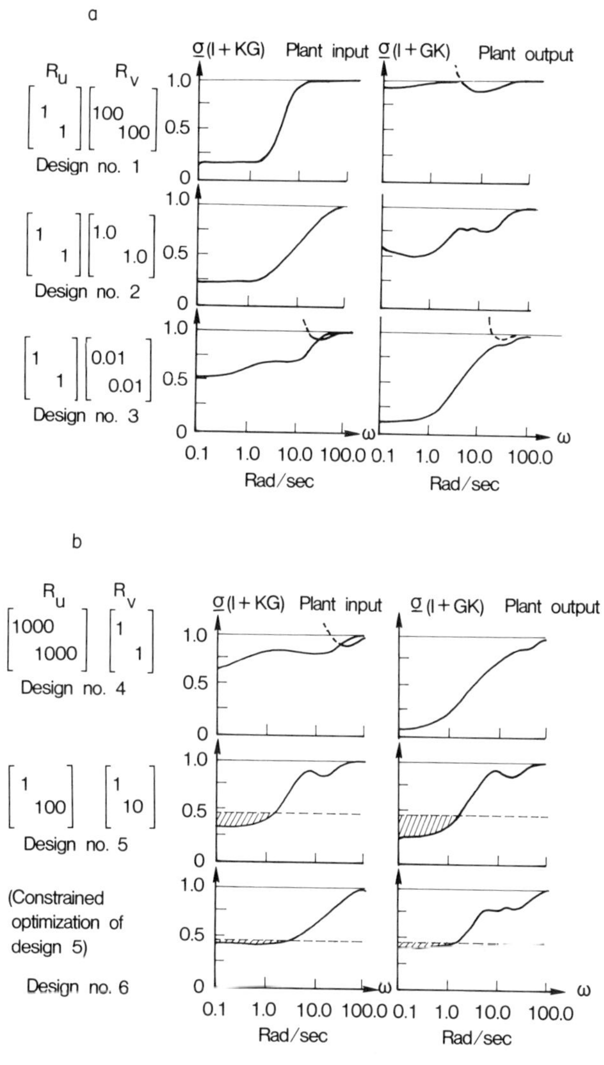

Fig. 8. Singular value shaping (a) by noise adjustment and (b) by noise adjustment and constrained optimization.

design, the weighting matrices on the output $Q_1 = I$ and on the controls $Q_2 = 0.5I$ where I is a unity matrix of appropriate order.

The full-order LQG controllers are designed by solving the Kalman state estimator and optimal controller Riccati equations to obtain the gain matrices B_0 and C_0, respectively. The matrix A is given by Eq. (81). In designs 1 to 3, the input noise intensity $R_u = I$ and the sensor noise intensity R_v take the values

$100I$, I, and $0.01I$, respectively. The resulting singular value plots are shown in Fig. 8a. In design 1, with large sensor noise, most of the stability robustness is at the plant output, along with rapid attenuation at higher frequencies. This is due to the dominant second and fourth terms in the cost function Eq. (21). With a lower sensor-to-input noise ratio in designs 2, 3, and 4, the robustness properties shift to the plant input since the first and third terms in Eq. (21) dominate. There is also a substantial loss of attenuation at higher frequencies. In design 5, the effect of unequal noise intensity in each loop is investigated by imposing more uncertainty in the rudder channel. The minimum singular value plot shown in Fig. 8b, indicates that the minimum $\boldsymbol{\sigma}(I + KG)$ is 0.33, the minimum $\boldsymbol{\sigma}(I + GK)$ is 0.25, and both have good high-frequency attenuation. This design is used as the starting point for the constrained optimization procedure to improve stability robustness at both plant input and plant output. In this design, the weighting matrices Q_1 and Q_2 are the same as before, but the noise intensity matrices are set to zero. The system is driven by a unit RMS white noise input at the elevon actuator. All the elements of the matrices B and C are chosen as design variables. The minimum desired singular value $\boldsymbol{\sigma}_D = 0.45$ is chosen to constrain $\boldsymbol{\sigma}(I + KG)$ and $\boldsymbol{\sigma}(I + GK)$ at the plant input and output, respectively. In the cumulative constraints of Eqs. (23, 24), the frequency points are uniformly chosen as 50 divisions per decade over the range 0.1–100 rad/sec.

After five iterations, the minimum singular value is reshaped as shown in Fig. 8b. The minimum singular value was raised to 0.4 at the plant input and plant output. The closed-loop eigenvalues (Table I) indicate adequate damping of the dutch-roll, heading, and roll modes for the drone aircraft. The variation of the normalized performance index and constraints on singular values at plant input and output is shown in Fig. 9. The RMS responses and

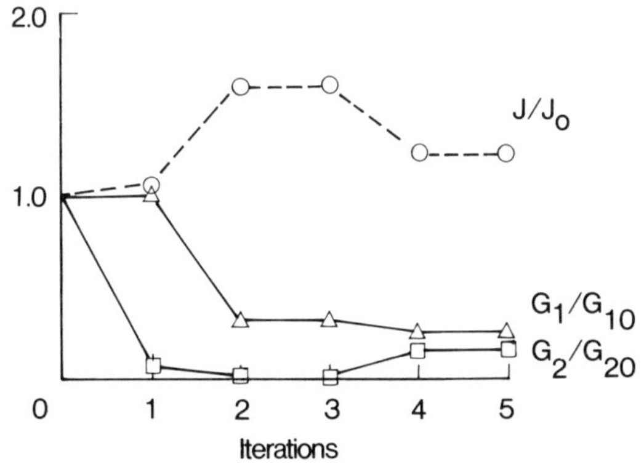

Fig. 9. Normalized cost function and constraints versus iteration (design 6).

weighting matrices indicate that the contribution of u' and y' to the cost function are roughly equal. After the first iteration, g_2 is nearly satisfied with a slight increase in J. After the second iteration, g_1 is also reduced at the cost of increased J. During iteration 4, the algorithm reduces the cost function J by slightly violating the second constraint g_2 to reach a compromise solution. This numerical example indicates that an increase in minimum singular value at the plant input is always accompanied by a decrease in the minimum singular value at the plant output, and vice versa. Using the present procedure, we can increase the minimum singular value at both the plant input and output, but only to a limited extent.

B. GUST LOAD ALLEVIATION

The parameter optimization procedure was applied to synthesize second-order digital control laws for gust load alleviation (GLA) of the flexible drone aircraft reported in [9]. The basic control scheme is shown in Fig. 10. In longitudinal motion, the symmetric elevator and outboard aileron deflections are used as the two control inputs. Accelerometer sensors positioned symmetrically near outboard ailerons and in the fuselage near the center of gravity are used as two measurement outputs. The linear, small perturbation equations of motion of the flexible aircraft in longitudinal, symmetric level flight was expressed by a 19th-order state-space system of equations. This basic model included rigid body plunge rate, pitch, pitch rate, three wing-flexure modes, and two aerodynamic lag terms [7] for each of the rigid and

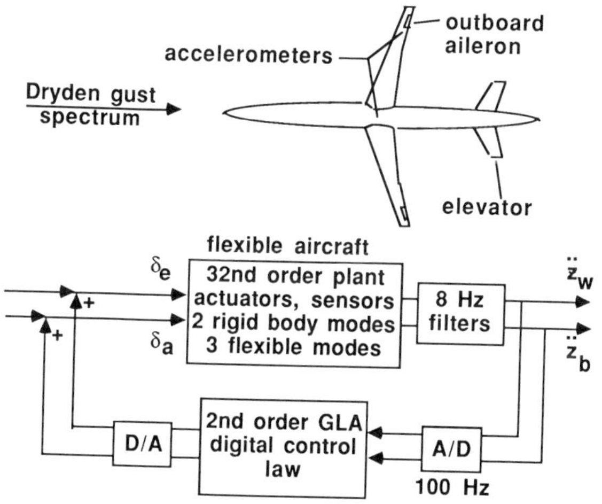

Fig. 10. Gust load alleviation (GLA) control system block diagram.

flexible modes. These lag terms are used to approximately model the unsteady aerodynamic effects. The rigid body plunge position mode was excluded since it does not contribute to the dynamics. A third-order elevator actuator dynamics [$20/(s+20)$ with a 100-Hz double pole filter] and an 8th-order aileron actuator dynamics were added. A second-order filter, shown in Eq. (91), which approximates the Dryden gust spectrum driven by a unit white noise w to generate a 1 in./sec RMS transverse gust velocity, was also added to derive a 32nd-order continuous plant model.

$$\frac{\xi_g}{w} = \sigma_{wg}\sqrt{\frac{3V}{l}}\,\frac{\left(\frac{V}{l\sqrt{3}}\right)+s}{(V/l+s)^2} \tag{91}$$

Here ξ_g is the gust state, σ_{wg} is the RMS gust velocity, l is the scale of turbulence or characteristic length, and V is the flight velocity. For numerical calculation, the design flight condition was chosen at 24,000 ft altitude and at dynamic pressure 2.95 psi, with $l = 2500$ ft. The corresponding flight velocity was 10,530 in./sec and the Mach number was 0.86. The open-loop eigenvalues corresponding to the plunge, pitch, and three wing-flexure modes were -1.466, $-0.1346 \pm j5.468$, $-13.4 \pm j86.89$, $-32.43 \pm j168.6$, and $-14.05 \pm j218.8$, respectively. Design responses were computed, such as wing-root bending moment (WRBM) and shear (WRS), wing-outboard bending moment (WOBM) and torsion (WOT), symmetric elevator and aileron deflections and rate.

The *design objectives* were to achieve a robust, low-order, digital GLA control law that would reduce the open-loop RMS values of the wing-root bending moment and shear by half, without increasing the RMS outboard bending moment and torsion, to avoid shifting the wing load outboard. The robustness requirement was specified in terms of the minimum singular value of the return difference matrix at the plant input and output. A minimum value of $\sigma_D = 0.6$ would provide a simultaneous guaranteed MIMO gain or phase margins of -6 dB, $+6$ dB or ± 35 deg, respectively. These design requirements are tabulated in Fig. 11.

C. GLA CONTROL LAW SYNTHESIS

The open-loop RMS values of WRBM, WRS, WOBM, and WOT were obtained first by solving the steady-state Lyapunov equation. These were found to be 209.6 lb-in. 3.75 lb, 1.66 lb-in. and 0.76 lb-in., respectively, for a 1 in./sec RMS gust. The maximum allowable RMS deflection and rate for the elevator and aileron were specified to be 0.00006981 rad, 0.0035 rad/sec, 0.000412 rad, and 0.0558 rad/sec, respectively, for a 1 in./sec RMS Dryden

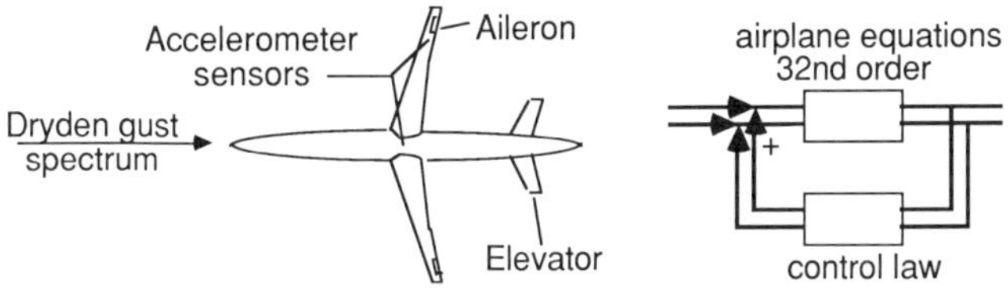

Physical quantities	Design objective	Design steps
Wing root BM	50% reduction	1. LQG design
Wing root shear	50% reduction	2. Control law order reduction
Wing outboard BM	No increase	
Outboard torsion	No increase	3. Discretize
Elevator deflection	Within max limit	4. Optimization
Elevator rate	Within max limit	5. Apply constraints on
Aileron deflection	Within max limit	a) rms loads
Aileron rate	Within max limit	b) singular values
Min. singular values at plant input & output	> 0.6 | ± 6 dB ± 35 deg	

Fig. 11. Design objectives of the GLA system.

gust. Second-order digital GLA control laws were synthesized to meet the design objectives and were compared with full-order LQG control laws. A summary of the result obtained is presented in Tables II–IV and Fig. 12. The RMS wing loads, as percentages of the corresponding open-loop values, for various control laws are presented in Table II. The control surface RMS

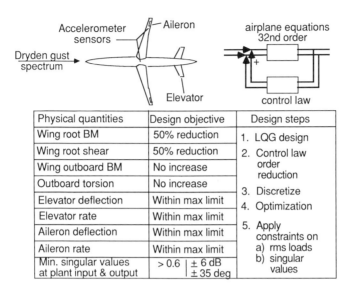

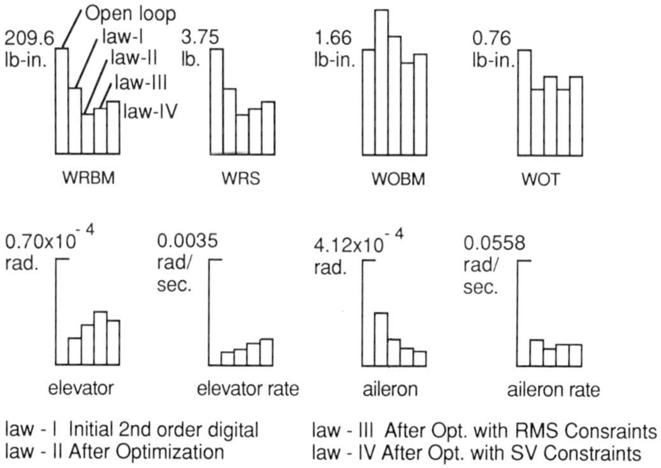

Fig. 12. Comparisons of normalized RMS responses due to a 1 in./sec Dryden gust.

TABLE II. ROOT-MEAN-SQUARE WING LOADS AS PERCENTAGES OF OPEN-LOOP VALUES, AND CONTROL SURFACE ACTIVITIES AS PERCENTAGES OF MAXIMUM ALLOWED DUE TO A UNIT RMS GUST

Design (order)	RMS loads on wing due to unit Dryden gust (% of open loop)				RMS control deflection and rate (% of maximum allowed)			
	Wing root		Wing outboard		Elevator		Aileron	
	BM	Shear	BM	Torsion	δ_1	$\dot{\delta}_1$	δ_2	$\dot{\delta}_2$
Open loop	100	100	100	100	0	0	0	0
Full state	26	25	23	17	49	6	35	32
LQG (32)	49	49	81	57	20	3	13	9
Law-I (2)	63	60	140	63	13	1.5	51	10
Law-II (2)	43	43	101	66	25	1.7	25	1.3
Law-III (2)	45	45	92	62	33	3	5	1
Law-IV (2)	46	46	93	63	27	3	2	1

deflections and rate, as percentages of maximum allowable values, are also shown in Table II. The peak transient loads and responses due to a 1 in./sec step gust input, for the open-loop system and the closed-loop system with different control laws, are presented in Table III. The short-period frequency and damping ratios are also shown in Table III. The second-order digital control law quadruples are shown in Table IV.

To obtain a stable initial control law, it was convenient to start with a continuous system, obtain a state feedback controller and a LQG state estimator, and then reduce the order of the resulting LQG control law by

TABLE III. PEAK TIME RESPONSES OF WING-ROOT BENDING MOMENT AND SHEAR, WING-OUTBOARD BENDING MOMENT AND TORSION (WRBM, WRS, WOBM, WOT), ELEVATOR AND AILERON DEFLECTIONS, SHORT-PERIOD FREQUENCY AND DAMPING RATIO, DUE TO A 1 IN./SEC STEP GUST INPUT

Design (order)	WRBM (lb-in.)	WRS (lb)	WOBM (lb-in.)	WOT (lb-in.)	δ_1 (rad $\times 10^{-4}$)	δ_2 (rad $\times 10^{-4}$)	ω_{sp} (rad/sec)	ζ_{sp} ζ_{sp}
Open loop	36	0.65	0.12	0.10	0	0	6.47	0.017
Full state	20	0.35	0.09	0.06	0.25	0.13	7.04	0.430
LQG (32)	32	0.58	0.12	0.08	0.29	0.30	5.50	0.170
Law-I (2)	32	0.55	0.28	0.05	0.04	0.40	5.86	0.060
Law-II (2)	30	0.55	0.26	0.12	0.05	0.46	5.82	0.175
Law-III (2)	28	0.52	0.12	0.07	0.16	0.16	5.75	0.136
Law-IV (2)	32	0.58	0.12	0.07	0.08	0.025	5.49	0.179

TABLE IV. SECOND-ORDER DIGITAL CONTROL LAW QUADRUPLES FOR GUST LOAD ALLEVIATION

Law	Quadruples	
I	$A = \begin{bmatrix} 0.9621 & 0 \\ 0 & 0.8706 \end{bmatrix}$	$C = \begin{bmatrix} -0.00141 & -0.00179 \\ -0.01196 & -0.0405 \end{bmatrix}$
II	$A = \begin{bmatrix} 0.9712 & 0 \\ 0 & 0.8646 \end{bmatrix}$	$C = \begin{bmatrix} -0.00201 & -0.00077 \\ -0.01424 & -0.01278 \end{bmatrix}$
III	$A = \begin{bmatrix} 0.9933 & 0 \\ 0 & 0.9944 \end{bmatrix}$	$C = \begin{bmatrix} -0.00245 & -0.00071 \\ -0.01531 & -0.01117 \end{bmatrix}$
IV	$A = \begin{bmatrix} 0.9698 & 0 \\ 0 & 0.9721 \end{bmatrix}$	$C = \begin{bmatrix} -0.00270 & -0.00068 \\ -0.01512 & -0.01133 \end{bmatrix}$
All	$B = \begin{bmatrix} 0.000208 & 0.000444 \\ -0.000263 & -0.000578 \end{bmatrix}$	$D = \begin{bmatrix} 0 & 0 \\ 0 & 0 \end{bmatrix}$

balanced truncation or residualization. The reduced-order controller in block diagonal form was then discretized, using Z transform with a zero-order hold and a sampling rate of 100 Hz. Two 8-Hz low-pass antialiasing filters were added to the two accelerometer measurements of the continuous plant model. The plant state-space model was then discretized using Z transform with a zero-order hold at a 100-Hz sampling rate. Unconstrained and constrained optimization procedures were applied to these discrete models of plant and control laws.

1. Full-Order LQG Control Laws

A state feedback optimal GLA control law for the continuous-time system was obtained using $J = E[y_d^T Q_1 y_d + u^T Q_2 u]$, where y_d consisted of WRBM, WRS, WOBM, and WOT, and u consisted of elevator and aileron input δ_1 and δ_2, respectively. The diagonal weighting matrix Q_1 was chosen as the inverse of the maximum desired mean-square value of the WRBM, WRS, WOBM, and WOT (i.e., $Q_1 = \text{diag}[1/(104.8)^2 \quad 1/(1.87)^2 \quad 1/(1.66)^2 \quad 1/(0.76)^2]$). The diagonal weighting matrix Q_2 was also chosen as the inverse of the maximum allowable mean-square elevator and aileron deflections (i.e., $Q_2 = \text{diag}[1/(0.00006981)^2 \quad 1/(0.0035)^2]$), following Bryson's rule [15]. The RMS responses due to a 1 in./sec RMS gust, are shown in Table II as percentages of open-loop responses for the wing loads and as percentages of the maximum allowable deflection and rate for the control surfaces. The peak transient loads and control surface deflections for the full-state design, due to a

1 in./sec step gust input, are shown in Table III. The corresponding short-period damping ratio is 0.43.

This full-state LQ control law satisfies all the design requirements, but it cannot be implemented because all the states are not available for feedback. The implementation can be possible with a LQG state estimator. This was designed using $R_u = [0]$, $R_w = 1$ (a unit intensity plant noise input corresponding to a 1 in./sec RMS Dryden gust) and measurement noise intensity $R_v = \text{diag}[2 \quad 1]$ for the wing and fuselage acceleration measurements, respectively. The closed-loop normalized RMS responses using the 32nd-order LQG state estimator are higher, as expected, compared with the full-state case, but they still satisfy the design requirements. This is shown in Table II, where all the RMS values were computed assuming zero measurement noise. The peak transient loads due to a unit step gust input increased considerably as shown in Table III. The corresponding short-period damping was reduced to 0.170.

2. Initial Second-Order GLA Control Law (Law-I)

The 32nd-order LQG control law is difficult to implement in a flight computer. A low-order control law with similar performance is often desirable. It was found that a stable second-order control law can be obtained by truncating the full-order LQG control law, retaining only the key controller states corresponding to the pitch angle and pitch rate perturbation state-estimates [7]. This second-order control law was transformed into block diagonal form and then discretized using Z transform with a zero-order hold, at 100 samples/sec. This is shown in Table IV as law-I. This truncated control law was stable, and the corresponding normalized RMS values of the closed-loop sampled-data system, using discrete plant input noise intensity R_w of $1/T$ (corresponding to approximately 1 in./sec RMS Dryden gust) are shown in Table II. Although the RMS values of WRBM, WRS, and WOT were reduced by 30%, the WOBM increased by 40% and none of the design requirements were satisfied. The aileron RMS deflections increased considerably but were still within the allowable limits. The short-period damping ratio was only 0.060.

3. Unconstrained Optimization (Law-II)

The present optimization procedure was applied next, using law-I as the initial value to satisfy the design requirements. First, the unconstrained optimization was attempted using the same weighting matrices on the design output and control input as in the full-state continuous case. A unit RMS gust was used to drive the system, and the measurement noises were set to zero. The four elements of matrix C and the diagonal elements of matrix A were used as the six design variables. The optimized control law, obtained after five iterations, is shown in Table IV as law-II. The corresponding closed-loop normalized RMS responses (Table II, Fig. 12) indicate 57% reduction in the WRBM and WRS and 37% reduction WOT. However, the WOBM was 1% higher than the corresponding open-loop value. The RMS control surface activities indicate equal sharing of work load by the elevator and aileron. The short-period damping ratio was about 0.175. The plot of normalized cost function versus number of iterations, shown in Fig. 13, indicates convergence in one iteration.

4. Constrained Optimization (Law-III)

To prevent the increase in the outboard bending moment, the constrained optimization procedure was attempted next, using the control law-II as the initial value. The RMS outboard bending moment was treated as a constraint, instead of lumping it with the cost function. The maximum allowable RMS value of WOBM was chosen as 1.6. After 20 iterations, an optimized control law was obtained. It is designated as law-III (Table IV). The corresponding closed-loop RMS values (Table II) indicate net reduction in the open loop WRBM, WRS, WOBM, and WOT by 55, 55, 8 and 38%, respectively. The

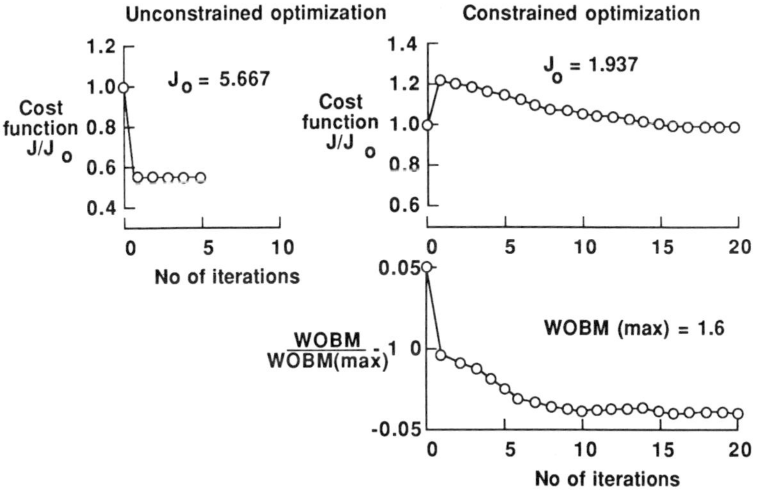

Fig. 13. Normalized cost function and constraints versus iteration (law-II and law-III).

RMS control surface activities indicate that most of the work load was shifted to the elevator. The peak transient loads were lower compared with law-II, though the short-period damping ratio was reduced to 0.136 (Table III). The plot of cost function and constraint versus iteration (Fig. 13) indicates that the constraint on WOBM was satisfied in one iteration at the expense of increased cost function, which was subsequently reduced along with the wing outboard bending moment.

The transient responses of the open-loop system and the closed-loop system with law-II for a 1 in./sec step gust (Fig. 14a) for the first wing flexure mode and pitch mode, indicate that the GLA control law-II damped out the transients in about 2.5 sec. To compare the transient response characteristics of the different control laws, the peak transient responses are tabulated in Table III. The transient responses of the elevator and aileron deflections of the closed-loop system using law-II and law-III are shown in Fig. 14b. From Table III and Fig. 14b, law-III appears to provide better transient response to a unit step gust than law-II.

5. Stability Margins (Laws II and III)

The stability margins at the plant input and output were evaluated by computing the minimum singular values of the corresponding return-difference and inverse return-difference matrices as in the continuous-time case. For the discrete system, the singular values were computed by replacing the term Z in the discrete domain transfer matrix with $\exp(j\omega)$, where ω is a set of N frequency points below the Nyquist frequency π/T radians, and T is the sampling period. The input and output signals were assumed to coincide with the sampling instant. The minimum singular value plots of the return-difference matrix and inverse return-difference matrix at the plant input and output, using law-II and law-III are shown in Fig. 15a. At the plant input, the minimum singular values of $(I + KG)$ and $I + (KG)^{-1}$ were -15 dB and -14.5 dB, respectively, for law-II and -10.0 dB and -7.5 dB, respectively, for law-III. From Fig. 3, and Eqs. (15) and (16), the corresponding maximum, guaranteed simultaneous gain or phase margins at the plant input were $+1.8$ dB, -1.9 dB, or ± 12 deg for law-II and $+3.4$ dB, -4.8 dB, or ± 24 deg for law-III, respectively. At the plant output, the minimum singular values of $(I + GK)$ and $I + (GK)^{-1}$ were -7 dB and -5 dB, respectively, for law-II and -9 dB and -5.6 dB, respectively, for law-III. These values correspond to gain or phase margins of $+5$ dB, -7 dB, or ± 33 deg for law-II and $+3.8$ dB, -6 dB, or ± 30 deg for law-III, respectively. From the singular value analysis, law-II and law-III appear to be robust to perturbations at plant output but not at plant input.

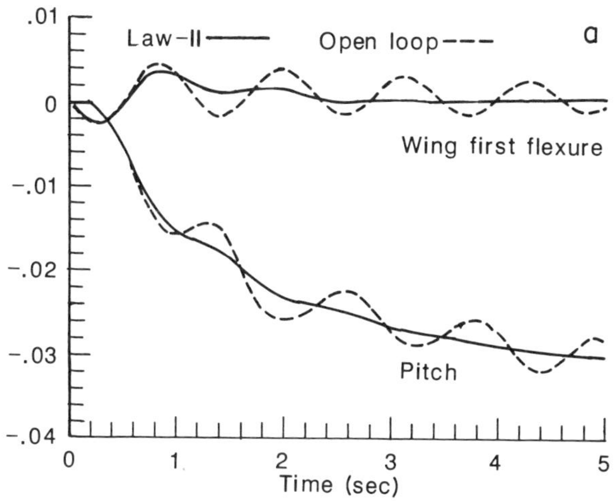

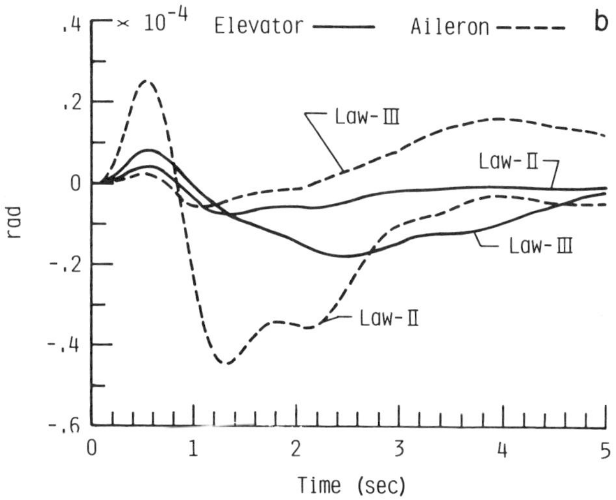

Fig. 14. Transient response due to unit gust of (a) wing first flexure and pitch and (b) elevator and aileron.

6. Stability Margin Improvement (Law-IV)

To improve stability robustness at both the plant input and output, law-III was reoptimized using two additional constraints corresponding to the required minimum singular value of $(I + KG)$ and $(I + GK)$ not less than 0.6 or -4.43 dB, as shown by the dashed lines in Fig. 15a. The constraint on

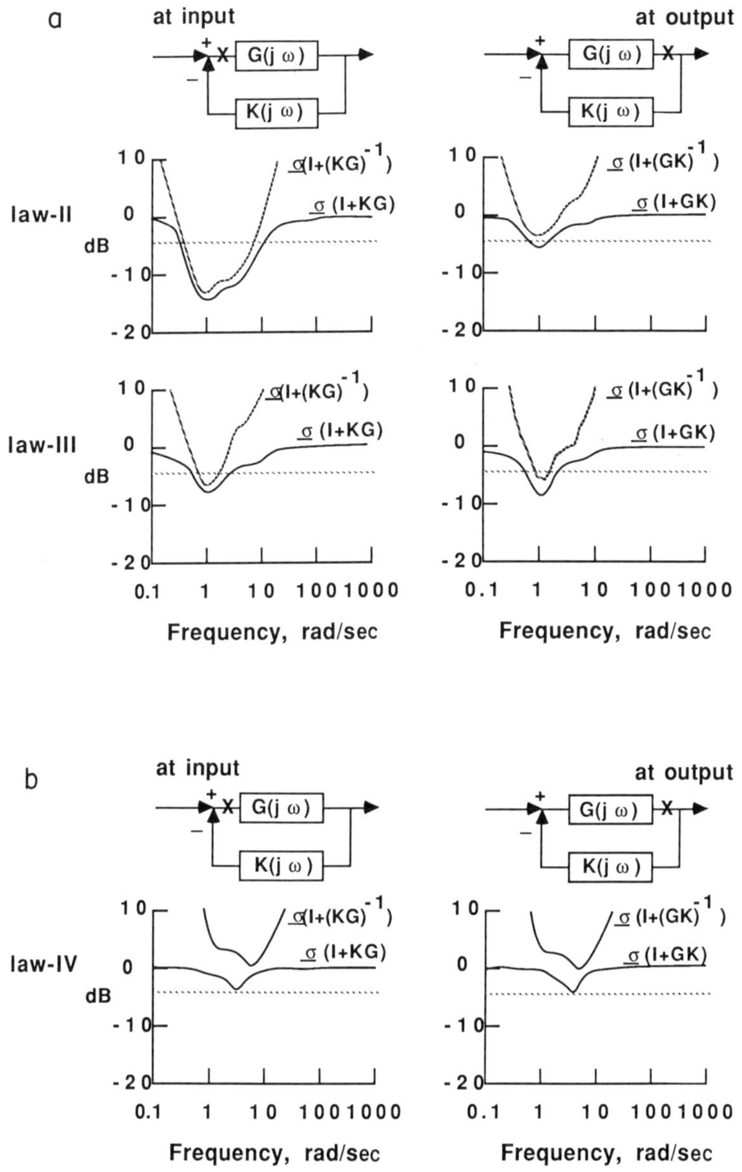

Fig. 15. (a) Minimum singular values at the plant input and output, and (b) stability margin improvement using singular value constraints.

the WOBM was also retained. After seven iterations, an optimized control law was obtained. It is designated as law-IV and is shown in Table IV. The corresponding closed-loop RMS loads and peak transient responses increased marginally from those of law-III and are presented in Tables II and III and in Fig. 12 as a bar chart. The minimum singular value plots at the plant input and output are shown in Fig. 15b. At the plant input, the minimum singular values of $(I + KG)$ and $I + (KG)^{-1}$ were -4.63 dB and -1 dB, respectively, for law-IV. These correspond to maximum gain or phase margins of $+7.5$ dB, -16 dB, or ± 53 deg, respectively, at the plant input. At the plant output, the minimum singular values of $(I + GK)$ and $I + (GK)^{-1}$ were -4.56 dB and -0.9 dB, respectively, for law-IV. These values correspond to gain or phase margins of $+7.7$ dB, -17 dB, or ± 53 deg for law-IV at the plant output. Thus, substantial improvement in stability robustness was obtained at the plant input and output by using the constrained optimization technique.

XI. CONCLUSIONS

A generic procedure was presented for optimization of a continuous or a discrete control law of arbitrary order for a multiinput–multioutput system. The constrained optimization technique was used to satisfy conflicting design requirements on the mean-square responses and the stability robustness at the plant input and output. The synthesis procedure is particularly suitable for flexible flight vehicles or large space-structures that are modeled by a high-order state-space system of equations. Analytical expressions for the gradients of the cost function and the design constraints on the mean-square response and minimum singular value were presented. The use of analytical gradient information facilitates fast convergence of the numerical optimization process. The gradient information can also be used for parameter sensitivity studies.

APPENDIX A. MATRIX DIFFERENTIATION

Here we present details of matrix differentiation used to arrive at the matrix Eq. (39) from the scalar Eqs. (38) and (32). All the other gradient expressions were obtained using the same basic technique. We use the basic matrix properties $\mathrm{tr}[AB] = \mathrm{tr}[BA]$ and $\mathrm{tr}[A] = \mathrm{tr}[A^{\mathrm{T}}]$. The quadratic and linear matrix differentiation relations are as follows. Let p be an element of a matrix P. Using the matrix trace properties, we can express the scalar cost function J or the RMS response constraints in the general form

$$J(p) = \mathrm{tr}[P^{\mathrm{T}}QPA + P^{\mathrm{T}}BA].$$

Then one can write the scalar equation $\delta J(p)/\delta p = \mathrm{tr}[QPA + Q^{\mathrm{T}}PA^{\mathrm{T}} + BA]$ and the matrix equation $\delta J(p)/\delta P = [QPA + Q^{\mathrm{T}}PA^{\mathrm{T}} + BA]$.

APPENDIX B. SINGULAR VALUE GRADIENTS

Consider a general complex matrix G whose distinct singular values are σ_n, and u_n and v_n are respectively the right and left normalized singular vectors of G. Hence, by definition,

$$Gv_n = u_n\sigma_n \tag{92}$$

$$G^*u_n = v_n\sigma_n, \qquad n = 1, 2, \ldots, N_c \tag{93}$$

where the superscript * denotes the complex conjugate transpose of a matrix. The normalized singular vectors satisfy the following orthogonal properties:

$$u_m^*u_n = \delta_{mn} \qquad v_m^*v_n = \delta_{mn} \tag{94}$$

where δ_{nm} is the Kroneker delta, which is unity when $m = n$ and zero when $m \neq n$. Let p be any real parameter for which the derivative information is needed. Differentiating Eqs. (92) and (93) with respect to p and then premultiplying the result by u_n^* and v_n^*, respectively, and adding them yields

$$u_n^*G'v_n + v_n^*G^{*\prime}u_n + (u_n^*G - v_n^*\sigma_n)v_n' + (v_n^*G^* - u_n^*\sigma_n)u_n' = \sigma_n'(u_n^*u_n + v_n^*v_n) \tag{95}$$

where ( )′ represents the partial derivative with respect to p. Using Eqs. (92–94) in Eq. (95) yields

$$\begin{aligned} \delta\sigma_n/\delta p &= 0.5[u_n^*G'v_n + v_n^*G^{*\prime}u_n] \\ &= \mathrm{Re}[u_n^*\,\delta G/\delta p\, v_n] \end{aligned} \tag{96}$$

ACKNOWLEDGMENTS

This research was partially supported by a National Research Council Fellowship, NASA Research Grant NAGI-199 and Contract NASI-18000 at the Aeroservoelasticity Branch, NASA Langley Research Center, Hampton, Virginia.

REFERENCES

1. M. G. SAFONOV, A. J. LAUB, and G. L. HARTMANN, "Feedback Properties of Multivariable Systems: The Role and Use of the Return Difference Matrix," *IEEE Trans. Autom. Control* **AC-26**, 47–65 (1981).
2. J. C. DOYLE and G. STEIN, "Multivariable Feedback Design: Concepts for a Classical/Modern Synthesis," *IEEE Trans. Autom. Control* **AC-26**, 4–16 (1981).

3. N. A. LEHTOMAKI, N. S. SANDELL, Jr., and M. ATHANS, "Robustness Results in Linear Quadratic Gaussian Based Multivariable Control Designs," *IEEE Trans. Autom. Control* **26**, 75–92 (1981).
4. V. MUKHOPADHYAY and J. R. NEWSOM, "A Multiloop System Stability Margin Study Using Singular Values," *J. Guidance, Control Dyn.* **7**, 582–587 (1984).
5. M. G. SAFONOV and B. S. CHEN, "Multi-variable Stability-Margin Optimization with Decoupling and Output Regulation," *IEE Proc. Part D: Control Theory Appl.* **129**, 276–282 (1982).
6. V. MUKHOPADHYAY and J. R NEWSOM, "A Multiloop Robust Controller Design Study Using Singular Value Gradients," *J. Guidance, Control Dyn.* **8**, 514–519 (1985).
7. V. MUKHOPADHYAY, J.R. NEWSOM, and I. ABEL, "A Method for Obtaining Reduced Order Control Laws for High Order Systems Using Optimization Techniques," *NASA* **TP-1876** (1981).
8. V. MUKHOPADHYAY, "Stability Robustness Improvement Using Constrained Optimization Techniques," *J. Guidance, Control Dyn.* **10**, 172–177 (1987).
9. V. MUKHOPADHYAY, "Digital Robust Control Law Synthesis Using Constrained Optimization," *J. Guidance, Control Dyn.* **12**, 175–181 (1989).
10. M. G. SAFONOV and R. Y. CHIANG, "Model Reduction for Robust Control: A Schur Relative Error Method," *Proc. Am. Control Conf., Atlanta Ga.*, 1685–1690 (1988).
11. K. E. LENZ, P. KHARGONEKAR, and J. DOYLE, "Controller Order Reduction With Guaranteed Stability and Performance," *Proc. Am. Control Conf., Atlanta Ga.*, 1697–1698 (1988).
12. D. S. BERNSTEIN and W. M. HADDAD, "Robust Stability and Performance for Fixed Order Dynamic Compensation via the Optimal Projection Equations with Guaranteed Cost Bounds," *Proc. Am. Control Conf., Atlanta, Ga.*, 2471–2478 (1988).
13. G. D. VANDERPLATTS, "CONMIN—A Fortran Program for Constraint Function Minimization. User Manual," *NASA Tech. Memo.* **NASA TM-X-62282** (1973).
14. K. KWAKERNAAK and R. SIVAN, "Linear Optimal Control Systems," Wiley, New York, 1972.
15. A. E. BRYSON, Jr., and Y. C. HO, "Applied Optimal Control," Hemisphere, Washington, D.C., 1975.
16. D. C. HYLAND and D. S. BERNSTEIN, "The Optimal Projection Equations for Fixed Order Dynamic Compensation," *IEEE Trans. Autom. Control* **AC-29**,1034–1037 (1984).
17. J. S. FREUDENBERG, D. P. LOOZE, and J. B. CRUZ, "Robustness Analysis Using Singular Value Sensitivities," *Int. J. Control* **35**, 95–116 (1982).
18. A. J. LAUB, "Efficient Multivariable Frequency Response Computations," *IEEE Trans. Autom. Control* **AC-26**, 407–408 (1981).
19. G. PETER and J. H. WILKINSON, "Eigenvectors of Real and Complex Matrices by LR and QR Triangularization," *Numer. Math.* **16**, 181–204 (1970).
20. D. F. FRANKLIN and D. POWELL, "Digital Control of Dynamic Systems," Addison-Wesley Reading, Massachusetts, 1980.
21. N. HALYO and J. R. BROUSSARD, "Investigation Development and Application of Optimal Output Feedback Theory," *NASA* [*Contract. Rep.*] *CR* **NASA-CR-3828 (NASI-15759)** (1984).
22. D. E. BERNSTEIN, L. D. DAVIS, and S. W. GREELEY, "The Optimal Projection Equations For Fixed-Order Sampled Data Dynamic Compensation with Computational Delay," *IEEE Trans. Autom. Control* **AC-31**, 859–862 (1986).
23. V. MUKHOPADHYAY, "Digital Active Control Law Synthesis for Aeroservoelastic Systems," *Proc. Am. Control Conf., Atlanta, Ga.*, 305–310 (1988).
24. V. MUKHOPADHYAY, J. R. NEWSOM, and I. ABEL, "Reduced Order Optimal Feedback Control Law Synthesis for Flutter Suppresion," *J. Guidance, Control Dyn.* **5**, 389–395 (1982).

COMPUTATIONAL METHODS FOR DECOY DISCRIMINATION AND OPTIMAL TARGETING IN BALLISTIC MISSILE DEFENSE

JOHN R. HOLDSWORTH

Systems Analysis
Lockheed Aeronautical Systems
Burbank, California 91520

C. T. LEONDES

Department of Mechanical, Aerospace, and Nuclear Engineering
School of Engineering and Applied Science
University of California
Los Angeles, California 90024

I. INTRODUCTION

A. PROBLEM BACKGROUND AND FORMULATION

For the past 30 years ballistic missile defense and offense have received a considerable amount of attention in the journal, industrial report, and classified literature. By 1970, the subject had gained its own acronym, MAP (the missile allocation problem), coined by Matlin in [1]. The class of problems reviewed by Matlin can be summarized as follows: Given an existing offensive weapon force and a set of targets, what is the optimal allocation of weapons to targets? As stated, the problem appears to deal only with the attacking force and makes no specific reference to the resources or defensive options available to the target complex under attack. The primary emphasis in the present research is on the decision problem presented to the defense. In general terms, the problem is the following. A target complex is under attack by a cloud of objects consisting of N_w warheads and N_d decoys, and the defense is assumed to know the values of the numbers of warheads and decoys in the cloud. The defense is equipped with a discrimination device capable of measuring some set of physical characteristics of each object as it reaches a decision altitude. For our purposes the discrimination device is characterized by two conditional probability density functions $f_w(x)$ and $f_d(x)$, where $f_w(x)$ is the probability density function of the observable given that the object being interrogated is a warhead, and $f_d(x)$ is the corresponding density function given that a decoy is being observed. Two cases are considered: (1) The objects arrive serially at the decision altitude, and (2) all of the objects in the cloud can be simultaneously examined. For each of these cases, two variations regarding the nature of the discrimination measurements are treated. First, the discrimination device is modeled as a single-threshold detector; that is, the only information passed to the defense about a reentry object is whether or not the measurement on the object exceeded a certain preset threshold. Rational ways of setting the threshold to provide the greatest resolving power will be discussed. Second, the discrimination device is assumed to provide the actual value of the physical measurement to the defense together with the knowledge of the conditional probability density functions $f_w(x)$ and $f_d(x)$; for want of a better term, we refer to this as an *analog measurement*. This should provide extra information to the defense and enable it to develop a targeting doctrine superior to that possible when only a single threshold discrimination is available. For the simultaneous arrival case, a third measurement variant is considered: The interceptor allocation is based on the rank-order statistics of the incoming objects.

In addition to the discrimination device, the defense has an initial inventory of N_I defensive missiles. Thus, the task of the defense is to optimally allocate its available defensive inventory based on the measurements made on the objects in the cloud. Optimality, of course, depends on the particular measure of effectiveness or cost function chosen. For example, one plausible cost function might be the expected number of surviving reentry warheads. Another might be the probability that some prespecified number K or more reentry warheads survive. For the serial-arrival case, the assignment of interceptors to an object must be made immediately after the measurement on the object. Thus for the kth object in the arrival sequence the information available to the defense consists of the measurements $x_1, \ldots, x_k$, together with its current interceptor missile inventory. In the second case, in which all measurements can be made simultaneously and the interceptor missile assignments can be made at one time, the information available to the defense consists of the results of the measurements on all of the objects. A further assumption is that once an interceptor missile is allocated, it cannot be redirected. Yet another assumption is that the only discrimination information on the reentry objects is provided by the measurement device. This precludes the possibility of using any posttargeting information on a reentry object as to whether it was a decoy or a warhead, to modify the conditional probability that a subsequent object arriving at the decision altitude is a warhead or a decoy.

The purpose of the decoys, of course, is to induce a wasteful disposition of the defensive assets and by so doing enhance the likelihood of a greater number of warhead penetrations. An interesting collateral problem is the inverse problem from the point of view of the offense. More precisely, because of weight, space, packaging, and cost constraints, there is an inevitable tradeoff between the quality of the decoys (i.e., their ability to impersonate a warhead) and the number of decoys. Thus, is it better to have a smaller number of "good" decoys or a greater number of poorer decoys, and what is the optimum decoy package? The term *goodness of a decoy* refers to the similarity between the conditional probability distributions $f_w(x)$ and $f_d(x)$. Clearly, when the distributions are identical, then no discriminatory information is provided by the measurements. The "distance" between the probability distributions defined by $f_w(x)$ and $f_d(x)$ is what provides the defense with the ability to discriminate between warheads and decoys. A brief digression pertinent to the single-threshold discriminator helps to illustrate this point.

For simplicity we assume that the discrimination device works on some type of a threshold principle and that it is capable of making a binary classification (i.e., classifying an object as either a decoy or a warhead). We further suppose that the performance of the discrimination device can be characterized by some known relationship between two parameters P_{ww} and P_{dw}, where P_{ww} is the probability that the discriminator will classify a warhead as a warhead and P_{dw} is the probability that the discriminator will classify a decoy as a warhead. Note that the classifications made by the discriminator are to be regarded merely as input data to the defensive decision process and that the fact that an object is classified as a decoy does not imply that it will not be targeted. In other words, the quantities P_{ww} and P_{dw} are simply the conditional probabilities that a measurement made by the defense on a warhead or decoy exceeds a certain predetermined threshold. It will be seen that the formulation of the decision problem in this way allows the defense the maximal use of all pertinent data and in fact enables the defensive decision procedure to function as an adaptive learning process.

A few explanatory comments are in order regarding the quantities P_{dw} and P_{ww}. First, for a perfect discriminator we should have $P_{ww} = 1$ and $P_{dw} = 0$. This is generally unattainable and reduces the defense's interceptor allocation problem to a triviality. Second, although the defense may fix a value of either of the parameters P_{ww} or P_{dw}, once it does so the value of the remaining parameter is determined. That is, the functional dependence of P_{dw} on P_{ww} depends on the quality of the decoys, which is ultimately controlled by the offense. This is a consequence of the offense's option of packaging a few very good decoys or a larger number of poorer decoys.

To further clarify these ideas, let $f_w(x)$ and $f_d(x)$ denote the conditional probability density function of the defense's measuring system given that the object measured is a warhead or decoy, respectively. Then if t denotes some threshold such that a measurement exceeding it is classified as coming from a warhead, we can write the following:

$$P_{ww}(t) = \int_t^\infty f_w(x)\,dx \tag{1}$$

$$P_{dw}(t) = \int_t^\infty f_d(x)\,dx \tag{2}$$

where the quality of the decoy is reflected in the closeness of the measurement distributions $f_d(x)$ and $f_w(x)$. For a fixed quality of decoy, we can parametrically vary the threshold and obtain from Eqs. (1) and (2) a functional relationship between P_{ww} and P_{dw}.

The quantity x appearing in the argument of $f_w(x)$ and $f_d(x)$ is a scalar that we have somewhat carelessly alluded to as a *measurement*. This should be interpreted in the following way. Several different physical measurements may well be made by the defense on an object at a particular time, such as radar cross-section and Doppler-shift measurements. In this case, the actual physical data obtained by the defense from measuring an object yield a 2-dimensional vector with components y_1 and y_2. If we let $g_w(y_1, y_2)$ and $g_d(y_1, y_2)$ be the bivariate density functions of returned radar signal strength and Doppler shift, given that the measurements come from a warhead or decoy, respectively, we form the likelihood ratio, $x = g_w(y_1\, y_2)/g_d(y_1, y_2)$. This scalar quantity x, or some minimal sufficient statistic determined from it, has a univariate distribution $f_w(x)$ or $f_d(x)$, depending on whether a warhead or decoy is being observed. It is this scalar quantity for which the threshold is set.Thus, the scalar x is a measurement in the sense that it is the observed value of the likelihood ratio, having measured a radar signal strength of y_1 and a doppler shift of y_2.

The optimal employment of the measurement data, whether single threshold or analog, is part of the optimization problem and is treated as such in the problem development. Furthermore, the relative gains in having the analog data, rank-order measurements or sequence of threshold exceedances are examined. The measure of effectiveness selected is the minimization of the expected number of surviving reentry warheads. The development of the optimum targeting doctrines for this cost function suggests the plausibility that these same targeting doctrines are also optimal for other cost functions, such as minimizing the probability that K or more warheads survive the defensive targeting.

B. RELATIONSHIP TO PRIOR WORK

The defensive problem, as broadly formulated in the preceding section, has received attention from several authors. In (2), Phillipson *et al.* treated the time sequential problem in which simultaneous observations were not possible and interceptors had to be assigned after each measurement was made. Their treatment assumed a threshold detector and did not account for the information inherent in the sequence of prior measurements. That is, at a fixed stage of the process, the number of interceptors allocated to the object depends on (1) the threshold being exceeded or not, (2) the serial position of the object in the reentry cloud, and (3) the remaining inventory of interceptors available at that stage. Furthermore, no systematic consideration was given to good ways of setting the threshold. In [3], Gorfinkel treated the case of a continuous detection device for both the serial and simultaneous arrival situations. He, at a given stage, based his interceptor allocation only on the stage number, the measurement based on the current object, and the current inventory. He further assumed that each cloud of objects contained exactly one warhead and did not discuss methods to scale his results when these could initially be multiple warheads in the set of reentry objects.

In [4], Holdsworth considered the sequential discrimination and assignment case for a threshold detector. He also mentioned the problem of adjusting the discrimination threshold so that the detector provides the best resolution between decoys and warheads; however, no quantitative comparisons were made. He did not consider the effects of the information lost by quantizing the measurement process and using a threshold detector. Layno [5] treated the problem in a very approximate sense. His assumptions and treatment leave it unclear as to whether the discrimination measurements and interceptor assignments must be made serially or can be done at once. His assignment policy is to allocate the same fixed number of interceptors to any object whose measurement exceeds a threshold and not to base the assignment on the computed a posteriori probability that the object is a warhead. Hershaft [6] also considered the quantized measurement problem for both the serial and the simultaneous discrimination and assignment cases. He did not address the question of threshold settings nor were interceptor assignments determined as a function of the a posteriori probability that an observed object was indeed a warhead.

C. AIMS OF THE PRESENT STUDY

This article presents a coherent extension of the work previously described. For most of the work, the same cost function is used (e.g., the expected number of surviving reentry warheads). Specifically, the following mathematical tasks are addressed:

1. Analysis of the sequential arrival, measurement, and targeting problem.
   a. Derivation of the optimum targeting doctrine for a single-threshold discriminator.
   b. Discussion of various criteria for setting the threshold for the single-threshold discriminator.
   c. Derivation of the optimum targeting policy when the defense has the actual measurements made on the reentry objects.
2. Analysis of the simultaneous arrival, measurement, and targeting problem.
   a. Derivation of the optimum targeting doctrine for the single-threshold discriminator.
   b. Derivation of the optimum targeting doctrine when the rank-order measurements on the reentry objects are available.
   c. Derivation of the optimum targeting doctrine when the actual analog measurements on the reentry objects are available.

Once the mathematical machinery is in place, it is used to develop a performance envelope of the targeting systems under consideration. Specifically, numerical comparisons are developed that address the following performance issues:

3. Numerical results.
   a. Parametrization of warhead and decoy measurement probability density functions with respect to a decoy quality parameter.
   b. Scaling of the fractional expected number of surviving reentry warheads with respect to the number of initial warheads.
   c. Dependence of the optimum targeting doctrine on the quality of the decoys.
   d. Comparison of the effectiveness of the proposed thresholding schemes for the single-threshold discriminator.
   e. Comparison of threshold discriminator versus analog measurement system performance for the sequential measurement and targeting problem.
   f. Comparison of threshold discriminator versus rank-order measurement versus analog measurement system performance for the simultaneous measurement and assignment problem.
   g. Bounds on possible performance improvement by adding "measurement memory" to single-threshold and analog measurements for the sequential measurement and interceptor assignment problem.
   h. Decoy optimization for various scaling laws.

II. ANALYSIS OF THE SEQUENTIAL ARRIVAL, MEASUREMENT, AND TARGETING PROBLEM

A. DERIVATION OF THE OPTIMUM TARGETING DOCTRINE FOR THE SINGLE-THRESHOLD DISCRIMINATOR

We now analyze the situation in which the problem time line imposes the condition that each object of the reentry cloud must be interrogated in a serial order and that, immediately after this interrogation by the discrimination device, an irrevocable decision must be made as to how many of the remaining defensive antimissile missile (AMM) interceptors to assign to that object. The measurement and subsequent targeting thus progresses serially until (1) all of the reentry objects have been dealt with or (2) the defense exhausts its inventory of interceptor weapons. As mentioned in Section I, the aim of the defense is to employ a targeting doctrine that minimizes the expected number of surviving reentry warheads. The role of the discrimination device is to permit the defense a greater ability to expend its interceptor assets against warheads and not to waste them against decoys. Conversely, the reason for decoys is to induce a wasteful disposition of defensive assets and by so doing enhance warhead survival. The following paragraph presents a typical situation in which it is plausible to assume, as we do here, the necessity of developing a serial measurement and targeting policy.

Assume that the discrimination device available to the defense is a radar. At high altitudes, where the atmosphere is rarified, it is easy to simulate warheads very cheaply by chaff or small pieces of wire that can be made to act as radiating dipoles at a given radar frequency. At high altitudes, chaff can be employed in sufficient quantity to saturate the defensive interceptor inventory. However, as these pieces of chaff approach lower altitudes where the atmospheric density is appreciable, they quickly burn up. Thus, the decoys that we are discussing are those that are at least massive enough to survive reentry without burning up. Now, it may well be, from time considerations, that it is necessary for the defense to decide whether or not to target an object shortly after it reaches this reentry altitude. In many cases the time interval between the arrival of an object at the reentry altitude and the time at which a targeting decision must be made is smaller than the average delay between the arrival of successive objects in the cloud at the reentry altitude. In this situation, a serial measurement and interceptor allocation policy is appropriate.

The immediate task in this section is the derivation of the optimum targeting doctrine when the discrimination device available to the defense is a single-threshold discriminator. Recall from Section I that $f_w(x)$ and $f_d(x)$ are the probability density functions of the quantity measured by the defense under the hypotheses that the received measurement x originated from a warhead or a decoy, respectively. From Eqs. (1) and (2) we recall that for a single-threshold discriminator the conditional probabilities that a measurement on a warhead or decoy, respectively, exceeded a certain preset threshold could be written as

$$P_{\mathrm{ww}} = \int_t^\infty f_{\mathrm{w}}(x)\,dx \tag{3}$$

$$P_{\mathrm{dw}} = \int_t^\infty f_{\mathrm{d}}(x)\,dx \tag{4}$$

For the moment we consider that the threshold t has been preset in some rational manner and that it remains static or constant throughout the problem. Various rationales leading to different settings of the threshold parameter will be discussed later.

Given this description of the single-threshold detector, we now formulate the decision or targeting problem for the defense. Initially, there is a cloud of $N_{\mathrm{w}} + N_{\mathrm{d}}$ objects consisting of N_{w} warheads and N_{d} homogeneous decoys of the same ability to mimic the warhead's measurement properties. The quantities N_{w} and N_{d} are both assumed to be known to the defense. At various times, one of the objects arrives at a decision altitude where it is interrogated by the threshold discriminator. Based on the output of the discriminator, the number of AMM interceptors remaining in inventory, the reliability and kill effectiveness of these interceptors, and the number of objects yet to reach the decision level, the defense decides the appropriate number of AMMs with which to target the current reentry object. The defense is assumed to initially possess N_{I} interceptors such that if a warhead is targeted by one of them its survival probability is P_{S} (also assumed known to the defense). For purposes of the following analysis, it is convenient to define an (n, i) situation as one in which a total of n objects remain in the cloud and the defense's remaining inventory consists of i interceptors. We further let $P(n)$ denote the probability, prior to interrogation by the threshold discriminator, that the next object to reach the decision level will be a warhead when there are n objects remaining to be interrogated. Nominally, there is little information available on the nature of the objects prior to interrogation, so for most of our analysis we assume that

$$P(n) = \frac{N_{\mathrm{w}}}{N_{\mathrm{w}} + N_{\mathrm{d}}} \tag{5}$$

This assumption is consistent with the assumption that the defense does not have a reliable posttargeting kill assessment capability against any earlier objects that were targeted, which would allow a dynamic refinement of the premeasurement probabilities $P(n)$. Knowledge of the quantities N_w and N_d should be available to the defense from *a priori* knowledge of the offense's penetration aid kit packaging policies together with the employment of other sensors used in the "cradle-to-grave" tracking process, which provide raid count but not discrimination information. It is felt that these assumptions provide a conservatively plausible representation of the information available to the defense for the formulation of its targeting doctrine.

For convenience in the development of the equations we define the following notational conversions.

N_w = Initial number of warheads in cloud of reentry objects
N_d = Initial number of decoys in cloud of reentry objects
N_I = Initial defensive interceptor inventory
P_S = Single shot survival probability of a warhead targeted by one interceptor
P_{ww} = Probability that a measurement on a warhead exceeds a preset classification threshold
P_{dw} = Probability that a measurement on a decoy exceeds the classification threshold
$PK(n)$ = *A priori* probability that the next object to emerge from a cloud of n objects is a warhead, given that K warheads remain in the cloud
$P(n)$ = Total a priori probability that the next emergent object from a cloud of n objects is a warhead
$L_n(k, i)$ = Expected number of surviving reentry warheads from stage n through stage 1, where n is the number of objects remaining in the cloud, given that k of the n are warheads, and that the defense has i remaining interceptors
rn = Random number of warheads remaining in the cloud when the cloud contains n elements
$\phi_1(n, i)$ = Optimum number of interceptors to target an object exceeding the threshold when n objects remain in the cloud and the defense has i interceptors.
$\phi_2(n, i)$ = Optimum number of interceptors to target an object not exceeding the threshold when n objects remain in the cloud and the defense has i interceptors.
$f_n(i)$ = Minimum expected number of surviving reentry warheads when n objects remain in the cloud and the defense has i interceptors remaining.

Initially, there are $N_w + N_d$ objects in the cloud, N_w of which are warheads and N_d of which are decoys of a prescribed quality. At discrete times, an object arrives at a decision point where it is interrogated by the threshold discriminator. The quantities N_w, N_d, N_I, P_S, P_{ww}, and P_{dw}, as well as the probabilities $P(n)$ and $PK(n)$, are assumed known to the defense. The number of objects n remaining in the cloud is also assumed known. Based on this information, the defense must decide how many, if any, interceptors should target the currently emerging object. The discrimination measurements and targeting are made serially and the targeting is irrevocable; that is, an interceptor is dispatched, it cannot be used for retargeting another. The goal of the defense is to use all available information to make those targeting assignments that minimize the expected number of surviving reentry warheads. The quantity

$$f_{N_w + N_d}(N_I) \tag{6}$$

is a direct measure of how well this goal is achieved. The targeting doctrine that is best in meeting this goal is explicitly contained in the functions

$$\phi_1(n, i) \tag{7}$$

and

$$\phi_2(n, i) \tag{8}$$

Thus, the present task is to calculate the functions shown in (7) and (8) as well as the measure of effectiveness given by (6).

We begin by working with the conditional loss function $L_n(k, i)$, where n is the number of objects remaining in the cloud, k is the number of warheads in the cluster, and i is the remaining interceptor inventory available to the defense. By its definition, $L_n(k, i)$ satisfies certain natural boundary conditions. For example, if the remaining cluster of n objects contains no warheads, then the expected number of surviving reentry warheads from that point on is zero. Thus,

$$L_n(0, i) = 0 \tag{9}$$

Next, if only one object remains in the cloud, then clearly the defense has nothing to lose by targeting that one object with all of its remaining interceptors. Hence we write

$$L_1(1, i) = P_S^i \tag{10}$$

In writing (10) we have used the assumption that warhead survivability from attacks by multiple defensive interceptors are statistically independent but equal. This is reasonable but not crucial to the analysis. If a survivability probability function $P_S(i)$ other than P_S^i were operative then the subsequent analysis would simply be modified by replacing P_S^i by $P_S(i)$. Next, if at any stage the defense has exhausted its interceptor inventory and if k of the remaining n objects are warheads, then all k of them survive, which enables us to write

$$L_n(k, 0) = k \tag{11}$$

Finally, to conclude the specification of the boundary conditions for $L_n(k, i)$, we note that since for n objects remaining in the cloud, the number of warheads among them k cannot exceed n, then there is no harm in writing

$$L_n(k, i) = 0 \qquad \text{for } k \geq n \tag{12}$$

Suppose for a moment that the defense is presented with an (n, k, i) situation; that is, there are n objects remaining in the cloud, k of which are warheads, and the defense has i remaining interceptors. The defense decides that it will target the next emergent object with a interceptors if it exceeds the threshold and with b interceptors if it does not exceed the threshold. The quantities (n, i) are known to the defense but k is not, except when

$$n = N_{\mathrm{w}} + N_{\mathrm{d}} \tag{13}$$

which is the initial stage where

$$k = N_{\mathrm{w}} \tag{14}$$

Under the conditions just stipulated, we can represent the possible one-step transitions for the triplet (n, k, i) as shown in Fig. 1.

In Fig. 1, the two leftmost paths are for cases in which the next object exceeds the threshold and the two rightmost paths are for the contingency that the object does not exceed the discrimination threshold. Specifically, on path 1 the next object is a warhead that exceeds the threshold. On path 2 the next

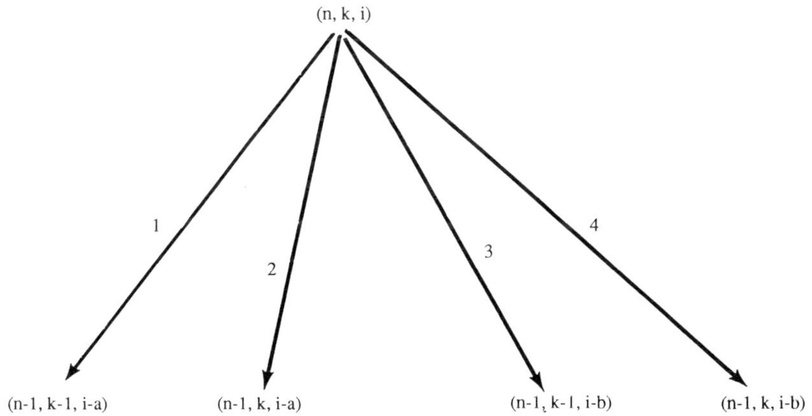

Fig. 1. Sketch of possible single-step transitions.

object is a decoy that exceeds the threshold. Path 3 represents a warhead that does not exceed the threshold, and path 4 represents a decoy that does not exceed the threshold. Now, since a warhead targeted with a interceptors survives the attack with probability P_S^a and since a warhead targeted with b interceptors survives with probability P_S^b, then from the definition of the probability $PK(n)$ and the enumeration of the contingencies in the description of Fig. 1, it follows that the conditional loss function satisfies the following partial difference equation.

$$\begin{aligned} L_n(k,i) = {} & PK(n)P_{ww}P_S^a + PK(n)P_{ww}L_{n-1}(k-1, i-a) \\ & + (1 - PK(n))P_{dw}L_{n-1}(k, i-a) \\ & + PK(n)(1 - P_{ww})P_S^b + PK(n)(1 - P_{ww})L_{n-1}(k-1, i-b) \\ & + (1 - PK(n))(1 - P_{dw})L_{n-1}(k, i-b) \end{aligned} \tag{15}$$

Although Eq. (15) describes the transition dynamics of the conditional loss function, in general, it cannot be used to sequentially compute the optimum a and b quantities, or equivalently, the functions $\phi_1(n,i)$ and $\phi_2(n,i)$. The reason for this is that if (15) is used directly, the optimizing quantities a and b generally depend on k, which is not known to the defense.

The exception to this difficulty exists in the special but important case of $N_w = 1$ (i.e., there is initially just one warhead in the cloud). For this special case, from the boundary condition (9), it follows that all of the loss-function terms with a first argument $k - 1$ must vanish. Since the only time there will be a nonzero expected survivability of the warhead is when $k = N_w = 1$, the k argument can be suppressed and Eq. (15) can be rewritten as

$$\begin{aligned} L_n(i) = {} & \pi(n)P_{ww}P_S^a + (1 - \pi(n))P_{dw}L_{n-1}(i-a) \\ & + \pi(n)(1 - P_{ww})P_S^b + (1 - (n))(1 - P_{dw})L_{n-1}(i-b) \end{aligned} \tag{16}$$

where $\pi(n)$ is now just the *a priori* probability that the next emergent object is the warhead. Then, from (16) and the definition of $f_n(i)$, the invocation of Bellman's *principle of optimality* [7] enables us to write

$$\begin{aligned} f_n(i) = {} & \min_{0 \le i \le a} (\pi(n)P_{ww})P_S^b + (1 - (n))(1 - P_{dw})f_{n-1}(i-a) \\ & + \min_{0 \le i \le b} (\pi(n))(1 - P_{ww})P_S^b + (1 - (n))(1 - P_{dw})f_{n-1}(i-b) \end{aligned} \tag{17}$$

Arguments similar to those employed in developing (10) and (11) can be used to show that $f_n(i)$ satisfies the boundary conditions given by (18) and (19).

$$f_1(i) = P_S^i \tag{18}$$

$$f_n(0) = 1 \tag{19}$$

In this case (17) together with the boundary conditions (18), (19) comprise an integer dynamic programming problem, and the techniques for solving that problem can be employed to calculate the optimal policy functions $\phi_1(n, i)$ and $\phi_2(n, i)$ as well as the desired minimum probability that the warhead survives, function (N_1). Since our more general discussion also includes this special case, we proceed to the more general treatment.

Returning to (15), recall that it was unsatisfactory as a vehicle for optimization because it was conditioned on there being precisely k remaining warheads in the set of n objects yet to arrive at the decision point. However, we can multiply both sides of Eq. (15) by the probability that, of the n objects yet to reenter, exactly k of them are warheads and sum the resulting expression over all possible values of k to obtain the following:

$$\phi_n(i, a, b) = \sum_{K=\max(0, n-N_d)}^{\min(n, N_w)} \Pr(rn = K) L_n(K, i) \tag{20}$$

$$\begin{aligned}\phi_n(i, a, b) = {} & \sum_K \Pr(r_n = K) P_{ww} P_S^a \\ & + \sum_K \Pr(rn = K) PK(n) P_{ww} L_{n-1}(k-1, i-a) \\ & + \sum_K \Pr(rn = K) PK(n)(1 - P_{ww}) P_S^b \\ & + \sum_K \Pr(rn = K) PK(n)(1 - P_{ww}) L_{n-1}(k-1, i-b) \\ & + \sum_K \Pr(rn = K)(1 - PK(n))(1 - P_{ww}) L_{n-1}(K, i-b)\end{aligned} \tag{21}$$

Since

$$\sum_K \Pr(rn = K) PK(n) = P(n) \tag{22}$$

then (21) can be rewritten as

$$\begin{aligned}\phi_n(i, a, b) = {} & P(n) P_{ww} P_S^a + \sum_K \Pr(rn = K) PK(n) L_{n-1}(K-1, i-a) \\ & + \sum_K \Pr(rn = K)(1 - PK(n)) P_{dw} L_{n-1}(K-1, i-a) \\ & + P(n)(1 - P_{ww}) P_S^b \\ & + \sum_K \Pr(rn = K) PK(n)(1 - P_{ww}) L_{n-1}(K-1, i-b) \\ & + \sum_K \Pr(rn = K)(1 - PK(n))(1 - P_{dw}) L_{n-1}(K, i-b)\end{aligned} \tag{23}$$

Now from the definition of $f_n(i)$, it follows that

$$f_n(i) = \min \phi_n(i, a, b) \qquad 0 \le a \le i \qquad 0 \le b \le i \tag{24}$$

which from (23) can be more explicitly written as

$$f_n(i) = \min_{0\le a\le i}\Big[P(n)P_{\mathrm{ww}}P_{\mathrm{S}}^{\mathrm{a}} + \sum_K \Pr(rn = K)PK(n)L_{n-1}(K-1, i-a)$$

$$+ \sum_K \Pr(rn = K)(1 - PK(n))P_{\mathrm{dw}}L_{n-1}(K, i-a)\Big]$$

$$+ \min_{0\le b\le i}\Big[P(n)(1 - P_{\mathrm{ww}}P_{\mathrm{S}}^{\mathrm{b}}$$

$$+ \sum_K \Pr(rn = K)PK(n)(1 - P_{\mathrm{ww}})L_{n-1}(K-1, i-b)$$

$$+ \sum_K \Pr(rn = K)(1 - PK(n))(1 - P_{\mathrm{dw}})L_{n-1}(K, i-b)\Big] \quad (25)$$

The optimization calculations are performed in the following way. From Eqs. (10) and (12) for the boundary conditions, the function $L, (k, i)$ is known for all pairs (k, i). Thus, for $n = 2$, Eq. (25) can be iteratively tested to calculate the minimizing values of a and b for all values i of the interceptor inventory between 1 and N_{I}. Thus, the functions $\varphi_1(2, i)$ and $\varphi_2(2, i)$ are determined for all values of i, and consequently by substitution so are all values of $f_2(i)$. Explicitly, from (24),

$$\phi_2(i, \varphi_1(2, i), \varphi_2(2, i)) \quad (26)$$

Having computed the optimum values of a and b as given by $\varphi_1(2, i)$ and $\varphi_2(2, i)$, we can use (15) to generate $L_2(k, i)$ as a function of k and i.

This process is iterated until all of the $f_n(i)$ are generated and, in particular, until the desired measure of effectiveness $f_{N_{\mathrm{w}}+N_{\mathrm{d}}}(N_{\mathrm{I}})$ is obtained. In particular, for each (n, i) situation, the quantities $\varphi_1(n, i)$ and $\varphi_2(n, i)$ are calculated. They determine the optimum targeting policy in the following sense. If there are n objects remaining in the cloud and if the defense has an inventory of i interceptors then the best decision is to target the next reentry object with $\varphi_1(n, i)$ interceptors if it exceeds the threshold and $\varphi_2(n, i)$ interceptors if it does not. This policy minimizes the expected number of surviving reentry warheads. A computer program was written to do these calculations and the results are discussed in Section IV. This corresponds to no *a priori* information about the location of the warheads in the incoming sequence of objects as well as no postattack or targeting information.

The case of most interest to us, which forms the basis of our numerical calculations, is that whenever there are n objects remaining in the cloud, the probability that exactly k of these are warheads is governed by the hypergeometric probability distribution. That is,

$$\Pr(rn = K) = \frac{\binom{N_w}{K}\binom{N_d}{n-K}}{\binom{N_w + N_d}{n}} \tag{27}$$

This is a conservative assumption for the defense. Similarly, for the conditional probabilities $PK(n)$, we can write

$$PK(n)\begin{cases} \min(1, k/n) & \text{for } k \leq n \\ 0 & \text{for } k > n \end{cases} \tag{28}$$

Furthermore, it is easy to show that

$$\sum_K \Pr(rn = K)PK(n) = \sum_K \frac{K}{n} \frac{\binom{N_w}{K}\binom{N_d}{n-K}}{\binom{N_w + N_d}{n}} \tag{29}$$

$$= \frac{N_w}{N_w + N_d}$$

With these specifications, the single-threshold discriminator serial targeting problem can be dealt with numerically.

B. CRITERIA FOR SETTING THE THRESHOLD FOR THE SINGLE-THRESHOLD DISCRIMINATOR

This section discusses various means of setting the threshold for a single-threshold discriminator. We make the assumption that the measurement probability density functions $f_w(x)$ and $f_d(x)$ are density functions of probability distributions belonging to a real parameter family of distributions that has the monotone likelihood property (see e.q., Ferguson [8]). For our case, this means that

$$g(x) = f_w(x)/f_d(x) \tag{30}$$

is a nondecreasing function of x. This is physically plausible since warheads tend to be bigger in terms of mass, cross-sectional area, volume, and so on than decoys.

Given these assumptions, the information carried by a threshold exceedance is that in some sense the a posteriori probability that an object is a warhead given that its measurement exceeded the threshold is greater than it would have been had its measurement failed to exceed the threshold. If the discriminator were perfect, then with probability 1, every warhead's measurement would exceed the threshold and no decoy's would. This situation, although in general not realizable, would provide perfect information to the defense and would ensure that all of its interceptors were assigned to warheads and were not wastefully expended against decoys.

For a given quality of decoy, the aim of the threshold setting should be to provide the maximum amount of "information" to the defense so that it can come as close as possible to the unrealizable perfect allocation in which all interceptors are allocated uniformly to warheads and none are allocated to decoys. As in classical statistical hypothesis testing, there are two kinds of errors. A warhead failing to exceed the threshold runs the risk of having too few if any interceptors assigned to it. A decoy exceeding the threshold wastefully attracts interceptors thus depleting the interceptor inventory available for targeting actual warheads. However, these two types of decoys may produce asymmetric effects, and their costs must actually be reckoned in terms of the degradation or increase that they induce in the cost function, the expected number of surviving reentry warheads. Because it seems analytically intractable to carry the single-threshold discrimination parameter as part of the optimization procedure, except in some simple cases to be discussed subsequently, we discuss certain possible ad hoc schemes that have the benefit of a cetain intuitive plausibility. The numerical consequences of these schemes is described in Section IV,D. For want of better names, the three thresholding schemes to be considered will be called maximum resolution (MR), best classification (BC), and constrained exceedance (CE).

Recalling from the definition of P_{ww} and P_{dw} given by (3) and (4), it follows that for a given quality of decoy, if the threshold parameter is varied, a plot can be made of P_{ww} versus P_{dw} as shown in Fig. 2.

The concavity of the solid curve in Fig. 2 follows from the fact that $f_w(x)$ and $f_d(x)$ have densities that have the monotone likelihood property. The degree of the concavity is inversely a function of the decoy quality (i.e., the poorer the quality the more concave the curve). In the limit of perfect decoy, the dashed linear curve is approached. Now, any value of the threshold t determines a point on the curve, and conversely. Moreover for a fixed value of P_{dw} the difference between the ordinate of the solid curve and the dashed line provides a measure of the ability of the threshold discriminator to resolve between a warhead and a decoy. That threshold t yielding the maximum difference we call the maximum resolution threshold.

This threshold setting is analytically determined as follows. Letting r be the resolution distance, from (3) and (4) we write

$$r = \int_t^\infty f_w(x)\,dx - \int_t^\infty f_d(x)\,dx \tag{31}$$

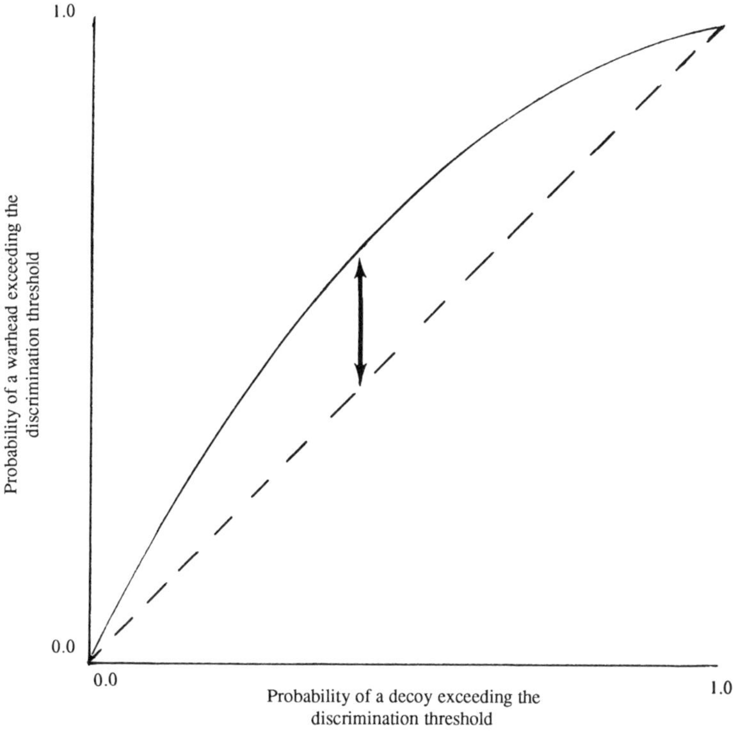

Fig. 2. Geometric illustration of maximum-discrimination threshold setting. Solid line, actual imperfect decoy; dashed line, perfect decoy limit; arrow, maximum-discrimination threshold setting.

Assuming $f_w(x)$ and $f_d(x)$ are continuous, we differentiate to obtain

$$\frac{dr}{dt} = -f_w(t_{mr}) + f_d(t_{mr}) = 0 \tag{32}$$

Thus, the maximum resolution threshold is obtained by inverting the following algebraic relation:

$$\frac{f_w(t_{mr})}{f_d(t_{mr})} = 1 \tag{33}$$

A closed-form expression for t_{mr} is given in terms of the decoy quality parameter in Section IV,A.

We now digress briefly to give a simple example for which the maximum resolution threshold is strictly optimum. Consider the case in which the defense has one interceptor and the reentry cloud consists of one decoy and one warhead that arrive serially in unknown order at the decision altitude. It is clear that the best targeting doctrine for the defense is to target the first reentry object if it exceeds the threshold. If the first object doesn't exceed the threshold, then the second object should be targeted. For this simple use, using our previously developed notation, we can write the following expression for the expectation that the warhead survives:

$$f_2(1) = 1 - (1 - P_S)\left(\frac{1}{2}P_{ww} + \frac{1}{2}(1 - P_{dw})\right) \tag{34}$$

where the bracketed term is just the probability that the interceptor targets the warhead. Rearranging (34) we get

$$f_2(1) = 1 - \frac{1}{2}(1 - P_S)(1 + (P_{ww} - P_{dw})) \tag{35}$$

$$f_2(1) = 1 - \frac{1}{2}(1 - P_S)\left(1 + \int_t^\infty f_w(x)\,dx - \int_t^\infty f_d(x)\,dx\right) \tag{36}$$

Thus, comparison of (36) and (31) show that when the resolution distance is maximized, the expectation of the warhead survival is minimized. Thus, in this simple case, the maximum-resolution discriminator threshold setting is optimum. One final comment: Calculation of the maximum resolution threshold depends only on the probability density functions f_w and f_d.

We now discuss the best classification threshold. The threshold discriminator acts as a classifier in the sense that the optimization algorithm treats an object exceeding the threshold as more likely to be a warhead than an object not exceeding the threshold. Since classifying a warhead as a decoy deprives it of targeting by enough interceptors and since a decoy classified as a warhead wastes warheads, it would appear reasonable that one might choose the threshold t such that in some way the greatest number of correct classifications would be made. One way to do this is to choose the threshold such that the expected number of correct classifications is maximized.

Now, a warhead is correctly classified if it exceeds the threshold, and this happens with probability P_{ww}. Similarly, a decoy is correctly classified if it does not exceed the threshold, and this happens with probability $1 - P_{dw}$. Since there are initially N_w warheads and N_d decoys, then letting C denote the expected number of correct classifications, we can write

$$C = N_w P_{ww} + N_d(1 - P_{dw}) \tag{37}$$

or, in terms of the threshold parameter, t

$$C = N_w \int_t^\infty f_w(x)\,dx + N_d \int_t^\infty f_d(x)\,dx \tag{38}$$

From (38),

$$\lim_{t \to \infty} C = N_d \tag{39}$$

$$\lim_{t \to \infty} C = N_w \tag{40}$$

thus, if there is some threshold t such that

$$C(t) > \max(N_w, N_d) \tag{41}$$

it is obtained by differentiation of (38) with respect to t and equating the result to zero. Performing this operation, we obtain

$$\frac{dC}{dt} = 0 = -N_w f_w(t) + N_d f_d(t) \tag{42}$$

Thus, from (42), we see that for the best classification, the threshold setting can be obtained by solving the transcendental equation

$$\frac{f_w(t)}{f_d(t)} = \frac{N_d}{N_w} \tag{43}$$

Again, a closed-form expression is given for this threshold setting in Section IV,A, and the numerical consequences of this thresholding technique will be evaluated in Section IV,D.

The last thresholding scheme that we discuss is the constrained exceedance scheme. Let E denote the expected number of threshold exceedances of the $N_w + N_d$ objects in the reentry cloud. Then, from our prior definitions, we can write

$$E = N_w P_{ww} + N_d P_{dw} \tag{44}$$

Explicitly, in terms of the threshold setting, (44) becomes

$$E = N_w \int_t^\infty f_w(x)\,dx + N_d \int_t^\infty f_d(x)\,dx \tag{45}$$

If the discriminator were perfect and acted without error, then only the warheads would exceed the threshold, and we would have $E = N_w$. This suggests setting the threshold t_{CE} by constraining the expected number of positive exceedances from the cloud of objects to equal the number of warheads initially in the cloud. Thus, from (45), t_{CE} is obtained by numerically inverting:

$$N_w \int_t^\infty f_w(x)\,dx + N_d \int_t^\infty f_d(x)\,dx = N_w \tag{46}$$

or

$$N_d \int_t^\infty f_d(x)\,dx = N_w \int_t^\infty f_w(x)\,dx \tag{47}$$

The numerical consequences of all these thresholding schemes are discussed in Section IV,D.

C. DERIVATION OF THE OPTIMUM TARGETING DOCTRINE FOR AN ANALOG DISCRIMINATOR

The previous section discussed the derivation of the best targeting doctrine when the only information available to the defense was whether a measurement on a reentry object exceeded a fixed threshold. *Best*, again, means the targeting policy that minimizes the expected number of surviving reentry warheads. Section II,B discussed possible ways for setting the threshold. This section develops the optimum targeting doctrine when the measurement x_i made on the ith reentry object is available in its entirety. We introduce two new pieces of notation for this case:

$p_j(n)$ = Probability of targeting a warhead with j interceptors at stage n

$q_j(n)$ = Probability of targeting a decoy at stage n with j interceptors

The defense now has more information with which to operate than in the threshold discriminator case. Recall that by an (n, i) situation we mean that there are n objects remaining in the cloud and that the defense has i defensive interceptors remaining in its inventory. The conditional loss function at stage n can be written in terms of the quantities just defined as

$$L_n(K, i) = \sum_{j=0}^{i} [PK(n)p_j(n)P_S^j + PK(n)p_j(n)L_{n-1}(K-1, i-j)$$

$$+ (1 - PK(n))q_j(n)L_{n-1}(K, i-j)] \tag{48}$$

In (48), the term $L_{n-1}(K-1, i-j)$ indicates that at stage n a warhead transited the decision altitude and was targeted by j interceptors, and $L_{n-1}(K, i-j)$ accounts for the nth object being a decoy and being twisted by j defensive interceptors. Equation (47) is not suitable for optimization as it stands since it is conditioned on there being exactly K warheads among the n objects in the (n, i) situation presented to the defense. Once more, the way out of this dilemma is to multiply both sides of (47) by the probability that there are indeed k warheads among the remaining n objects and sum the result over all possible values of k. Performing this operation yields

$$F_n(i) = \sum_K \Pr(r_n = K)L_n(K, i) \tag{49}$$

or

$$F_n(i) = P(n) \sum_{j=0}^{i} p_j(n)P_S^j + \sum_{j=0}^{i} p_j(n) \sum_K \Pr(r_n = K)(PK(n))L_{n-1}(K-1, i-j)$$

$$+ \sum_{j=0}^{i} q_j(n) \sum_K \Pr(r_n = K)(1 - PK(n))L_{n-1}(k, i-j) \tag{50}$$

Equation (50) has averaged over all values of k and as such is suitable for optimization. Since the full analog measurement is available, the decision problem for the defense in an (n, i) situation requires a partitioning of the measurement space into regions

$$t_0 < t_1 < \cdots < t_{i+1} \tag{51}$$

such that if a measured value x satisfies

$$t_j \leq x < t_{j+1} \tag{52}$$

then exactly j interceptors are targeted against that object. The optimization reduces to a choice of the t quantities. Note that for an (n, i) situation these quantities depend on n and i. We suppress making this explicit dependence for reasons of notational tidiness.

Since $p_j(n)$ is by definition the probability in an (n, i) situation that j interceptors will be targeted a warhead, then (52) implies that we can write

$$p_j(n) = \int_{t_j}^{t_{j+1}} f_w(x)\,dx \tag{53}$$

Similarly, since $q_j(n)$ is the probability of targeting a decoy with j interceptors, we can write

$$q_j(n) = \int_{t_j}^{t_{j+1}} f_d(x)\,dx \tag{54}$$

Furthermore, since the defense in an (n, i) situation can never assign more than i interceptors or less than zero interceptors, it is permissible to set

$$t_0 = -\infty \tag{55}$$

$$t_{i+1} = +\infty \tag{56}$$

Now, substitution of (53) and (54) into (50) yields

$$F_n(i) = \sum_{j=0}^{i} [P(n)P_S^j + \sum_K \Pr(rn = K)PK(n)L_{n-1}(K-1, i-j)] \int_{t_j}^{t_{j+1}} f_w(x)\,dx$$

$$+ \sum_{j=0}^{i} \sum_K \Pr(rn = K)(1 - PK(n))L_{n-1}(K, i-j) \int_{t_j}^{t_{j+1}} f_d(x)\,dx \tag{57}$$

Assume for a moment that the conditional loss functions for the decremental index $n - 1$ are known in (57). Since we are trying to choose the best set of t quantities, we can differentiate (57) with respect to t_j to obtain

$$\frac{\partial F_n(i)}{\partial t_j} = 0 \tag{58}$$

or

$$\begin{aligned}
&[P(n)P_S^{j-1} + \sum_K P(rn = K)PK(n)L_{n-1}(K-1, i-j+1)]f_w(t_j) \\
&\quad - [P(n)P_S^j + \sum_K \Pr(rn = K)PK(n)L_{n-1}(k-1, i-j)]f_w(t_j) \\
&\quad + \sum_K \Pr(rn = K)(1 - PK(n))L_{n-1}(K, i-j+1)f_d(t_j) \\
&\quad - \sum_K \Pr(rn = K)(1 - PK(n))L_{n-1}(K, i-j)f_d(t_j) = 0
\end{aligned} \tag{59}$$

Equation (59) can be solved for $f_w(t_j)/f_d(t_j)$ to yield

$$\begin{aligned}
\frac{f_w(t_j)}{f_d(t_j)} &= \frac{\Sigma_K \Pr(rn = K)(1 - PK(n))(L_{n-1}(K, i-j) - L_{n-1}(K, i-j+1)}{P(n)(P_S^{j-1} - P_S^j) + \Sigma_K \Pr(rn = K)PK(n)} \\
&\quad \times (L_{n-1}(K-1, i-j+1) - L_{n-1}(K-1, i-j))
\end{aligned} \tag{60}$$

Now, under the assumption that the measurement distributions satisfy the monotone likelihood property, (60) can be uniquely-solved for a given (n, i) situation to yield

$$t_1, t_2, \ldots, t_i \tag{61}$$

In the solution of (60) certain situations might arise. Thus, if $t_j = \infty$ for some $j < i$, then $1 > j$ implies $t_1 = \infty$ also. This just means that no more than $j - 1$ interceptors are ever assigned to an object. For example, with $P_S = 0$ it would be pointless to assign more than one interceptor to a reentry object; thus, we would expect for $j \geq 2$ that $t_j = \infty$. Conversely, if for $j > 0$, $t_j = -\infty$, then $1 < j$ implies that $t_1 = -\infty$, which implies that in the given (n, i) situation at least j interceptors will target the object. For example, since at the last stage (i.e., $n = 1$), all remaining interceptors will be expended, we should expect that (60) would show that $j \leq i$ implies that $t_j = -\infty$, and $t_{i+1} = +\infty$.

We mention once more that the optimum partitioning quantities t_j depend on (n, i), P_S, and the decoy quality parameter. We also note that the best partitioning of the measurement space is calculated from a likelihood ratio principle.

In summary, the complete computational sequence proceeds as follows. The conditional loss function $L_1(K, i)$ is known from Eqs. (10) and (12) since the same boundary conditions apply for both the single-threshold and the analog measurement serial measurement and targeting problem. Thus, for $n = 2$ and arbitrary interceptor inventory i, Eq. (60) can be used to calculate the optimal partitioning of the measurement space. After the partitioning parameters are fixed, Eq. (57) can be used together with the $L_1(K, i)$ to compute the minimum number of expected surviving warheads $F_2(i)$, where i is the second-stage interceptor inventory. Next, since for $n = 2$ and arbitrary i, the t_j and hence, from (53) and (54), the terms $p_j(n)$ and $q_j(n)$ are known. After these quantities are available, Eq. (48) can be used to generate the second-stage conditional loss function $L_2(k, i)$, and the process can be iterated to calculate the final desired result $F_{N_w+N_d}(N_I)$. Note that for any (n, i) the partitioning constants t_j define the optimal targeting doctrine for the defense in that if the measured value x satisfies $t_j \le x < t_{j+1}$, then exactly j interceptors should be assigned to the object. Thus, the optimum targeting doctrine for the analog measurement serial targeting problem has been developed together with the algorithm to compute the expected number of surviving reentry warheads using the optimal targeting doctrine. Numerical results for this problem are described in Section IV.

III. ANALYSIS OF SIMULTANEOUS ARRIVAL, MEASUREMENT, AND TARGETING PROBLEM

A. DERIVATION OF THE OPTIMUM TARGETING DOCTRINE FOR THE SINGLE-THRESHOLD DISCRIMINATOR

Section II presented an analysis of the targeting problem when the physical time line was such that it was necessary to make measurements on each reentry object serially and that the targeting assignment on an object must be made prior to the availability of the next reentry object for interrogation. Moreover, it was assumed that defensive interceptor targeting assignments were final and irrevocable, an assumption that will be retained throughout this section. In contrast, this section supposes that the cluster of reentry objects arrives in the field of view of the discrimination device in a span of time that permits each of the objects to be interrogated prior to the allocation of any of the defensive assets. For brevity we refer to this situation as the *simultaneous-arrival* case. Clearly, the situation treated in Section II provides the minimal information base to the defense, whereas the simultaneous-arrival case provides the maximum amount. This attainable defense system performance for intermediate situations, in which more than one but not all of the reentry objects are simultaneously in the discriminator field of view, is bounded by computations using the results of Sections II and III. Moreover, the analysis in Section II assumed a memoryless system on the part of the defense. Numerical comparison between results for the simultaneous and serial targeting cases allow the determination of bounds on possible system improvement attainable by adding memory to the system for the serial arrival case. Some examples are presented in Section IV,B. By *memoryless* we simply meant that at any stage the targeting allocations were based on (1) the measurement made on the present object, (2) the number of defensive interceptors still in inventory, and (3) the number of objects still to reenter. In particular, knowledge of the measurements on the preceding objects was not used in the calculations. However, as stated previously, bounds are presented in Section IV,G that put a cap on the improvement to be gained by adding that considerable mathematical complexity to the analysis of the sequential targeting problem.

Our immediate task in this section is the derivation of the optimal targeting policy when all of the objects in the cloud can be interrogated by a single-threshold discriminator prior to the allocation of any defensive interceptors. Again, we assume that the total number of warheads N_w and decoys N_d in the cloud are known and that prior to interrogation by the threshold discriminator the a priori probabilities that an object is a warhead or a decoy are $N_w/(N_w + N_d)$ and $N_d/(N_w + N_d)$, respectively. We furthermore retain our assumption that interceptor targeting assignments are final in the sense that retargeting is not permitted.

The development of the targeting doctrine is based on the following observation. Since the only measurement information provided on an object by the threshold discriminator is whether the threshold is exceeded, and since there is no a priori information available about the objects other than the total number of warheads and decoys in the cloud, then after all of the threshold measurements have been made, all objects exceeding the threshold have the same *a posteriori* probabilities of being warheads. Similarly, any two objects not exceeding the threshold have equal *a posteriori* probabilities of being warheads. These *a posteriori* probabilities depend on k, the total number of observed threshold exceedances. This implies that the optimal targeting policy assigns the same number of interceptors, or as nearly as posible, to all objects recording positive exceedances. Similarly, since any two objects not exceeding the threshold have the same *a posteriori* probability of being warheads, then the optimal targeting policy dictates that, as nearly as possible, all objects not exceeding the threshold are targeted by the same number of interceptors. Thus, the determination of the optimal targeting doctrine is achieved by specifying how many of the N_I available interceptors, say N^+, should be uniformly assigned to those objects exceeding the threshold, with the understanding that the remaining $N_I - N^+$ interceptors should be assigned to target those objects not exceeding the threshold as uniformly as possible. We do this in the following way, conforming to the notational conventions set in Section II,A.

Before proceeding we need some new notation. Accordingly we define the following:

$P(w \mid 1, k) =$ Conditional probability that an object exceeding the threshold is a warhead given that k objects exceed the threshold.

$P(w \mid 0, k) =$ Conditional probability that an object not exceeding the threshold is a warhead given that k objects exceed the threshold.

$P(w, 1, k) =$ Joint probability that an object selected at random is a warhead and exceeds the threshold.

$P(w, 0, k) =$ Joint probability that an object selected at random is a warhead and does not exceed the threshold.

The quantities $P(d \mid 1, k)$, $P(d \mid 0, k)$, $P(d, 1, k)$, and $P(d, 0, k)$ are analogously defined by replacing the word *warhead* by *decoy* in the preceding definitions.

Assume first that $0 < K < N_w + N_d$ where k is the number of threshold exceedances. Since for any sensible single-threshold discriminator and for homogeneous decoys of less than perfect quality, we have

$$P_{ww} > P_{dw} \tag{62}$$

it follows that for $K > 0$,

$$P(w \mid 1, K) > P(w \mid 0, K) \tag{63}$$

Thus, for $P_S < 1$, there is an integer I_1 defined by the following conditions:

$$P_S^{I_1} P(w \mid 1, K) < P(w \mid 0, K) \tag{64}$$

$$P_S^{I_1 - 1} P(w \mid 1, K) \geq P(w \mid 0, K) \tag{65}$$

The interpretation of I_1, which depends on the quantities N_w, N_d, P_{ww}, P_{dw}, and k, is that subject to available inventory, I_1 interceptors should target each of the k objects with positive exceedances before any objects not exceeding the threshold are targeted. After each of the k objects with positive exceedances is targeted by I_1 interceptors, then each object not exceeding the threshold should be targeted by one interceptor. This weighted layering of interceptors should proceed until the entire inventory of N_I defensive interceptors has been assigned.

The correctness of this targeting doctrine for minimizing the expected number of surviving reentry warheads becomes clear from the following considerations. For some k such that $0 < k < N_w + N_d$, assume that we are at some intermediate point in our interceptor allocation process and assume further that the ith object exceeding the threshold has been targeted by n_i interceptors and that the ith object not exceeding the threshold has been targeted by m_i interceptors. Then, given the assignments thus far and the total number of exceedances k, the conditional probability that the ith object that exceeds the threshold is a surviving warhead is given by (66).

$$P_i(S \mid 1, K) = P_S^{n_i} P(w \mid 1, K) \tag{66}$$

Similarly, the probability that the ith object that does not exceed the threshold is a surviving warhead is given by (67).

$$P_i(S \mid 0, k) = P_S^{m_i} P(w \mid 0, K) \tag{67}$$

Since the goal is to minimize the expected number of surviving reentry warheads, the next interceptor should be assigned to the greatest threat, that is, to the object having the greatest possibility of being a surviving warhead. Moreover, since this policy should be pursued from the initial allocation, it is clear that the layered policy just described is optimal when the N_I interceptors are distributed as uniformly as possible so that each object exceeding the threshold is targeted by I_1 interceptors for each interceptor that targets an object not exceeding the threshold.

We now proceed with the specifics of computing the optimum targeting allocations. First, assume that

$$KI_1 \geq N_I \tag{68}$$

Thus, in accordance with Eqs. (64) and (65), none of the interceptors should be allocated to objects not exceeding the threshold; instead, all N_I interceptors should be assigned as uniformly as possible to objects whose measurements exceed the threshold. Thus, letting

$$N^- = N_I - N^+ \tag{69}$$

denote the optimal number of interceptors to allocate to those objects not exceeding the threshold, we have for the present case

$$N^+ = N_I \tag{70}$$

and

$$N^- = 0 \tag{71}$$

For the second case, assume that

$$KI_1 < N_I \tag{72}$$

When this situation obtains, a certain number of the objects not exceeding the threshold should be targeted.

Let N_u denote the number of interceptors used in one complete covering of the K positive exceedances with I_1 interceptors each, and the remaining objects with one interceptor each. Then,

$$N_u = KI_1 + N_w + N_d - k \tag{73}$$

Now, if N_c denotes the number of complete layered coverings of all the objects provided by the N_I interceptors, then

$$N_c = \left[\frac{N_I}{N_u}\right] \tag{74}$$

where [ ] denotes the integer part. The remaining number of interceptors after all of the possible complete layered coverings have been made is given by (75):

$$N_R = N_I - N_C N_u \tag{75}$$

Now if

$$N_R \leq KI_1 \tag{76}$$

then all of the remaining interceptors should target those objects with positive exceedances. Thus, in this case

$$N^+ = N_c I_1 + N_R \tag{77}$$

and

$$N^- = N_I - N^+ = N_I - N_c I_1 - N_R \tag{78}$$

On the other hand, if

$$N_R > KI_1 \tag{79}$$

then some of the remaining interceptors should target those objects not exceeding the threshold, in which case

$$N^+ = (N_c + 1)I_1 \tag{80}$$

and

$$N^- = N_I - N^+ = N_I - (N_c + 1)I_1 \tag{81}$$

To complete this discussion, we now calculate the various probabilities defined earlier. First note from the theorem relating joint and conditional probabilities that

$$P(w \mid 1, K) = P(w, 1, K)/P(1, K) \tag{82}$$

$$P(w \mid 0, K) = P(w, 0, K)/P(0, K) \tag{83}$$

$$P(w, 1, K) = \left(\frac{N_w}{N_w + N_d}\right) P_{ww} \sum_j \binom{N_w - 1}{j} P_{ww}^j (1 - P_{ww})^{N_w - 1 - j} \times \binom{N_d}{K - j - 1} P_{dw}^{K-j-1} (1 - P_{dw})^{N_d - K + j + 1} \tag{84}$$

where

$$\max(K - N_d, 0) \le j \le \min(K - 1, N_w - 1) \tag{85}$$

$$P(d, 1, K) = \left(\frac{N_d}{N_w + N_d}\right) P_{dw} \sum_j N_w P_{ww}^j (1 - P_{ww})^{N_w - j} \times \binom{N_d - 1}{K - 1 - j} P_{dw}^{K-1-j} (1 - P_{ww})^{N_d - K + j} \tag{86}$$

where

$$\max(K - N_d, 0) \le j \le \min(K - 1, N_w)$$

Since an object is either a decoy or a warhead (i.e., exclusive events), then

$$P(1, K) = P(w, 1, K) + P(d, 1, K) \tag{87}$$

Thus (86) and (87) explicitly specify $P(1, K)$. Hence, substitution of (84) and (81) into (82) specifies $P(w \mid 1, K)$ in closed form.

Next we can write

$$P(w, 0, K) = \left(\frac{N_w}{N_w + N_d}\right)(1 - P_{ww}) \sum_j \binom{N_w}{j} P_{ww}^j (1 - P_{ww})^{N_w - 1 - j} \times \binom{N_d - 1}{K - j} P_{dw}^{K-j} (1 - P_{dw})^{N_d - k + j} \tag{88}$$

where

$$\max(0, K - N_d) \le j \le \min(K, N_w - 1) \tag{89}$$

Similarly,

$$P(d, 0, K) = \left(\frac{N_d}{N_w + N_d}\right)(1 - P_{dw}) \sum_j \binom{N_w}{j} P_{ww}^j (1 - P_{ww})^{N_w - j} \times \binom{N_d - 1}{K - j} P_{dw}^{K-j} (1 - P_{dw})^{N_d - 1 - K + j} \tag{90}$$

where

$$\max(K + 1 - N_d, 0) \le j \le \min(K, N_w) \tag{91}$$

Hence,

$$P(0, K) = P(w, 0, K) + P(d, 0, k) \tag{92}$$

Therefore, substituting (88) and (90) into (92), and (88) and (92) into (83), establishes $P(w \mid 0, K)$ explicitly. Thus, since for $P_{ww} > P_{dw}$ it follows that

$$P(w \mid 1, K) > P(w \mid 0, K) \tag{93}$$

then the integer I_1 is well defined by (64) and (65). Thus, the optimum targeting policy is completely defined. Thus far we have assumed that

$$0 < K < N_w + N_d \tag{94}$$

We now consider what happens to our conditional probabilities $P(w \mid 1, N_w + N_d)$ and $P(w \mid 0, 0)$ in the extreme cases. First, when $K = N_w + N_d$, then from (84) we have

$$P(w, 1, N_w + N_d) = \left(\frac{N_w}{N_w + N_d}\right) P_{ww}^{N_w} P_{dw}^{N_d} \tag{95}$$

Similarly,

$$P(d, 1, N_w + N_d) = \left(\frac{N_d}{N_w + N_d}\right) P_{ww}^{N_w} P_{dw}^{N_d} \tag{96}$$

Thus

$$P(1, N_w + N_d) = P_{ww}^{N_w} P_{dw}^{N_d} \tag{97}$$

and

$$P(w \mid 1, N_w + N_d) = \frac{P(w, 1, N_w + N_d}{P(1, N_w + N_d)} = \frac{N_w}{N_w + N_d} \tag{98}$$

In a similar manner it follows that

$$P(d \mid 1, N_w + N_d) = \frac{N_d}{N_w + N_d} \tag{99}$$

and

$$P(w \mid 0, 0) = \frac{N_w}{N_w + N_d} \tag{100}$$

and

$$P(d \mid 0, 0) = \frac{N_d}{N_w + N_d} \tag{101}$$

In other words, when $k = 0$ or $N_w + N_d$, observing the threshold exceedances provides no discrimination information as to whether an object is a decoy or a warhead. In those degenerate cases it is clear that the optimum targeting doctrine is to allocate the N_I interceptors as uniformly as possible over the total cluster of $N_w + N_d$ objects.

We are now in a position to write an explicit, albeit complicated, expression for the expected number of surviving reentry warheads for the simultaneous measurement single-threshold detector. We treat first the degenerate case in which $k = N_w + N_d$ or $k = 0$. Since the best targeting policy for this case is the uniform allocation of the N_I interceptors of the total complex of $N_w + N_d$ objects, the conditional expected number of surviving warheads, given either of these extreme threshold measurement realizations, can be written as

$$N_w\left(fP_S^{\left[\frac{N_I}{N_w+N_d}\right]+1} + (1-f)P_S^{\left[\frac{N_I}{N_w+N_d}\right]}\right) \tag{102}$$

where

$$f = \frac{N_I - (N_w + N_d)\left[\dfrac{N_I}{N_w + N_d}\right]}{N_w + N_d} \tag{103}$$

and where [ ] denotes the integer part of the expression included in the brackets. Now, since the probability of the threshold exceedance being either all positive or all negative is

$$P_{ww}^{N_w} P_{dw}^{N_d} + (1 - P_{ww})^{N_w}(1 - P_{dw})^{N_d} \tag{104}$$

then the net contribution to the total unconditional expectation of surviving warheads for this degenerate case is simply

$$N_w(P_{ww}^{N_w} P_{dw}^{N_d} + (1 - P_{ww})^{N_w}(1 - P_{dw})^{N_d}) \times \left(fP_S^{\left[\frac{N_I}{N_w+N_d}\right]+1} + (1-f)P_S^{\left[\frac{N_I}{N_w+N_d}\right]}\right) \tag{105}$$

We now consider the nondegenerate case in which $0 < K < N_w + N_d$ positive exceedances are observed from the results of the single-threshold discriminator. Recalling that for $K > 0$, N^+ and N^- are the number of interceptors assigned to that set of objects with positive and negative exceedances, respectively, we define f^+ and f^- as follows:

$$f^+ = N^+ - K\left[\frac{N^+}{K}\right] \tag{106}$$

$$f^- = N^- - (N_w + N_d - K)\left[\frac{N^-}{N_w + N_d - K}\right] \tag{107}$$

where we recall that

$$N^+ + N^- = N_I \tag{108}$$

Since for $0 < dK < N_w + N_d$ positive exceedances, it has been shown that the optimum targeting plan is to allocate N^+ interceptors uniformly to those K objects with positive exceedances and N^- interceptors to those $N_w + N_d - K$ objects with negative exceedances, then given K positive exceedances,

j of which are warheads, the conditional expected number of surviving reentry warheads is expressed as

$$j\left(f^+P_S^{\left[\frac{N^+}{K}\right]+1} + (1-f^+)P_S^{\left[\frac{N^+}{K}\right]}\right) + (N_w + N_d - j)$$

$$\times\left(f^-P_S^{\left[\frac{N^-}{N_w+N_d-K}\right]+1} + (1-f^-)P_S^{\left[\frac{N^-}{N_w+N_d-K}\right]}K\right) \quad (109)$$

Now, the probability that the threshold discriminator will produce a total of K positive exceedances, j of which are warheads, is

$$P(j,K) = \binom{N_w}{j} P_{ww}^j(1-P_{ww})^{N_w-j}\binom{N_d}{K-j}P_{dw}^{K-j}(1-P_{dw})^{N_d-K+j} \quad (110)$$

Hence, noting in the degenerate cases that

$$K = N_w + N_d \Rightarrow N^+ = N_I, \qquad N^- = 0 \quad (111)$$

$$K = 0 = N^+ = 0, \qquad N^- = N_I \quad (112)$$

we can write Eq. (113) for the total expected number of surviving reentry warheads $\langle S\rangle$ as

$$\langle S\rangle = \sum_{K=0}^{N_w+N_d}\sum_j\left(j(f^+P_S^{\left[\frac{N^+}{K}\right]+1} + (1-f^+)^+P_S^{\left[\frac{N^+}{K}\right]}\right)$$

$$+ (N_w + N_d - j)\left(f^-P_S^{\left[\frac{N^-}{N_w+N_d-K}\right]+1} + (1-f^-)P_S^{\left[\frac{N^-}{N_w+N_d-K}\right]}\right)$$

$$\times\binom{N_w}{j}P_{ww}^j(1-P_{ww})^{N_w-j}\binom{N_d}{K-j}P_{dw}^{K-j}(1-P_{dw})^{N_d-K+j} \quad (113)$$

where

$$\max(0, K - N_d) \leq j \leq \min(N_w, K)$$

In summary, Eq. (113) gives a closed-form but complicated expression for the expected number of surviving reentry warheads, given that an optimal target assignment policy is followed for the simultaneous assignment problem when a single-threshold discriminator is used. Prescription of the optimum policy defines the quantities N^+, N^-, f^+, and f^- appearing in Eq. (113). Thus, for this problem the optimum targeting doctrine, as well as a closed-form expression for the minimum expected number of surviving reentry warheads, has been attained. A computer program was written to perform these computations, and numerical results are discussed in Section IV. The problem of determining a suitable setting for the threshold discriminator applies to the present situation as well as to the sequential single-threshold discriminator problem discussed in Section II. The efficacy of the threshold setting schemes described in Section II,B when applied to the present simultaneous problem is numerically evaluated in Section IV,D.

B. DERIVATION OF THE OPTIMAL TARGETING DOCTRINE WHEN ONLY THE RANK-ORDER STATISTICS ON THE REENTRY OBJECTS ARE AVAILABLE

For the situation hypothesized in this section, which is that all measurements can be made on the objects prior to making the targeting assignments, the single-threshold discriminator analyzed in Section III,A represents the minimum information situation available to the defensive data processor. The maximum information situation is when the actual analog measurements made on the reentry objects are recorded and optimally factored into the development of the targeting doctrine. The problem treated in this section occupies an intermediate position in that the rank-order statistics are available on all of the objects. Thus, the number of interceptors targeting a given object is driven by the rank-order of that particular measurement relative to the measurements made on the other objects. Again we invoke the assumption that the decoy and warhead measurement distributions belong to a family of probability distributions processing the monotone likelihood property as defined in [8]. Thus, we can assume that after the measurements are made, those objects with larger measured values are more likely to be warheads than those objects with smaller measurements. Or if we rank the measurements in reverse order, $x_1 \geq x_2 \cdots \geq x_{N_w+N_d}$, the object yielding the measurement x_1 has the highest a posteriori probability of being a warhead, and so on down the line. The problem then is the following. Given the single-shot survival probability P_S of a warhead targeted by an interceptor and an inventory of N_I defensive interceptors, how should the targeting of the objects be done when the only information preserved by the targeting mechanism is the rank-order statistics of the measurement. Again, the cost function of the defense is the expected number of penetrating enemy warheads.

As in the preceding sections, we assume that the only information available to the defense prior to interrogation by the discriminator is the knowledge of the number of warheads N_w and decoys N_d in the cloud. Thus, before the measurements are made, each object has an *a priori* probability of $N_w/(N_w + N_d)$ of being a warhead. Now, let P_k be the *a* posteriori probability, given the observed ranks of the discriminator output, that the kth ranked or largest object is a warhead. Our ranking convention is that 1 corresponds to the object yielding the largest measured value. Thus, P_1 is the *a posteriori* value that the largest object is a warhead, given the observed ranks, and $P_{N_w+N_d}$ is the *a posteriori* probability that the smallest ranked object is a warhead. We now consider the probability that the kth ranked object is a warhead, given that it produced a measured value of x and that there are exactly j warheads producing measurements that exceed x. Thus, defining

$$F_w(x) = \int_{-\infty}^{x} f_w(y)\,dy \tag{114}$$

$$F_d(x) = \int_{-\infty}^{x} f_d(y)\,dy \tag{115}$$

we can write this probability as

$$N_w \binom{N_w - 1}{j} F_w(x)^{N_w - 1 - j}(1 - F_w(x))^j \\ \times \binom{N_d}{K - 1 - j} F_d(x)^{N_d - K + j + 1}(1 - F_d(x))^{K - 1 - j} \tag{116}$$

P_k is obtained from (115) by summation over all possible values of j, multiplication by the warhead probability density function, and integration with respect to x:

$$P_K = N_w \sum_j \binom{N_w - 1}{j}\binom{N_d}{K - 1 - j} \int_{-\infty}^{\infty} F_w(x)^{N_w - 1 - j}(1 - F_w(x)) \\ \times F_d(x)^{N_d - K + j + 1}(1 - F_d(x))^{K - 1 - j} f_w(x)\,dx \tag{117}$$

where

$$\max(0, K - 1 - N_d) \leq j \leq \min(N_w - 1, K - 1)$$

We now make some preliminary observations regarding Eq. (117). Consider the case in which the decoys are perfect [i.e., $F_w(x) \equiv F_d(x)$]. Then, suppressing the w and d subscripts on the probability density and distribution functions in (117) enables us to write (117) as

$$P_K = N_w \sum_j \binom{N_w - 1}{j}\binom{N_d}{K - 1 - j} \int_{-\infty}^{\infty} F(x)^{N_d + N_w - K}(1 - F(x))^{K - 1} f(x)\,dx \tag{118}$$

Using an elementary combinatorial identity yields

$$P_k = N_w \binom{N_w + N_d - 1}{K - 1} \int_{-\infty}^{\infty} F(x)^{N_w + N_d - K}(1 - F(x))^{K - 1} f(x)\,dx \tag{119}$$

Now, noting that

$$f(x) = \frac{dF}{dx} \tag{120}$$

and making the change of variable

$$u = F(x) \tag{121}$$

we can write

$$P_k = N_w \binom{N_w + N_d - 1}{K - 1} \int_0^1 u^{N_w + N_d - K}(1 - u)^{K-1}\, du \tag{122}$$

But

$$\int_0^1 u^{N_w + N_d - K}(1 - u)^{K-1}\, du = B(K, N_w + N_d - dK + 1) \tag{123}$$

where $B(,)$ is the beta function and

$$B(K, N_w + N_d - K + 1) = \frac{(K-1)!(N_w + N_d - K)!}{(N_w + N_d)!} \tag{124}$$

Thus, for the special case of perfect decoys, we obtain

$$P_k = \frac{N_w}{N_w + N_d} \tag{125}$$

for all k. This is intuitively correct since for perfect decoys the measurements provide no discrimination information so that the *a posteriori* probabilities conditioned on the rank-order statistics must equal the *a priori* probabilities.

Next from (117), if we sum both sides over k and interchange the order of interaction and summation, we obtain the following:

$$\sum_{K=1}^{N_w + N_d} P_K = \int_{-\infty}^{\infty} \left(\sum_{j=0}^{N_w - 1} \binom{N_w - 1}{j} F_w(x)^{N_w - 1 - j}(1 - F_w(x))^j \right) \times \left(\sum_{K=j+1}^{N_d + j + 1} \binom{N_d}{K - 1 - j} F_d(x)^{N_d + j + 1}(1 - F_d(x))^{K-1-j} f_w(x)\, dx \right) \tag{126}$$

But both of the summations sum the unity, hence

$$\sum_{K=1}^{N_w + N_d} P_k = N_w \int_{-\infty}^{\infty} f_w(x)\, dx = N_w \tag{127}$$

which simply expresses the conservation of warheads. Equations (125) and

(127) are not meant to be profound but rather to provide a commonsense consistency check on a rather complicated equation.

We now determine the optimal targeting doctrine for the simultaneous order statistic assignment problem. As a by-product, we obtain an expression for the expected number of surviving warheads given that an optimal targeting policy is followed. To this end we define $W(n, i)$ to be the probability that the nth-ranked object is a surviving warhead given that i of the N_I defensive interceptors have been allocated in an optimum way. We note first that

$$W(n, 0) = P_n \tag{128}$$

where P_n is given by (117).

Because of our assumption that the decoy and warhead measurement probability distributions possess the monotone likelihood ratio property, it follows that

$$P_1 \geq P_2 \cdots \geq P_{N_w + N_d} \tag{129}$$

Thus, since the first-ranked object has the highest *a posteriori* probability of being a warhead, the first interceptor should be assigned to the first-ranked object. Now, if the ith interceptor is assigned to the nth-ranked object,

$$W(n, i) = P_S W(n, i - 1) \tag{130}$$

otherwise,

$$W(n, i) = W(n, i - 1) \tag{131}$$

At any stage of the assignment process, the defense should clearly allocate the next interceptor to that object posing the greatest probability of being a surviving warhead. Specifically the ith interceptor should be assigned to the labeled object n_i, when n_i is determined by (132)

$$W(n_i, i - 1) = \max_{1 \leq k \leq N_w + N_d} W(k, i - 1) \tag{132}$$

Equations (130), (131), and (132), together with the prescription that the first interceptor should be assigned to the first-ranked object, determine the best targeting procedure. The resultant expected number of surviving reentry warheads, given this optimal policy, is then given by (133).

$$\langle S \rangle = \sum_{n=1}^{N_w + N_d} W(n, N_I) \tag{133}$$

In Section IV,A, a specific model is assumed for the decoy and measurement distributions. Specifically, the physical discriminant is assumed to be the radar cross section, and both decoys and warheads are postulated to be Swerling type I fluctuating targets. This assumption permits a closed-form evaluation of the P_K probabilities given by Eq. (116) in terms of a decoy quality parameter as well as other problem variables. These calculations are discussed in Section IV,A. A computer program was written to generate numerical results on the performance of the rank-order statistic discriminator. The comparative performance of this system is discussed in Sections IV,F and IV,G.

One final comment regarding the implementation of the rank-order discriminator is relevant, namely, that the decision rule can be calculated before the fact. That is, it is not necessary to record the value of the largest object to know how many interceptors to assign to it. This is not true for the analog discriminator to be discussed in the next section and indeed it is this difference that provides some improvement in the statistical resolving power of the analog discriminator.

C. DERIVATION OF THE OPTIMUM TARGETING DOCTRINE FOR THE SIMULTANEOUS ANALOG DISCRIMINATOR

The present section discusses the development of the optimum targeting doctrine and the resulting minimum expected number of surviving warheads for the case where the actual physical measurements, $x_1, \ldots, x_{N_w+N_d}$, made on the objects are recorded and processed optimally prior to making the allocation of the defensive interceptors. This situation provides the maximum amount of information available to the defense. Again we assume that the defense knows the conditional probability density functions $f_w(x)$ and $f_d(x)$. Thus, given a particular realization of the measurements, the most informative numbers on which the defense should base its targeting doctrine are the conditional probabilities that the individual objects are warheads given the realized set of data $x_1, \ldots, x_{N_w+N_d}$. In this section the x_i are not ranked. Recall that by *analog* we simply mean that the entire measurements rather than just the rank-orders are used in computing the various conditional probabilities.

The calculation of the conditional probability that the kth object is a warhead given the observed data is conceptually straightforward though notationally awkward. If we let **x** denote the $N_w + N_d$ dimensional vector of measurements, we shall write $PK(x)$ to denote the conditional probability that the kth object is a warhead, given the observed set of measurements. $PK(x)$ is the ratio of two quantities to be described. The numerator consists of the sum of

$$\binom{N_w + N_d - 1}{N_w - 1}$$

terms each consisting of a product of $N_w + N_d$ of the probability density functions representing the totality of ways these products can be formed such that the kth measurement was made on a warhead [i.e., such that $f_w(x_k)$ is one of the factors]. The denominator is the sum of

$$\binom{N_w + N_d}{N_w}$$

terms, each consisting of the product of $N_w + N_d$ of the probability density functions.

We continue the details of the calculation for the important special case in which there is one warhead in the cloud: $N_w = 1$. In this case, the notational problems are tractable. Since *a priori*, each object has a probability of $N_w/(N_w + N_d)$ of being a warhead, then the conditional probability that the kth object [i.e., the object yielding the measurement xK_1 can be written as

$$P_k(\mathbf{x}) = \frac{f_w(x_k)\prod_{i \neq K, i=1}^{N_d+1} f_d(x_i)}{\sum_{j=1}^{N_d+1} f_w(x_j)\prod_{i \neq j, i=1}^{N_d+1} f_d(x_i)} \tag{134}$$

Dividing numerator and denominator of (134) by

$$\prod_{i=1}^{N_d} f_d(x_i) \tag{135}$$

we obtain the following:

$$P_K(\mathbf{x}) = \frac{f_w(x_k)/f_d(x_k)}{\sum_{j=1}^{N_d+1} f_w(x_j)/f_d(x_j)} \tag{136}$$

where we have explicitly indicated the dependence of these conditional probabilities on the particular realization of the measurement vector $\mathbf{x}$.

Again, for a particular $\mathbf{x}$ we let $W(n, i \mid \mathbf{x})$ denote the conditional probability that the nth object is a surviving warhead given that an optimal allocation thus far has been made of i of the N_I defensive interceptors. For $i = 0$ we clearly have

$$W(n, 01\mathbf{x}) = P_n(\mathbf{x}) \tag{137}$$

Clearly the defense wants to assign the first interceptor to that object K_1 so that

$$P_{K_1}(\mathbf{x}) = \max_{1 \leq k \leq N_d+1} P_k(\mathbf{x}) \tag{138}$$

As before, if the ith interceptor is assigned to the nth object, then

$$W(n, i1\mathbf{x}) = P_S W(n, i - 1 \mid \mathbf{x}) \tag{139}$$

otherwise,

$$W(n, i \mid \mathbf{x}) = W(n, i - 1 \mid \mathbf{x}) \tag{140}$$

Similarly, the ith interceptor should be assigned to the jth object, where

$$W(j, i-1 \mid \mathbf{x}) = \max_{1 \le K \le N_d + 1} W(K, i-1 \mid \mathbf{x}) \tag{141}$$

Hence, the conditional minimum expected number of surviving reentry warheads is given by

$$\langle S \mid \mathbf{x} \rangle = \sum_{n=1}^{N_d+1} W(n, N_I \mid \mathbf{x}) \tag{142}$$

Equation (142) is conditional on the observed measurement set. The unconditional minimum expected number of surviving warheads is given by multiplying (142) by the joint unconditional likelihood of the measurements and performing an $(N_w + 1)$-dimensional integration of (142) with respect to

$$\begin{aligned} \langle S \rangle &= \int \langle S \mid \mathbf{x} \rangle L(x)\, d\mathbf{x} \\ &= \sum_{n=1}^{N_d+1} \int W(n, N_I \mid \mathbf{x}) L(\mathbf{x})\, d\mathbf{x} \end{aligned} \tag{143}$$

Finally, because the assumption is that prior to making the measurements each object has equal *a priori* probability of being the warhead, we can write (143) for the joint likelihood function:

$$L(x) = \frac{1}{N_d + 1} \sum_{K=1}^{N_d+1} f_w(xK) \prod_{\substack{i \ne K \\ i=1}} f_d(x_i) \tag{144}$$

The fact that in the present case the probabilities $PK(\mathbf{x})$ are conditional on the actual observed measured values instead of merely the rank-order statistics accounts for their increased resolving power and the improved system performance of the rank-order discriminator discussed in Section III,C. The integral in (143) is very difficult to evaluate analytically. However a Monte Carlo simulation is easy to develop where the measurements are sampled from the appropriate Swirling type I distribution. A computer program was developed to do this. Numerical comparisons between the analog and rank-order discriminator are presented in Section IV,F.

One final comment should be made regarding a comparison between the implementation of the rank-order statistic and the analog discriminator. For the rank-order discriminator, the targeting doctrine was precomputable in the sense that one could prescribe beforehand how many interceptors should be allocated to the kth largest object. For the present situation that is no longer the case. For example, for the analog discriminator, the optimum number of interceptors allocated to the largest object depends on how large it and the remaining measurements are. That is, it depends on the actual value of the measurements and is itself a statistic or funtion of random variables whose sample values must be observed to be computed. This is both a strength and a weakness. It is the price the system must pay in real-time data processing to achieve the improved resolving power of the analog discriminator. The performance improvement is quantified in Section IV,F.

IV. NUMERICAL RESULTS

A. PARAMETRIZATION OF WARHEAD AND DECOY MEASUREMENT PROBABILITY DENSITY FUNCTIONS WITH RESPECT TO A DECOY-QUALITY PARAMETER

In this section we perform certain quantitative and parametric analyses based on the numerical results that were developed in Sections II and III. To do this, it is necessary to specify the probability density functions $f_w(x)$ and $f_d(x)$ at least up to a finite set of distribution parameters. Fortunately there is a parametrization of the family of measurement probability density functions that is physically plausible and permits, after rescaling, a simple relationship between the probability density functions in terms of a decoy-quality parameter. Moreover, this decoy-quality parameter is dimensionless and assumes the value unity for perfect decoys, which are statistically indistinguishable from warheads, and 0 for useless decoys, which can be resolved with probability 1.

We therefore assume for our numerical work that the physical parameter being measured by the discrimination device is the radar cross section of the object. We also assume that the radar cross-section distribution of the decoys and the warheads can be modeled as Swerling type I fluctuation targets, as described in [9]. The, if θ_w and θ_d denote the mean radar cross sections of a warhead and a decoy, respectively, from [9] it follows that we can write the conditional probability density functions as

$$f_w(y) = \begin{cases} 1/\theta_w e^{-y/\theta_w} & y \geq 0 \\ 0 & y < 0 \end{cases} \tag{145}$$

and

$$f_d(y) = \begin{cases} 1/\theta_d e^{-y/\theta_d} & y \geq 0 \\ 0 & y < 0 \end{cases} \tag{146}$$

Recalling from Section II the definitions of P_{ww} and P_{dw} for a given preselected discriminator threshold, we can write

$$P_{ww}(t) = \int_t^{\infty} f_w(x)\,dx = e^{-t/\theta_w} \tag{147}$$

and

$$P_{\text{dw}}(t) = \int_t^{\infty} f(x)\,dx = e^{-t/\theta_{\text{d}}} \tag{148}$$

If we now define

$$q = \theta_{\text{d}}/\theta_{\text{w}} \tag{149}$$

then from (147) and (148) it follows that we can write

$$P_{\text{ww}} = P_{\text{dw}}^{q} \tag{150}$$

where q is a dimensionless quality parameter. Since from cost and energy considerations we can be certain that the mean decoy cross section will never exceed that of a warhead, then q varies between zero and unity. Referring back to Fig. 2, the curve for the perfect decoy corresponds to a value of $q = 1$ and the curve for an extremely poor decoy could be easily resolved as the quality parameter q approaches zero.

The relationship given by (150) is implied by an even more general set of expressions between the warhead and decoy measurement probability density functions. Thus for a nonnegative parameter k, if we write

$$f_{\text{w}}(y) = \frac{Ky^{K-1}}{\theta_{\text{w}}} e^{-y^K/\theta_{\text{d}}} \tag{151}$$

$$f_{\text{d}}(y) = \frac{Ky^{K-1}}{\theta_{\text{d}}} e^{-y^K/\theta_{\text{d}}} \tag{152}$$

an easy integration shows that (150) is still satisfied. For subsequent calculations we work with the dimensionless variable $x = y/\theta_{\text{w}}$, which permits us to write equations (153) and (154) for the conditional probability density functions of x under the warhead and decoy hypothesis, respectively:

$$f_{\text{w}}(x) = \begin{cases} e^{-x} & x \geq 0 \\ 0 & x < 0 \end{cases} \tag{153}$$

$$f_{\text{d}}(x) = \begin{cases} x/q\, e^{-x/q} & x \geq 0 \\ 0 & x < 0 \end{cases} \tag{154}$$

References [10] and [11] define various metrics or distance functions that are sometimes used to calculate a "distance" between two probability distributions. We compute the Bhattacharrya and the variational distance between the warhead and the decoy measurement distributions as a function of the decoy-quality parameter. The Bhattacharrya distance between the decoy and warhead probability distributions is given by

$$\rho_{\text{B}}(f_{\text{w}}, f_{\text{d}}) = -\ln \beta \tag{155}$$

where β is the Bhattacharrya coefficient given by

$$\beta = \int \sqrt{f_{\mathrm{w}}(x) f_{\mathrm{d}}(x)}\, dx \tag{156}$$

Using (153) and (154), we can compute the Bhattacharrya distance as

$$\rho_{\mathrm{B}}(f_{\mathrm{w}}, f_{\mathrm{d}}) = \ln\left(\frac{q+1}{2\sqrt{q}}\right) \tag{157}$$

We note from (157) that for $q = 1$ (i.e., perfect decoys) that the Bhattacharrya distance between the measurement distributions is zero. Similarly as q tends to zero the distance becomes infinite.

We next compute the variational distance between the warhead and measurement probability distributions. From [12] we can write the following expression for this quantity:

$$\rho_{\mathrm{v}}(f_{\mathrm{w}}, f_{\mathrm{d}}) = \int_{-\infty}^{\infty} |f_{\mathrm{w}}(x) - f_{\mathrm{d}}(x)|\, dx \tag{158}$$

Equation (158) can be easily evaluated to yield

$$\rho_{\mathrm{v}}(f_{\mathrm{w}}, f_{\mathrm{d}}) = 2\left(\frac{1}{q}\right)^{q/q-1} - \left(\frac{1}{q}\right)^{1/q-1} \tag{159}$$

Using L'Hospital's rule, it follows that for the limiting conditions of perfect and terrible decoys, we have

$$\lim_{q \to 1} \rho_{\mathrm{v}}(f_{\mathrm{w}}, f_{\mathrm{d}}) = 0 \tag{160}$$

$$\lim_{q \to 0} \rho_{\mathrm{v}}(f_{\mathrm{w}}, f_{\mathrm{d}}) = 2 \tag{161}$$

The significance of (159) will be pointed out in Section IV,D when the various thresholding schemes are discussed.

In conclusion we also note that the analytic form assumed for the decoy and warhead measurement probability density functions permits a closed-form but messy expression for P_K, the probability that the kth largest object is a warhead. Substitution of (153) and (154) into (117) and performing the integrations finally yields

$$P_K = N_{\mathrm{w}} \sum_i \binom{N_{\mathrm{w}} - 1}{i} \binom{N_{\mathrm{d}}}{K - 1 - i} \sum_{=0}^{N_{\mathrm{w}} - 1 - i} \sum_{j=0}^{N_{\mathrm{d}} - K + 1 + i} \times \binom{N_{\mathrm{w}} - 1 - i}{l} \binom{N_{\mathrm{d}} - K + i + 1}{j} \times \left(\frac{q}{K - 1 - i + j + q(i + \quad + 1)}\right) \tag{162}$$

where

$$\max(0, K - N_d - 1) \leq i \leq \min(N_w - 1, K - 1)$$

This is the expression used for the calculation of the performance of the rank-order discriminator.

B. SCALING OF THE FRACTIONAL NUMBER OF EXPECTED SURVIVING WARHEADS WITH RESPECT TO THE INITIAL NUMBER OF WARHEADS

The primary measure of effectiveness or, more correctly, the cost function selected for minimization in this study is the expected surviving number of reentry warheads. It is clearly possible to divide this number by the initial number of warheads in the cloud and to speak of the expected fraction of surviving reentry warheads, which will, of course, always lie between zero and one.

If the defense had no power to achieve any discrimination between the decoys and warheads in the cluster, then its best policy would be to allocate its defensive interceptor inventory as uniformly as possible all over all incoming objects. Given that it has total raid count information, which has been assumed from the outset, the defense can always do this. Thus, if we let S_u denote the fractional number of expected reentry warheads under a uniform targeting doctrine and S denote the minimum expected fractional number of surviving reentry warheads, we clearly have

$$S \leq S_u \tag{163}$$

Moreover, if we define the fractional improvement factor F as in Eq. (164), then F is a direct measurement of the possible improvement due to the ability of the discrimination device to resolve between decoys and warheads.

$$F = \frac{S_u - S}{S_u} \tag{164}$$

The scaling question of interest is the following. For an arbitrary number of warheads, decoys, and interceptors, N_w, N_d, N_I, let S_1 denote the optimal expected fraction of surviving reentry warheads. Now let K denote any positive integer and consider the situation where there are KN_w, KN_d, and KN_I warheads, decoys, and interceptors, respectively, and let S_K and S_{uK} denote the expected fraction of surviving warheads under the optimal and uniform targeting doctrines. It is easy to show for the uniform targeting doctrine that

$$S_{uK} = S_{u1} \tag{165}$$

It is also easy to show numerically that, in general,

$$S_K \neq S_1 \tag{166}$$

Nonetheless, intuition suggests that S_K should approximately scale so that

$$S_K \cong S_1 \tag{167}$$

Extensive numerical work was done using computer programs produced by exercising the algorithms described thus far. In all cases, it was found numerically that S_K depends only weakly on K. Figures 3a,b show the scaling sensitivity of the expected fraction of surviving warheads as well as the improvement factor. These figures are for the case of the sequential analog discriminator but are virtually the same for all of the discrimination situations discussed thus far. Considerable effort was expended in trying to identify cases in which there were appreciable departures between S_K and S_1 for $K \neq 1$ but to no avail. In Fig. 3a, the curve denoted by open squares is the baseline case for $K = 1$. Inspection shows that there is some slight loss to the defense in the fractional number of survivors in having to deal with more objects even if the interceptor inventory is scaled up accordingly.

In Figs. 3a,b, the measures of effectiveness are plotted as functions of the normalized decoy-quality parameter. Many of the numerical sensitivities are examined as a function of this parameter since it is a quantity of great interest.

C. DEPENDENCE OF THE OPTIMUM TARGETING DOCTRINE ON THE DECOY-QUALITY PARAMETER

The optimization procedures we have developed provide as by-products the optimum targeting doctrines for the interceptor allocation problems considered. These optimum allocation policies depend on the quality of the decoys, the single-shot survival probability of a warhead targeted by an interceptor, the data available on an object to be targeted, the number of warheads and decoys initially in the reentry cloud, the interceptor inventory, and for the sequential arrival case, the relative position of the object in the cloud. Intuition suggests that for very poor decoys and appropriate threshold settings, the optimum policy is very selective and tends to assign multiple interceptors to objects exceeding the threshold or with large measured values. Conversely, since in the limit of perfect decoys, the optimum allocation is the uniform allocation, then one would expect to see this naturally evolve in the assignment policy as a function of the decoy-quality parameter. The purpose of this section is to provide numerical examples of this phenomenon.

First, consider the situation in which the objects arrive sequentially at a given decision altitude and a single threshold discriminator is employed. Then,

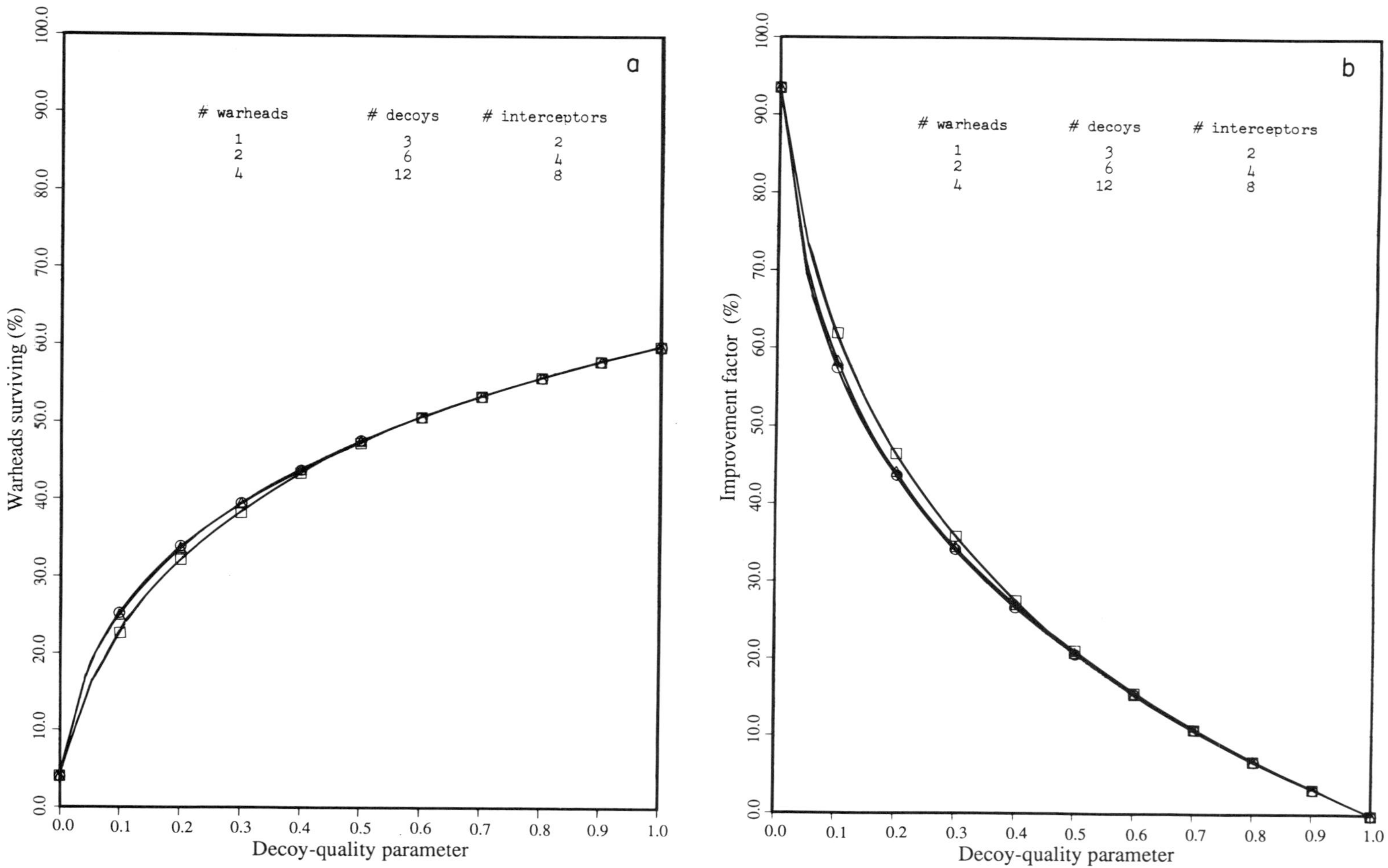
a
warheads
1
2
4
decoys
3
6
12
interceptors
2
4
8
Warheads surviving (%)
Decoy-quality parameter
b
warheads
1
2
4
decoys
3
6
12
interceptors
2
4
8
Improvement factor (%)
Decoy-quality parameter

TABLE I. OPTIMUM TARGETING POLICY SINGLE-THRESHOLD DISCRIMINATOR[a]

Optimal assignment of AMM missiles to those objects exceeding the threshold for a decoy quality of 0.05 $P_{dw} = 0.043$, $P_{ww} = 0.854$

A(1, 1) = 1	A(2, 1) = 1	A(3, 1) = 1	A(4, 1) = 1	A(5, 1) = 1
A(6, 1) = 1	A(7, 1) = 1	A(8, 1) = 1	A(9, 1) = 1	A(10, 1) = 1
A(1, 2) = 2	A(2, 2) = 2	A(3, 2) = 2	A(4, 2) = 2	A(5, 2) = 2
A(6, 2) = 2	A(7, 2) = 2	A(8, 2) = 2	A(9, 2) = 2	A(10, 2) = 2
A(1, 3) = 3	A(2, 3) = 3	A(3, 3) = 3	A(4, 3) = 3	A(5, 3) = 3
A(6, 3) = 3	A(7, 3) = 3	A(8, 3) = 2	A(9, 3) = 2	A(10, 3) = 2
A(1, 4) = 4	A(2, 4) = 4	A(3, 4) = 4	A(4, 4) = 3	A(5, 4) = 3
A(6, 4) = 3	A(7, 4) = 3	A(8, 4) = 3	A(9, 4) = 3	A(10, 4) = 3
A(1, 5) = 5	A(2, 5) = 5	A(3, 5) = 4	A(4, 5) = 4	A(5, 5) = 4
A(6, 5) = 4	A(7, 5) = 4	A(8, 5) = 3	A(9, 5) = 3	A(10, 5) = 5

Optimal assignment of AMM missiles to those objects not exceeding the threshold for a decoy quality of 0.05 $P_{dw} = 0.043$, $P_{ww} = 0.854$

B(1, 1) = 1	B(2, 1) = 0	B(3, 1) = 0	B(4, 1) = 0	B(5, 1) = 0
B(6, 1) = 0	B(7, 1) = 0	B(8, 1) = 0	B(9, 1) = 0	B(10, 1) = 0
B(1, 2) = 2	B(2, 2) = 0	B(3, 2) = 0	B(4, 2) = 0	B(5, 2) = 0
B(6, 2) = 0	B(7, 2) = 0	B(8, 2) = 0	B(9, 2) = 0	B(10, 2) = 0
B(1, 3) = 3	B(2, 3) = 0	B(3, 3) = 0	B(4, 3) = 0	B(5, 3) = 0
B(6, 3) = 0	B(7, 3) = 0	B(8, 3) = 0	B(9, 3) = 0	B(10, 3) = 0
B(1, 4) = 4	B(2, 4) = 1	B(3, 4) = 0	B(4, 4) = 0	B(5, 4) = 0
B(6, 4) = 0	B(7, 4) = 0	B(8, 4) = 0	B(9, 4) = 0	B(10, 4) = 0
B(1, 5) = 5	B(2, 5) = 1	B(3, 5) = 0	B(4, 5) = 0	B(5, 5) = 0
B(6, 5) = 0	B(7, 5) = 0	B(8, 5) = 0	B(9, 5) = 0	B(10, 5) = 0

[a] $N_w = 1$, $N_d = 9$, $q = 0.05$, $P_S = 0.50$, $N_I = 5$.

for an (n, i) situation, in which there are n objects remaining in the cloud and the defensive inventory contains i interceptors, the problem for the defense is to calculate the quantities $A(n, i)$, $B(n, i)$ (i.e., the number of interceptors to assign to the next object given that it exceeds or does not exceed the threshold) such that the total expected number of surviving reentry warheads is minimized. Table I displays those quantities for a scenario consisting of one warhead and nine decoys for a relatively poor decoy-quality parameter of 0.05. The single-shot survival probability of a warhead targeted by a decoy was 0.05, and the number of interceptors was 5.

Fig. 3. (a) Scaling sensitivity comparison for percent surviving warhead, serial arrival single-threshold discriminator; (b) scaling sensitivity comparison for percent improvement factor, serial arrival single-threshold discriminator. Single-shot survival probability is 20%.

Inspection of this table shows that for this situation (i.e, a poor-quality decoy) the best defense has considerable confidence in the ability of its detector to discriminate between decoys and warheads. Thus, at the initial stage it is willing to allocate three of its five interceptors to an object exceeding the threshold. Conversely, it is unwilling to assign any interceptors to an object not exceeding the threshold until the next to the last stage (i.e., $n = 2$).

In contrast consider Table II for the same scenario except that $q = 0.95$, a relatively high-quality decoy. For this situation the algorithm has much less confidence in the resolution power of its discriminator. This is shown by the relative unwillingness of the defense to target an object exceeding the threshold with multiple interceptors, even with a full inventory, until well into the game, as well as by its willingness to assign some interceptors to objects not exceeding the threshold as early as the fifth stage. This stems the tendency of the optimal allocation policy to approach the uniform assignment policy

TABLE II. OPTIMUM TARGETING POLICY SEQUENTIAL SINGLE-THRESHOLD DISCRIMINATOR[a]

Optimal assignment of AAM missiles to those objects exceeding the threshold for a decoy quality of 0.95 $P_{dw} = 0.358$, $P_{ww} = 0.377$

A(1, 1) = 1	A(2, 1) = 1	A(3, 1) = 1	A(4, 1) = 1	A(5, 1) = 1
A(6, 1) = 1	A(7, 1) = 1	A(8, 1) = 1	A(9, 1) = 1	A(10, 1) = 1
A(1, 2) = 2	A(2, 2) = 1	A(3, 2) = 1	A(4, 2) = 2	A(5, 2) = 1
A(6, 2) = 1	A(7, 2) = 1	A(8, 2) = 1	A(9, 2) = 2	A(10, 2) = 1
A(1, 3) = 3	A(2, 3) = 2	A(3, 3) = 1	A(4, 3) = 3	A(5, 3) = 1
A(6, 3) = 1	A(7, 3) = 1	A(8, 3) = 1	A(9, 3) = 2	A(10, 3) = 1
A(1, 4) = 4	A(2, 4) = 2	A(3, 4) = 2	A(4, 4) = 3	A(5, 4) = 1
A(6, 4) = 1	A(7, 4) = 1	A(8, 4) = 1	A(9, 4) = 3	A(10, 4) = 1
A(1, 5) = 5	A(2, 5) = 3	A(3, 5) = 2	A(4, 5) = 4	A(5, 5) = 1
A(6, 5) = 1	A(7, 5) = 1	A(8, 5) = 1	A(9, 5) = 3	A(10, 5) = 1

Optimal assignment of AMM missiles to those objects not exceeding the threshold for a decoy quality of 0.95 $P_{dw} = 0.358$ $P_{ww} = 0.377$

B(1, 1) = 1	B(2, 1) = 0	B(3, 1) = 0	B(4, 1) = 0	B(5, 1) = 0
B(6, 1) = 0	B(7, 1) = 0	B(8, 1) = 0	B(9, 1) = 0	B(10, 1) = 0
B(1, 2) = 2	B(2, 2) = 1	B(3, 2) = 0	B(4, 2) = 0	B(5, 2) = 0
B(6, 2) = 0	B(7, 2) = 0	B(8, 2) = 0	B(9, 2) = 0	B(10, 2) = 0
B(1, 3) = 3	B(2, 3) = 1	B(3, 3) = 1	B(4, 3) = 0	B(5, 3) = 0
B(6, 3) = 0	B(7, 3) = 0	B(8, 3) = 0	B(9, 3) = 0	B(10, 3) = 0
B(1, 4) = 4	B(2, 4) = 2	B(3, 4) = 1	B(4, 4) = 0	B(5, 4) = 0
B(6, 4) = 0	B(7, 4) = 0	B(8, 4) = 0	B(9, 4) = 0	B(10, 4) = 0
B(1, 5) = 5	B(2, 5) = 2	B(3, 5) = 1	B(4, 5) = 0	B(5, 5) = 1
B(6, 5) = 0	B(7, 5) = 0	B(8, 5) = 0	B(9, 5) = 0	B(10, 5) = 0

[a] $N_w = 1$, $N_d = 9$, $q = 0.95$, $P_S = 0.50$, $N_I = 5$.

in the limit as the decoys become statistically indistinguishable from the warheads.

For the simultaneous assignment case in which the rank-order discriminator is used, the problem for the defense is to determine how many interceptors to the kth largest object. The algorithm producing this optimum assignment was developed and discussed in Section III. For the similar case of $N_w = 1$, $N_d = 9$, $N_I = 5$, and $P_S = 0.5$, Table III showss the optimal number of interceptors to be assigned to the ranked objects when the rank increases from left to right (i.e., the leftmost rank is the largest object). Inspection of this table shows the same progression as in the sequential single-threshold case (that is, the tendency to a uniform allocation policy in the limit of perfect decoy quality.

Figure 4 shows the same information in a different format. The optimum number of interceptors allocated to the largest five objects is plotted versus decoy quality. For this situation the only object ever targeted by multiple interceptors is the first-ranked or largest object. Those values of the decoy-quality parameter at which each of the higher ranked objects is targeted are shown in the figure. By the time the decoy-quality parameter reaches 0.75, the uniform targeting policy has been reached, or more precisely, each of the five top-ranked objects is targeted by one interceptor.

D. COMPARISON OF THE EFFECTIVENESS OF THE PROPOSED THRESHOLDING SCHEMES FOR SINGLE-THRESHOLD DETECTORS

In section II,B, various criteria for setting the fixed threshold for the single-threshold discriminator were discussed. Three criteria were considered: (1) setting the threshold to maximize the difference between P_{ww} and P_{dw},

TABLE III. OPTIMAL ASSIGNMENT POLICIES FOR SIMULTANEOUS RANK-ORDER DISCRIMINATOR[a]

Decoy-quality parameter	Optimal number of interceptors									
0.50	5	0	0	0	0	0	0	0	0	0
0.25	3	1	1	0	0	0	0	0	0	0
0.50	2	1	1	1	0	0	0	0	0	0
0.75	1	1	1	1	1	0	0	0	0	0

[a] $N_w = 1$, $N_d = 9$, $N_I = 5$, $P_S = 0.50$.

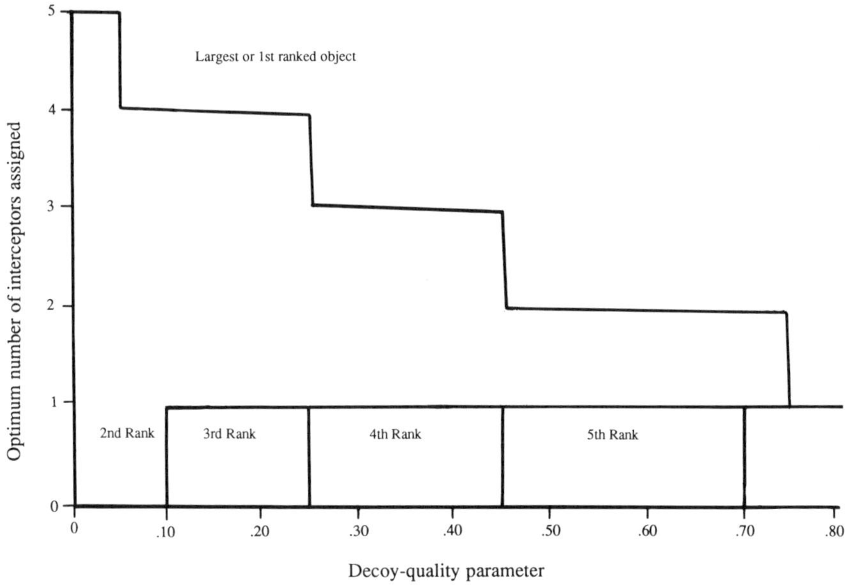

Fig. 4. Simultaneous rank-order static, discriminator optimum assignment policy; for case of 1 warhead, 9 decoys, 5 interceptors, and $P_S = 0.50$.

(2) setting the threshold to maximize the expected number of correct classifications, and (3) setting the threshold so that the expected number of threshold exceedances equals the number of warheads initially present in the cloud of objects. These thresholding schemes were called maximum resolution, best classification, and constrained exceedance, respectively. With the decoy-quality parametrization described in Section IV,A we are now in a position to quantitatively evaluate the consequences of these schemes in terms of their impact on the expected number of surviving reentry warheads.

For the maximum-resolution and best-classification threshold schemes, we can compute single closed-form expressions for P_{ww} and P_{dw} as functions of the decoy-quality parameter q. For the constrained-exceedance threshold, we can write a simple algebraic equation that can be numerically solved for the appropriate threshold or the equivalent value of P_{dw}. We now proceed to do this. For the maximum-resolution threshold determination from (150) we can write

$$d = P_{ww} - P_{dw} = P_{dw}^{q} - P_{dw} \tag{168}$$

where q is the decoy-quality parameter. From (153), (154), (3), and (4) it follows that determination of the threshold is equivalent to setting a threshold value of P_{dw}. Thus from (167) we maximize d by differentiating with respect to P_{dw} to obtain

$$\frac{dd}{dP_{\mathrm{dw}}} = qP_{\mathrm{dw}}^{q-1} - 1 = 0 \tag{169}$$

from which we obtain

$$P_{\mathrm{dw}} = (1/q)^{1/q-1} \tag{170}$$

and

$$P_{\mathrm{ww}} = P_{\mathrm{dw}}^{q} = (1/q)^{q/q-1} \tag{171}$$

Thus we have

$$d_{\max} = (1/q)^{q/q-1} - (1/q)^{1/q-1} \tag{172}$$

Comparing (172) with (160), we see that

$$d_{\max} = \frac{1}{2}\rho_{\mathrm{v}}(f_{\mathrm{w}}, f_{\mathrm{d}}) \tag{173}$$

where $\rho_{\mathrm{v}}(f_{\mathrm{w}}, f_{\mathrm{d}})$ is the variational distance between the measurement probability distributions. We note that P_{dw} and P_{ww} corresponding to the maximum-resolution threshold setting depend only on the decoy-quality parameter q and not on the number of decoys or warheads in the cloud.

We next derive the expressions for P_{dw} and P_{ww} corresponding to the best-classification threshold setting. In our terminology, a warhead is considered correctly classified if it exceeds the discriminator threshold. A decoy is considered correctly classified if it does not exceed the threshold. Thus, if we let c denote the expected number of correct classifications, we can write

$$c = N_{\mathrm{w}}P_{\mathrm{dw}}^{q} + N_{\mathrm{d}}(1 - P_{\mathrm{dw}}) \tag{174}$$

Equation (174) can be used to maximize c by differentiating with respect to P_{dw} and setting the result to zero. Performing this operation yields

$$P_{\mathrm{dw}} = (N_{\mathrm{d}}/qN_{\mathrm{w}})^{1/q-1} \tag{175}$$

and

$$P_{\mathrm{ww}} = (N_{\mathrm{d}}/qN_{\mathrm{w}})^{q/q-1} \tag{176}$$

From (175) and (176) the maximum expected number of correct classifications can be written as

$$c = N_{\mathrm{w}}(N_{\mathrm{d}}/qN_{\mathrm{w}})^{q/q-1} + N_{\mathrm{d}}(1 - (N_{\mathrm{d}}/qN_{\mathrm{w}})^{1/q-1}) \tag{177}$$

We note that in this case the $(P_{\mathrm{dw}}, P_{\mathrm{ww}})$ pair depends not only on the decoy-quality parameter but also on the number of warheads and decoys in the cloud. We also note that when the number of warheads and decoys are equal, the $(P_{\mathrm{dw}}, P_{\mathrm{ww}})$ pair for the best-classification threshold is the same as for the maximum-resolution threshold. Since the number of decoys will generally exceed the number of warheads, then comparison of (176) and (177) with (170) and (171) shows that fewer threshold exceedances will be expected under the best-classification threshold setting. We mention again that *best* is a terminological connection and that the consequences of this setting in terms of the expected number of surviving warheads must be considered.

The last threshold setting that we consider is the constrained-exceedance threshold. The rationale for this threshold setting is that since there is a known number N_w of warheads in the cloud, it makes some sense to set the discriminator threshold such that the expected number of threshold exceedances is N_w. Thus, for this threshold setting we have

$$N_w = N_w P_{ww} + N_d P_{dw} \tag{178}$$

or from (150),

$$N_w = N_w P_{dw}^q + N_d P_{dw} \tag{179}$$

For given values of N_w, N_d, and q, it is easy to solve (178) numerically for P_{dw} and then to use equation (150) to compute the (P_{dw}, P_{ww}) pair.

A number of numerical runs were made, using the computer programs developed for this study to examine the consequences of these threshold settings. Figures 5a and 5b show results for the sequential and simultaneous assignment problems, respectively, for the case that has is one warhead, nine decoys, and five defensive interceptors with a single-shot survival probability of 50%. These curves show virtually identical performance for the maximum-resolution and constrained-exceedance thresholds but a noticeable degradation for the best-classification threshold. These curves are typical of all the runs that were made.

The reason for the noticeably poorer performance of the best-classification threshold is that it achieves the maximum average number of current classifications at the expense of failing to classify enough warheads as warheads. For the measure of effectiveness considered (i.e., the expected number of surviving warheads), the two types of classification errors produce asymmetric effects. That is, it is more serious to classify a warhead as a decoy than it is to classify a decoy as a warhead. Figure 6 shows the probability of classifying a warhead correctly for the three thresholding schemes.

This figure clearly shows the tendency of the best-classification threshold to fail to classify a warhead as a warhead. Figures 7a and 7b show the probabilities of both warheads and decoys exceeding the threshold for the maximum-resolution and constrained-exceedance threshold settings. Thus, in summary, the best-classification threshold appears to be misnamed.

Fig. 5. Comparison of thresholding schemes for (a) serial assignment problem and (b) simultaneous assignment problem.

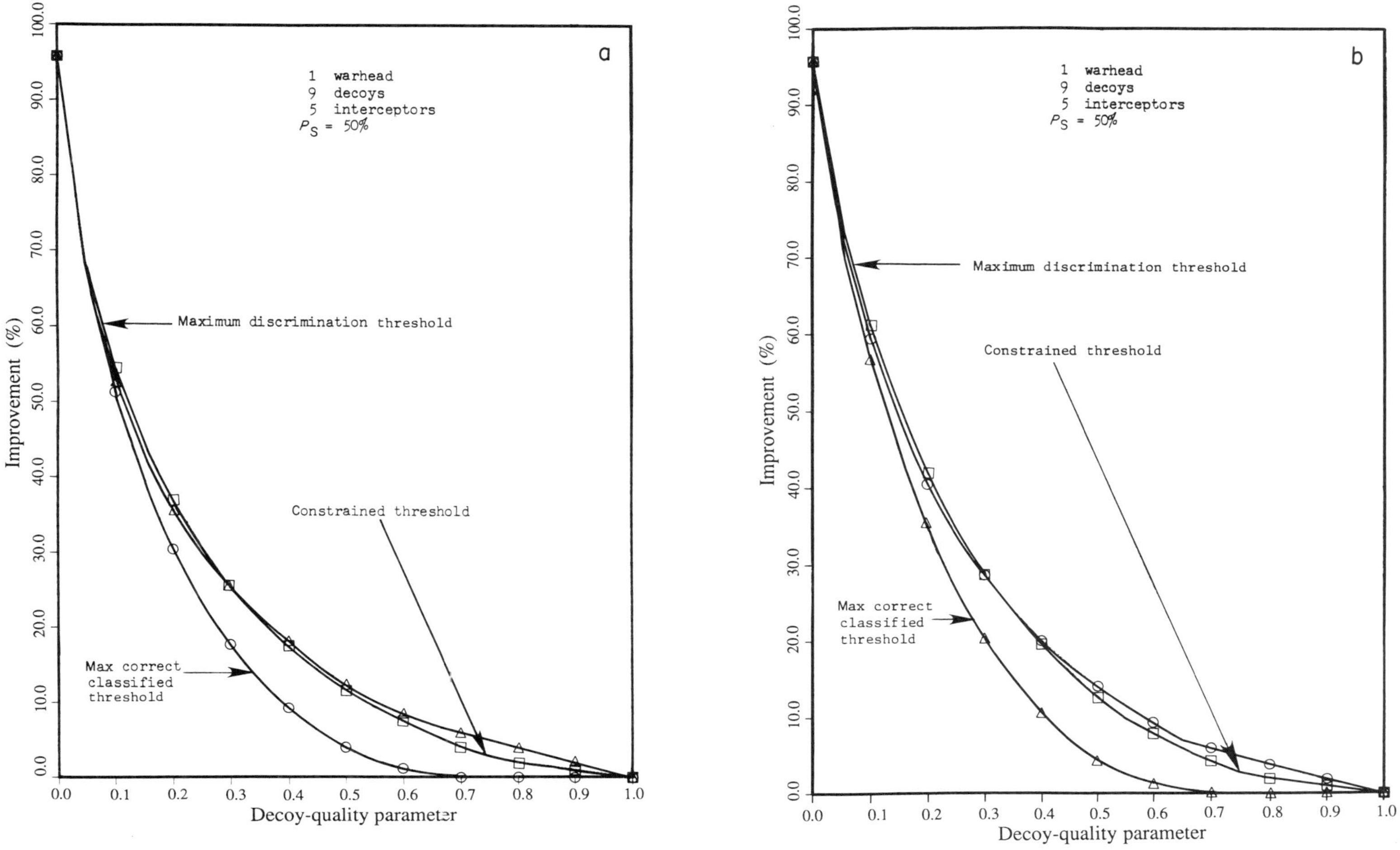
a
1 warhead
9 decoys
5 interceptors
P_S = 50%
Maximum discrimination threshold
Constrained threshold
Max correct
classified
threshold
Improvement (%)
Decoy-quality parameter
b
1 warhead
9 decoys
5 interceptors
P_S = 50%
Maximum discrimination threshold
Constrained threshold
Max correct
classified
threshold
Improvement (%)
Decoy-quality parameter

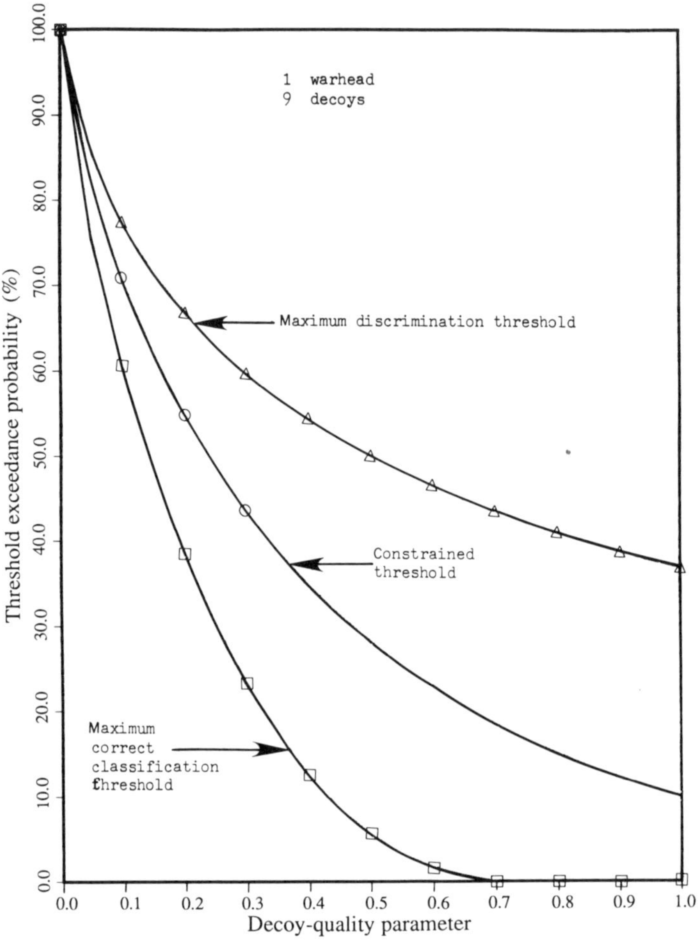

Fig. 6. Threshold exceedance probabilities for different thresholding schemes.

E. THRESHOLD DISCRIMINATOR VERSUS ANALOG DISCRIMINATOR PERFORMANCE FOR THE SERIAL TARGETING PROBLEM

In the preceding sections, algorithms have been developed for analog and single-threshold discriminator for both the serial and simultaneous targeting problems. Since there is more information in the analog measurements, the

---

Fig. 7. Warhead and decoy threshold exceedance probabilities for (a) maximum-discrimination threshold setting and (b) contrained exceedance threshold setting.

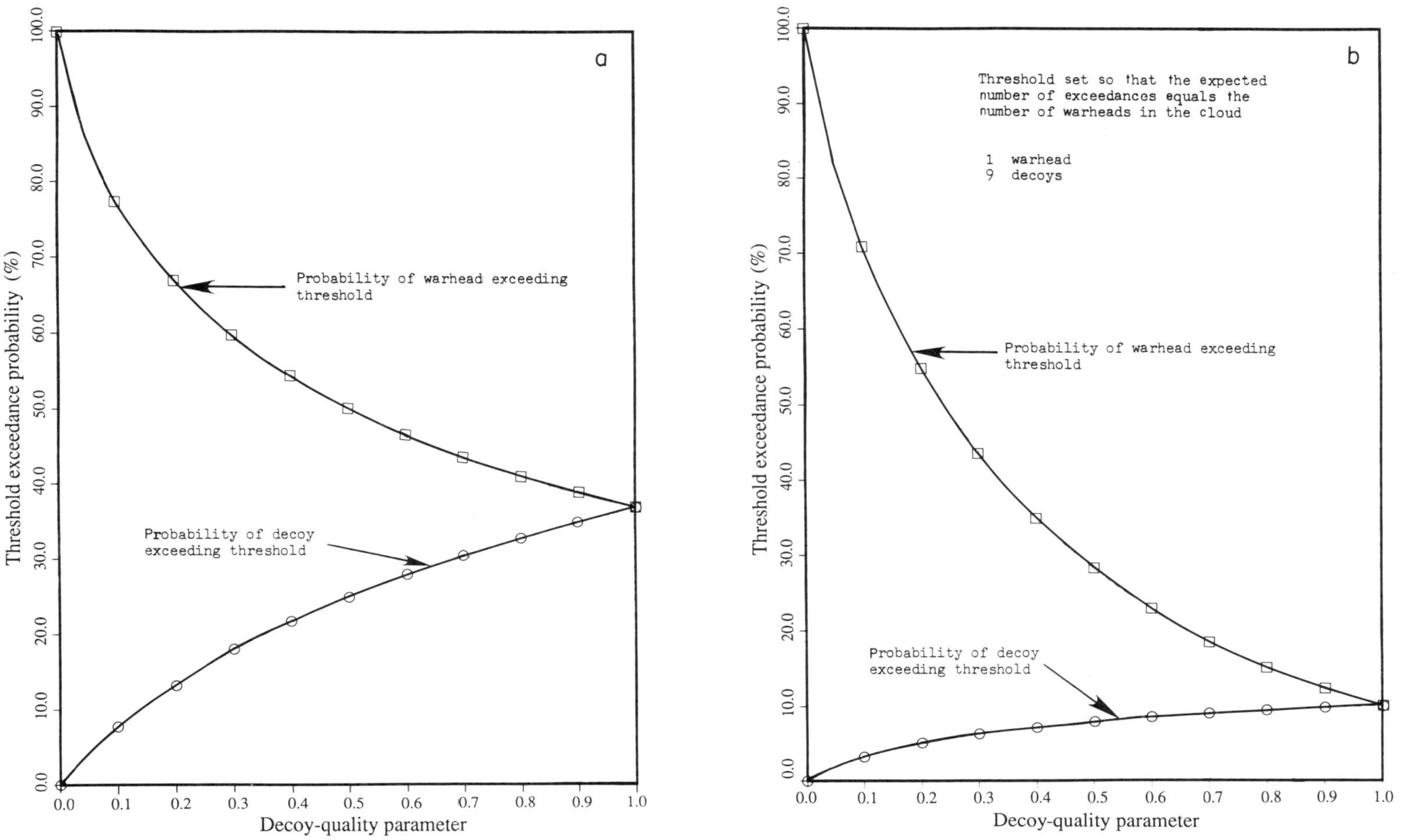
a
Threshold exceedance probability (%)
Decoy-quality parameter
Probability of warhead exceeding threshold
Probability of decoy exceeding threshold
b
Threshold set so that the expected number of exceedances equals the number of warheads in the cloud
1 warhead
9 decoys
Threshold exceedance probability (%)
Decoy-quality parameter
Probability of warhead exceeding threshold
Probability of decoy exceeding threshold

defense can do a better job with a knowledge of the actual measurement rather than with just the information that a fixed threshold is exceeded or not. How much better depends, of course, on the interceptor inventory, lethality, number of decoys, and so on. The purpose of this section is to look at a representative example. Figure 8 shows plots of the improvement factor versus the decoy-quality parameter for the analog and single-threshold discriminator. For this example there was one warhead, nine decoys, and five defensive interceptors. The single-shot survival probability of a warhead targeted by a defensive interceptor is 50%. For decoys of very poor quality, either

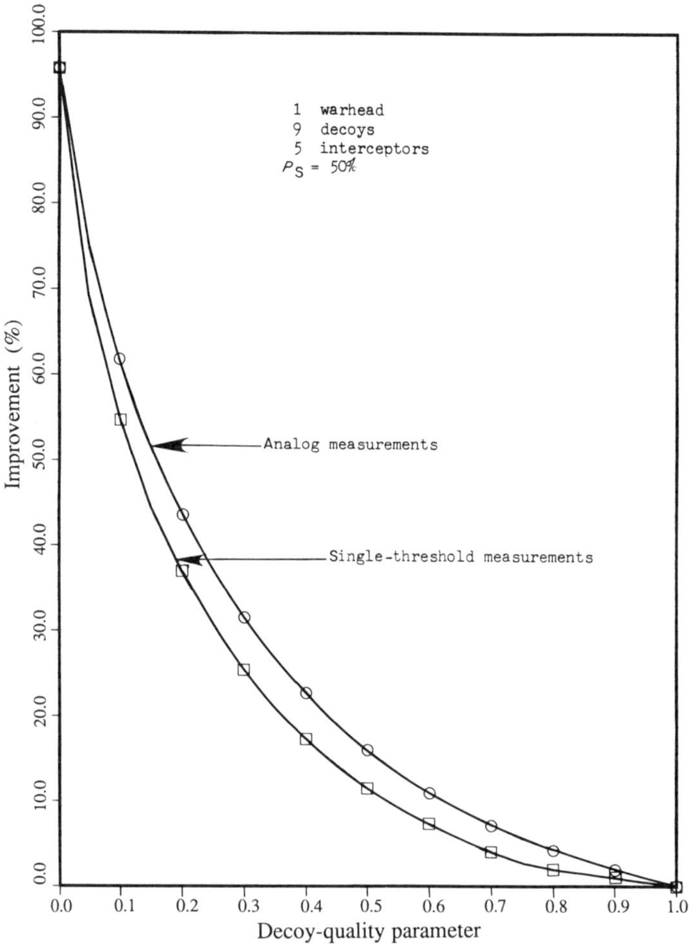

Fig. 8. Analog versus single-threshold performance comparison for the serial arrival problem.

discriminator will do very well whereas for very high quality decoys neither discriminator can do any better than uniform targeting. Thus, it is for the midrange of decoy quality that the analog discriminator would be expected to show the greatest relative improvement. Figure 10 bears this out and shows that the maximum gain in improvement factor is about 10%.

F. THRESHOLD DISCRIMINATOR VERSUS RANK-ORDER DISCRIMINATOR VERSUS ANALOG DISCRIMINATOR PERFORMANCE FOR THE SIMULTANEOUS TARGETING PROBLEM

For the simultaneous targeting problem, the most information is presented to the defense when the analog measurements themselves are available. The next best situation is that in which the rank-order statistics are available, and the least informative situation is that in which the only information preserved is whether a single preset threshold is exceeded. A large number of computer runs were made to see how much difference there was in the behavior of the analog and rank-order discriminator. In all cases the performance was almost identical. Figure 9a shows a case corresponding to one of the largest observed differences in performance. In no case was it possible to show that the analog discriminator has any real advantage over the rank-order discriminator. This is of some significance since for the rank-order discriminator the best targeting doctrine can be determined *a priori*. Figure 9b shows the comparison in improvement factors between the analog and single-threshold discriminator. The gains in going from a single-threshold to the analog measurement for the simultaneous targeting case are comparable but slightly less than for the serial case.

G. EFFECTS OF ADDING MEMORY TO THE SEQUENTIAL TARGETING SYSTEMS

We recall from Section II that for the sequential targeting problem the targeting assignments for a given object were based on (1) the number of objects remaining in the cloud, (2) the current interceptor inventory, (3) assumed decoy quality, and (4) interceptor lethality or the single-shot survival probability of a warhead targeted by a defensive interceptor. There is also some information in the sequence of prior measurements. The development of the targeting doctrine did not exploit this information.

It is clear that any gains in defense system performance achievable by exploiting the prior stage observed data must be bounded by the performance achieved by the simultaneous targeting system. Thus, comparison of

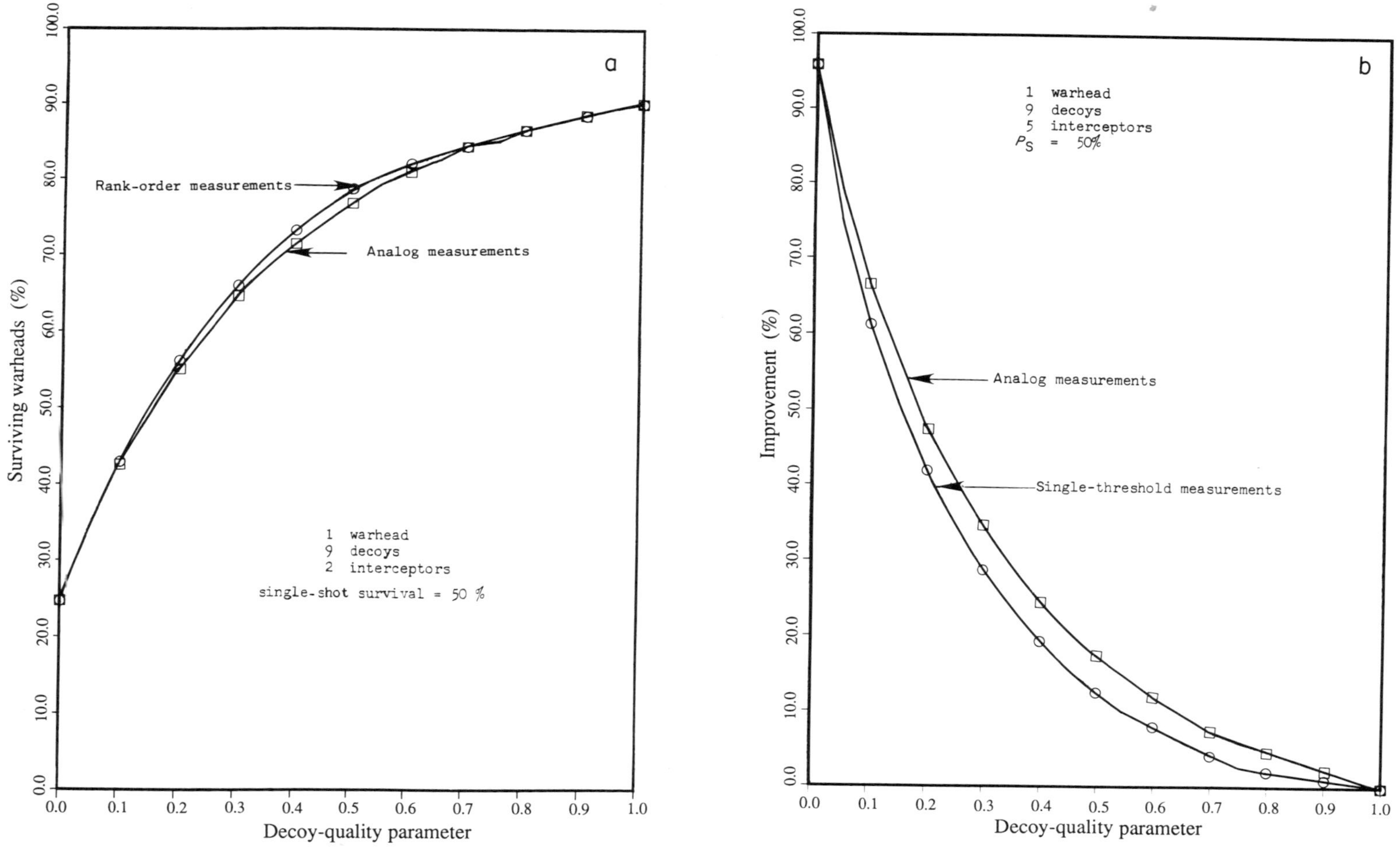

a
Surviving warheads (%)
Rank-order measurements
Analog measurements
1 warhead
9 decoys
2 interceptors
single-shot survival = 50 %
Decoy-quality parameter
b
Improvement (%)
1 warhead
9 decoys
5 interceptors
P_S = 50%
Analog measurements
Single-threshold measurements
Decoy-quality parameter

performance between the sequential and simultaneous targeting problems enables one to bound the maximum performance gain that could be achieved by adding computational memory to the system.

Many simulations were run in an effort to judge the magnitude of the potential improvement. Figures 10a and 10b show bounds on achievable improvement for the discrete threshold and analog discriminator. The maximum achievable improvement appears to be slightly greater for the single-threshold discriminator than for the analog discriminator. However, in both cases, the results are sufficiently close so that it does not appear warranted to add the considerable complexity to the sequential targeting calculations to account for prior stage measurements.

Figure 10c shows a three-way comparison for the example we have been considering, in which the serial single-threshold, serial analog, and simultaneous analog discriminator are compared. This figure shows that, for this engagement, more can be gained by going from the threshold to the analog measurements than by adding memory to the system.

All of the numerical work done thus far suggests that it is unwarranted to complicate the serial targeting problem by conditioning the assignment policy on the results obtained from prior stage observations.

H. DECOY OPTIMIZATION FOR VARIOUS SCALING LAWS

Thus far the discussion has focused on the problem presented to the defense: the development of the optimum targeting doctrine for various given situations. The various measures of effectiveness were calculated and displayed as functions of a normalized decoy quality parameter to examine sensitivities to variation in decoy quality. However, the offense has certain options at its disposal relating to the quality of the decoys. Because of weight, space, and form-factor constraints it is reasonable to assume that there exists some adjustable compromise between decoy quality and quantity. In other words, the offense probably has some choice that would permit it to package a smaller number of high-quality decoys or greater number of lesser-quality decoys. The nature of the relationship between decoy quality and quantity depends on the nature of the sensor and the physical observable that is measured by the discrimination device. The purpose of this section is to look at one or two simple examples in which the discrimination device is a radar.

For the numerical example we assume that the discrimination sensor is a radar and that the radar cross section is the physical observable. Furthermore,

Fig. 9. The simultaneous assignment problem. (a) Rank order versus analog discriminator performance; (b) analog versus single-threshold discriminator performance.

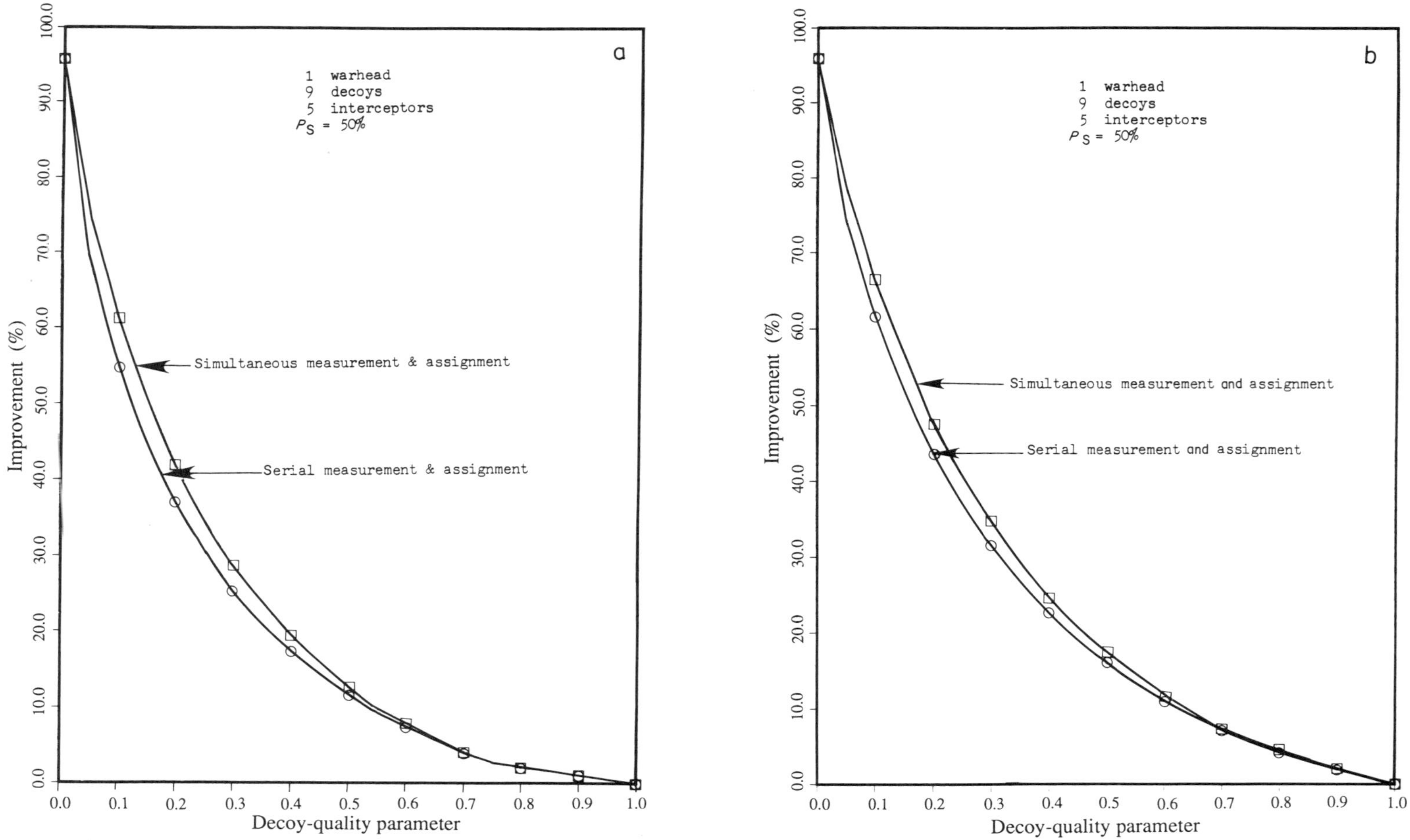

Fig. 10. Memory comparison for (a) single-threshold discriminator and (b) analog discriminator. (c) Summary improvement factor comparison.

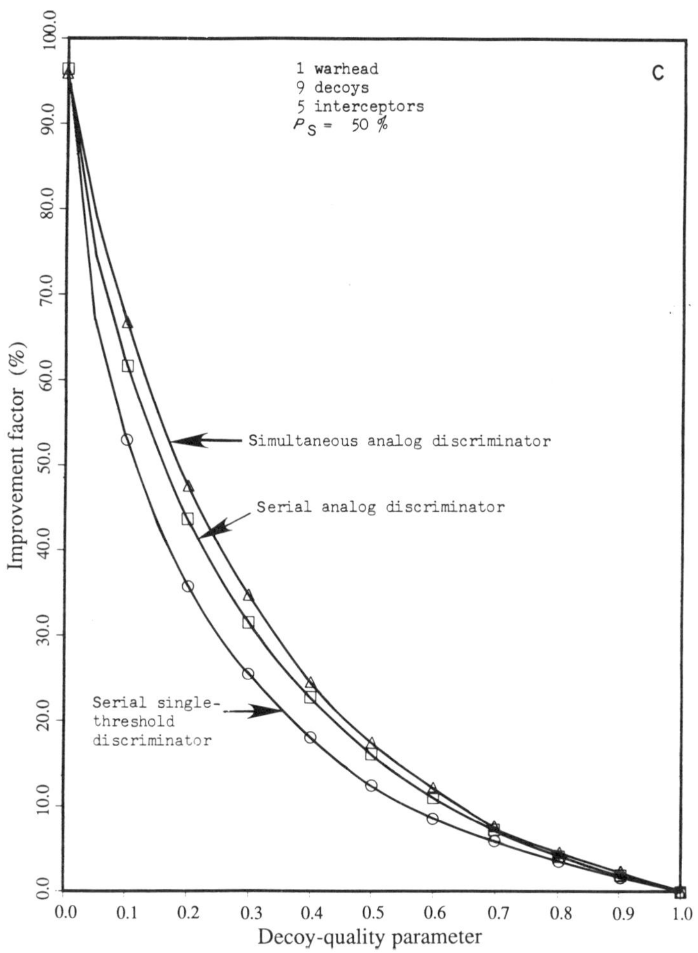

Fig. 10. (*Continued.*)

let us assume that there is a volume constraint such that the total volume of all of the decoys cannot exceed some fixed volume V. Then, if it is possible to have n_0 decoys of quality q_0 and then if there are $n > n_0$ decoys of quality q_n, the quality of each of the n decoys can be written as

$$q_n = (n_0/n)^{2/3} q_0 \tag{180}$$

The assumption made in (180) is that the decoy quality is proportional to the mean surface area of the decoy. We refer to this scaling law as spherical scaling. As an alternative, we also consider the scaling relationship given by (181), which we refer to as linear scaling:

$$q_n = (n_0/n)q_0 \tag{181}$$

Figure 11a plots the percentage of surviving warheads as a function of the number of decoys for the serial and simultaneous analog discriminator. In this figure, $q_0 = 1$, $n_0 = 1$, $N_I = 1$ and $P_S = 0.0$. The spherical scaling law given by (180) is assumed. For the case in which all of the objects can be examined simultaneously, the best packaging for the offense is to have two decoys of quality $q = \sqrt{2/2}$. For the serial case, the best offensive packaging is three decoys, each with quality $\sqrt{3/3}$. In both cases the tail-off is very slow.

Figure 11b considers the simultaneous rank-order discriminator for spherical and linear scaling when there are nine perfect interceptors and, initially, nine perfect decoys. The bottom curve considers the case in which the scaling is only on the basis of nine decoys of quality 0.50. A sharp maximum does not develop, but for all of these cases there seems little point in packaging more than 20 decoys with the warhead.

V. SUMMARY

This study set out to provide a unifying framework for the development of the optimum targeting doctrine for a defensive site whose aim was to minimize the expected number of surviving reentry warheads. Two major scenarios were examined. In the first, elements of a cloud of objects consisting of a known number of warheads and decoys were assumed to be serially interrogated by a discrimination device. Immediately after the interrogation, the defense had to decide how many interceptors, if any, should target the object just interrogated. The conditional statistical distributions of the discriminator measurements were assumed known, as well as the conditional single-shot survival probability of a warhead targeted by a defensive interceptor.

Three types of discriminator were modeled: a single-threshold discriminator, a rank-order discriminator, and an analog discriminator. Optimal targeting policies were developed and equations were written allowing the calculation of the minimum expected number of surviving reentry warheads. Plausible ways of setting the threshold for the single-threshold discriminator were discussed, and equations were derived that permitted the calculation of these thresholds as functions of the problem parameters. For the second scenario, it was assumed that the defense's discrimination device could make measurements on all of the reentry objects prior to allocation of its inventory of defensive interceptors. Optimal targeting policies were calculated for the second scenario for both the single-threshold and analog discriminator.

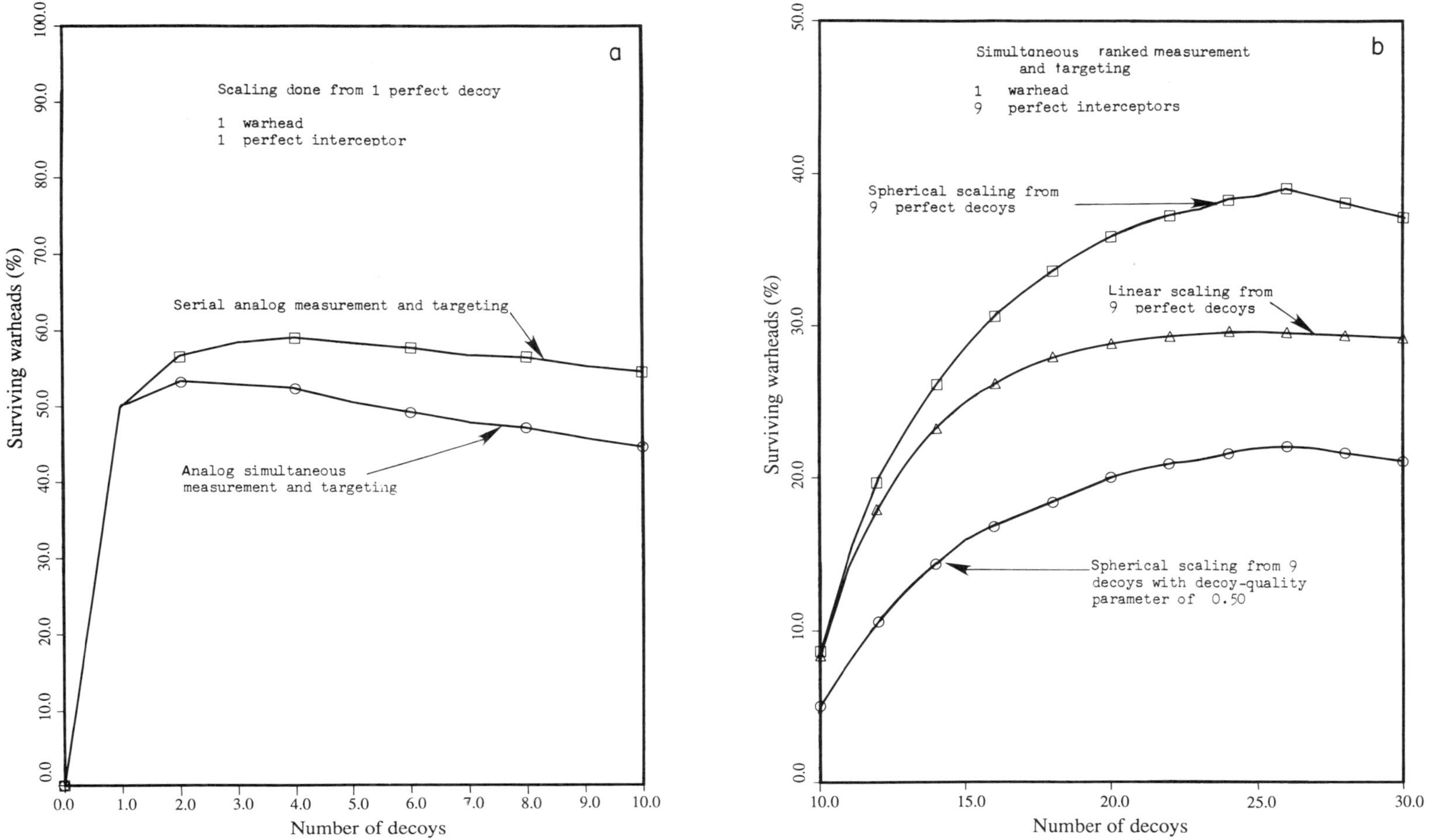

Fig. 11. Decoy quality–quantity optimization for (a) serial and simultaneous analog discriminators and (b) spherical and linear scaling.

For the numerical work, a parametric form was postulated for the conditional measurement probability distributions. With this parametrization it was possible to define a normalized decoy-quality parameter. Next it was shown that the fractional number of surviving reentry warheads for a given decoy-quality parameter is almost constant for (KN_w, KN_d, KN_I) situations where K is a positive integer.

Specific examples of the optimum targeting policies were calculated for various decoy qualities, and the tendency toward the uniform targeting doctrine was noted as the decoy quality became perfect. This was noted to hold for both the serial and simultaneous targeting problems.

With the assumed parametrization of the measurement distribution, the quantities P_{ww} and P_{dw} could be simply related in terms of the decoy-quality parameter. The effectiveness of the various thresholding schemes for the single-threshold discriminator were evaluated, and the maximum resolution threshold was found to yield the best performance. Various forms of statistical distances between the conditional measurement distributions were computed as functions of the decoy-quality parameter.

Next, a series of numerical comparisons were made. For the serial targeting problem, numerical results were shown that illustrated the amount of improvement attainable in employing an analog discriminator instead of a single-threshold discriminator. For the simultaneous targeting problem, similar comparisons were made between the single-threshold discriminator, a rank-order discriminator, and the analog discriminator. Various cross comparisons were made between the simultaneous and serial targeting problems to gain a feeling for the maximum improvement to be expected from adding measurement memory in the serial targeting problem.

Most of the work was looked at from the point of view of the defense. Finally, brief mention was made of the inverse problem of the offense; that is, given a scaling law between decoy quality and quantity, what is the best decoy packaging so that the offense can maximize the minimum expected number of surviving reentry warheads. Some simple calculations were made.

REFERENCES

1. S. MATLIN, "A Review of the Literature on the Missile Allocation Problem," *J. Oper. Res. Soc. AM.* **18**, 344–373 (1970).
2. L. PHILLIPSON, Y. FUKUDA, M. SCHAEFFER, and W. FARRAGHER, "Ballistic Missile Decoy Optimization Through Dynamic Programming," *USAF 7th Symp. Ballist. Missile Space Technol., Boulder, Colo.* **1**, 238–254 (1962).
3. M. GORFINKEL, "A Decision Theory Approach to Missile Defense," *J. Oper. Res. Soc. Am.* **2**, 194–209 (1963).
4. J. R. HOLDSWORTH, "A Dynamic Detection and Sequential Allocation Problem," *31st Nat. ORSA Meet., New York* (1967).

5. S. B. LAYNO, "A Model of the AMB vs. RV Engagement with Imperfect RV Discrimination," *J. Oper. Res. Soc. Am.* **19**, 1502–1517 (1971).
6. A. HERSHAFT, "Effectiveness of Imperfect Decoys," *J. Oper. Res. Soc. Am.* **16**, 10–17 (1968).
7. R. BELLMAN and S. DREYFUS, "Applied Dynamic Programming, p. 15. Princeton Univ. Press, Princeton, New Jersey, 1962.
8. T. S. FERGUSON, "Mathematical Statistics, A Decision Theoretic Approach," p. 208. Academic Press, New York, 1967.
9. D. K. BARTON, "Radar System Analysis," p. 22. Prentice-Hall, Englewood Cliffs, New Jersey, 1968.
10. A. J. VITERBI and J. K. OMURA, "Principles of Digital Communication and Coding," p. 63. McGraw-Hill, New York, 1979.
11. W. FELLER, "An Introduction to Probability Theory and its Applications," Vol. 2, p. 277. Wiley, New York, 1966.

INDEX

C

G

H

N

O

T